Directory of
Water Related
International Cooperation

Editor :

Motokazu ANDO

Assistant editors :

Martin Piddington & Joe Banerjee

1995

International Lake Environment Committee Foundation

This book is published with support from the Nippon Foundation.

Editor   : Motokazu Ando
Assistant editors : Martin Piddington and Joe Banerjee
Coordinator   : Kazukiyo Fukui
Cover design   : Uemura Design Office, Tokyo, Japan
Text layout   : Soken Layout Studio, Kadoma, Japan
Printing   : Hanroku Type Ltd., Otsu, Japan

International Lake Environment Committee Foundation (ILEC)
1091 Oroshimo-cho, Kusatsu, Shiga 525 Japan
Tel : +81-775-68-4567
Fax : +81-775-68-4568
Email : LDA02313@niftyserve.or.jp
ISBN 4-906356-14-1

INTERNATIONAL LAKE ENVIRONMENT COMMITTEE FOUNDATION

Secretariat

1091 Oroshimo-cho, Kusatsu, Shiga 525, JAPAN
TEL : +81-775-68-4567, FAX : +81-775-68-4568

6th November 1995

Dear Sir,

Request for cooperation

I am pleased to enclose herewith a complimentary copy of "Directory of Water Related International Cooperation". This book was originally intended to serve as a background material for the International Cooperation Session of the 6th International Conference on Conservation and Management of Lakes (World Lake Conference). The Conference which was held in October 1995 at Tsukuba Science City in Japan, brought more than 8,000 participants together successfully.

This is a source book on "who is doing what" in international cooperation for promoting conservation of freshwater resources with emphasis on lakes/reservoirs and their basins. Activities of multilateral, bilateral and non-governmental agencies are examined with regard to their water-related environmental projects as well as development projects which might affect lake/reservoir environments.

As mentioned in the Foreword by the Director of UNEP International Environmental Technology Centre, it is clear that this is but an initial effort in producing a reference document of this kind, and that this must be corrected and updated regularly.

ILEC is now going to initiate this updating work by requesting your cooperation in supplying latest and/or additional information to us. Though printing of a revised edition may take some time, at least we can maintain latest version of this book in our computer and supply you with latest information upon request. Supply of such database through INTERNET is also in our short-term scope.

We would be more than happy if you can supply us with such information (both an original manuscript and existing materials are welcome) and/or comments to the following address :

Postal :   International Lake Environment Committee Secretariat
          1091 Oroshimo-cho, Kusatsu, Shiga, 525 Japan
Fax :   +81-775-68-4568
Email :   LDA02313@niftyserve.or.jp

Thanking for your cooperation in advance.

Sincerely yours,

Motokazu Ando
Programme Coordinator, ILEC Secretariat

Remote sensing imagery of two troubled lakes in 1989

Tokai University, Reseach and Information Center

The Aral Sea (right) started to shrink in early 1960s due to over - use of irrigation water from inflow rivers. Some drainage water from the irrigation area of Amu river flows into Lake Sarykamyshkoya (southwest of the Aral Sea) and it tends to enlarge. On the other hand, the water level of the Caspian Sea (left) has been rising quickly in recent years.

Remote sensing imageries showing encroaching plantations around Tasek Bera, a wetland lake in Malaysia

by M. Nakayama

Open water of Tasek Bera is seen at down left in each scene.

↑ expansion of plantation areas during nine years

↑ in 1988 with smoke for forest clearing

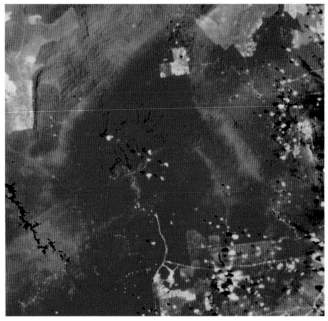

↑ scene in 1979

Foreword

Both physical and social statistics bear out the claim that "freshwater will be the petroleum of the 21st century". Only 2.5 percent of all the water on the planet is freshwater and only a very small percentage of that amount is available for human use, the rest being out of reach in the icecaps or buried too deep to economically exploit at present. A recent UN survey also noted the toll that mis-management of this precious resource has on the quality of human life. Each day some 25,000 people die from either a lack of water or being forced to drink contaminated water, and the numbers continue to increase.

No one doubts the fact that demand for freshwater has already exceeded production capacity in most of the world. In addition, many major river and lake systems are so contaminated that the scale of investment required to reverse this state is beyond even the largest aid agencies. Therefore, even more integration of development activities will be required if scarce financial resources are to be efficiently and effectively expended resulting in tangible results.

Lakes and reservoirs are increasingly important in the water management equation as are the rivers, springs and aquifers that feed them. However, the continued productivity of these resources is obviously directly tied to the management of the surrounding lands. This presents managers with a demand for integrated management of the land and water resource, one which is even more complex where a lake or reservoir defines an international boarder.

This text fills an important niche by assisting development, finance and technical assistance agencies and organizations in planning and implementing international cooperation efforts. UNEP and the International Environmental Technology Centre applaud this effort by the International Lake Environment Committee Foundation to document ongoing efforts as a means of stimulating a more coordinated exchange of ideas among scientists, planners, managers and policy makers as to the future management of these invaluable resources. It must be clear however that this is but an initial effort in producing a reference document that to remain current, must be updated regularly.

Therefore, IETC is prepared to join forces with ILEC to ensure that this text is kept current and provides the information desired by those involved maintaining the viability of lakes and reservoirs in contributing to the quality of the human condition.

Richard A. Meganck, Director
UNEP International Environmental Technology Centre
Osaka and Shiga, Japan
September 1995

In terms of available water mass and stability, lakes are the richest freshwater resource on earth. Aside from their value as water sources, lakes serve as fisheries, recreation sites and avenues of transport. They also provide many other practical and aesthetic benefits to human beings, and serve as habitats for other diverse biological species. Despite their importance, lakes are suffering severely from human mistreatment, and yet relatively little attention has been paid to their environmental deterioration. Environmental issues concerning lakes and reservoirs may take place in not only highly populated and industrialized areas but also less developed places, as typically shown in the case of the Aral Sea disaster. Therefore, international cooperation is indispensable in coping with the situation.

This book is a survey of "who is doing what" in international cooperation for promoting conservation of freshwater resources with emphasis on lakes/reservoirs and their basins. Activities of multilateral, bilateral and non-governmental agencies are examined with regard to their water-related environmental projects as well as development projects which might affect lake/reservoir environments. Information sources are mainly reports, documents and leaflets that the International Lake Environment Committee (ILEC) has obtained during its lake conservation activities. Therefore, this is not a balanced introduction of water related international cooperation projects of the world. For example, introduction of projects in French speaking countries are insufficient. Description of a small-scale NGO may be longer than that of a large UN organization. Moreover, this is only a partial introduction of water-related activities of each organization. Absence of description does not mean that the organization is not involved in such activities.

This book mainly introduces international cooperation projects directly targeted at developing countries and countries in economic transitions by multilateral, bilateral and non-governmental organizations. Though such international cooperation as joint research among developed countries may help developing countries, this book does not lay emphasis on 'north to north' cooperation. Consulting activities on a commercial basis is also not included. In development assistance the definition of 'environment' is very broadly used. For instance, the following components of respective areas may be regarded as freshwater-related environment projects :

Pollution :	Water quality conservation measures
Living environment :	Water supply for safe drinking water, Sewage for sanitation, Well digging for WID
Forest conservation :	Afforestation as a source of stable water resources
Natural environment and biodiversity :	Ecosystem conservation of lakes, rivers and wetlands
Disaster prevention :	Flood control
Capacity building :	Augmenting institutional capabilities for environmental issues (e.g. manpower development for administration, research and monitoring)
Natural resources :	Irrigation, sustainable inland fisheries, erosion control for prevention of eutrophication and siltation

The aim of this book is to collect diverse projects related to freshwater conservation. However, such projects as disaster prevention, irrigation, WID, afforestation are not sufficiently introduced in this book. As a key measure for securing sustainable development, the importance of environmental impact assessment (EIA) in the formulation of varied development projects has become recognized. In a sense this type of consideration could be more important in the prevention of freshwater deterioration than in rehabilitation projects. But investigation is also inadequate with this respect. In an international cooperation project, it is normal that more than a few organizations are involved in it. For instance, international cooperation of the Japanese Environment Agency is mainly made through the Japan International Cooperation Agency (JICA). GEMS/WATER, an United Nation's global water quality monitoring system, is a joint project of UNEP/WHO/WMO/UNESCO and many domestic organizations are collaborating to it. Such projects are introduced arbitrarily in a certain organizations column.

This book is originally intended to serve as background material for the International Cooperation Session of the 6th International Conference on Conservation and Management of Lakes (World Lake Conference) which takes place in October 1995 at Tsukuba in Japan. Chapter 1 is a translation of a report entitled "A Survey of International Cooperation Projects for Conservation of Lakes/Reservoirs and their Basins" which was prepared by ILEC in Japanese in 1994. Though updates and supplemental data were added for some organizations, it may not be sufficient to reflect the quickly changing trends in the field of 'environment', and continuous efforts will be necessary for this kind of directory work. Thanks are due to the Asian Wetland Bureau (AWB) which cooperated in compiling information on southeast Asian projects and many other organizations which kindly offered us information on their activities.

Motokazu Ando
Programme Coordinator, ILEC Secretariat

Contents

Chapter 1

Chapter 2

Chapter 3

Chapter 4

Chapter 5

Annex

Glossary

Organizations involved in international cooperation for freshwater conservation

■ UN Organizations and Projects

CSD	Committee for Sustainable Development
ECA	Economic Commission for Africa
ECE	Economic Commission for Europe
ECLAC	Economic Commission for Latin America and the Caribbean
ESCAP	Economic and Social Commission for Asia and the Pacific
ESCWA	Economic and Social Commission for Western Asia
FAO	Food and Agriculture Organization of the United Nations
GEF	Global Environment Facility
GEMS	Global Environment Monitoring System
GRID	Global Resources Information Database
HABITAT	United Nations Centre for Human Settlements
IAEA	International Atomic Energy Agency
IBRD	The World Bank (International Bank for Reconstruction and Development)
IETC	UNEP International Environmental Technology Centre
IHP	International Hydrological Program
INFOTERRA	International Referral System for Sources of Environmental Information
IHP	International Hydrological Programme
ILO	International Labour Organization
INSTRAW	International Research and Training Institute for The Advancement of Women
UNCED	United Nations Conference on Environment and Development
UNCHS	United Nations Centre for Human Settlements
UNDIESA	United Nations Department of International Economic and Social Affairs
UNDP	United Nations Development Programme
UNCRD	United Nations Centre for Regional Development
UNDDSMS	United Nations Department of Development Support and Management Services
UNDRO	Office of the United Nations Disaster Relief Co-ordinator
UNEP	United Nations Environment Programme
UNESCO	United Nations Educational, Scientific and Cultural Organization
UNICEF	United Nations Children's Fund
UNIDO	United Nations Industrial Development Organization
UNITAR	United Nations Institute for Training and Research
UNRISD	United Nations Research Institute for Social Development
UNU	United Nations University
WFP	World Food Programme
WHO	World Health Organization
WMO	World Meteorological Organization

■ Intergovernmental Organizations

AsDB	Asian Development Bank
AfDB	African Development Bank
AIT	Asian Institute of Technology
APO	Asian Productivity Organization
DAC	Development Assistance Committee (OECD)
IIASA	International Institute for Applied Systems Analysis
LCBC	Lake Chad Basin Commission
NATO	North Atlantic Treaty Organization
ICIMOD	International Centre for Integrated Mountain Development
OECD	Organization for Economic Co-operations and Development
REC	Regional Environmental Centre for Central and Eastern Europe
SADC	Southern African Development Community
SEAFDEC	Southeast Asian Fisheries Development Centre

■ Bilateral Aid Agencies and Domestic Governmental Institutes and Projects

AIDAB	Australian International Development Assistance Bureau
CIDA	Canadian International Development Authority
CITEC	Centre for International Technical and Educational Cooperation
CRAES	Chinese Research Academy of Environmental Sciences
DANIDA	Danish International Development Agency
DCA	Swiss Directorate of Development Cooperation and Humanitarian Aid
DGIS	International Development Cooperation Agency of the Netherlands
ERTC	Environmental Research and Training Center
FINNIDA	Finnish International Development Agency
GRDC	Global Runoff Data Center
GTZ	Deutsche Gesellschaft fur Technische Zusammenarbeit
JEC	Japan Environment Corporation
JICA	Japan International Cooperation Agency
LBDA	Lake Basin Development Authority
LBRI	Lake Biwa Research Institute
LLDA	Laguna Lake Development Authority
NASA	National Aeronautics and Space Administration
NIES	National Institute for Environment Studies
NIVA	Norwegian Institute for Water Research
NORAD	Norwegian Agency for Development Cooperation
NWRI	National Water Research Institute
ODA	Overseas Development Administration
OECF	The Overseas Economic Cooperation Fund
SIDA	Swedish International Development Authority

USAID	United States Agency for International Development
WASH	Water and Sanitation for Health Project

NIVA	Norwegian Institute for Water Research
SIL	International Association of Theoretical and Applied Limnology
WRI	World Resources Institute

■ Non-governmental Organizations (International and Domestic)

AWB	Asian Wetland Bureau
BICER	Baikal International Center for Ecological Research
CIP	Centre for International Projects
IOW/CEFIGRE	Department of International Cooperation, International Office for Water
IAHR	International Association for Hydraulic Research
IAWQ	International Association for Water Quality
ICBP	International Council for Bird Preservation
ICID	International Commission on Irrigation and Drainage
ICOLD	International Congress of Large Dam
INTECOL	International Society of Ecology
IRC	International Water and Sanitation Centre
IUCN	World Conservation Union
IWRA	International Water Resources Association
IWRB	International Waterfowl and Wetlands Research Bureau
MARC	Monitoring and Assessment Research Centre
NALMS	North American Lake Management Society

■ Non-governmental Organizations in Japan

FOEJ	Friends of the Earth Japan
GIF	Global Infrastructure Fund Research Foundation Japan
GISPRI	Global Industrial and Social Progress Research Institute
ICETT	International Center for Environmental Technology Transfer
IDI	Infrastructure Development Institute - Japan
ILEC	International Lake Environment Committee
JABIRP	Japanese Association for Baikal International Research Programme
JRAK	Japan Research Association Kazakhstan
KITA	Kitakyushu International Technol-cooperative Association
KIWC	Kushiro International Wetland Center
OECC	Overseas Environment Cooperation Center
OISKA	The Organization for Industrial, Spiritual and Cultural Advancement - International
RITE	Research Institute of Innovative Technology for the Earth

Chapter 1

◆

Water Related Activities of Multilateral, Bilateral and Non-governmental Agencies

United Nations Children's Fund (UNICEF)

Work Outline

UNICEF's work for children includes healthcare and sanitation, nutrition improvement education, and parent and child welfare.

Water Related Work

It's easy to see why water, faeces and dirt linked diseases still account for estimated 12.4 million deaths each year (children being the most vulnerable) as approximately 1,800 million people around the world have no access to adequate excreta disposal systems and 1,200 million people are wishing for, but still waiting for, improved water supply. With water being the only transmission route for the likes of guinea worm (*dracunculiasis*), safe water supply is the only answer to combating disease, which affects approximately 23 developing countries and has an enormous detrimental impact on rural development, as both agriculture and education are seriously affected, particularly in tropical Africa.

The current UNICEF expenditure of approximately US$90 million per year in more than 90 countries for the water and sanitation sector comes from the premise that improved water supply and sanitation backed by hygiene education (WATSAN in UNICEF terminology) can reduce water and excreta carried diseases amongst children and women in developing countries.

As well as preventing diarrhoeal morbidity and deaths, WATSAN action is helpful in subduing cholera, typhoid, amoebiasis,giardiasis and various helminthic diseases that sap limited food supplies and exacerbate malnutrition in children.

UNICEF aid to the water and sanitation sector pinpoints rural areas with little action in areas fringing urban districts. UNICEF backed WATSAN projects have annually reached some 16 million people during the last ten years with improved water supply. This has been made possible through the use of low-cost technologies and approaches, support of the low-cost action by the governments of developing countries, and increasing community participation in the implementation process during the late 1980s. The following are WATSAN interventions.

- **Water Supply**

  Low-cost appropriate technologies - headed by handpump shallow (<100m) borewells and followed by handdug wells - typically for 70% of WATSAN Project budgets. Gravity-fed systems (particularly in Asia) and rainwater catchment are increasingly being used.

- **Sanitation**

  A huge sanitation-improvement effort is needed as present sanitation reaches less than 50% of the world's rural areas. The demand for improved excreta disposal is often much less than the demand for water supply. UNICEF support in this area includes training of skilled workers, establishing of pre-cast latrine slab bases with revolving funds, construction of demonstration units in schools, clinics and market places, and support for the private sector to help it take over these projects.

- **Hygiene and Health Education**

  This education promotes sustainable behavioral changes in personal, household and environmental health, hygiene and sanitation practices, including the increase of demand for latrines. It also brings about community participation at the planning, implementation and post-implementation phases of projects.

United Nations Development Programme (UNDP)

One United Nations Plaza, New York, NY 10017 USA

Work Outline

Overseas development aid directed through the UN is 14% of the worldwide total. Of this, UNDP receives 30%. UNDP is fundamentally a finance organization often with the risk of not being able to function on a business base. In the case of reform projects, UNDP also provides venture capital assistance for developing countries and supports activities that find it difficult to get funding from other financial sources. UNDP also has a facet resembling the World Bank. Moreover, these activities include pre-investment studies, system setups, creation of economic development plans, dispatching of specialists, equipment contribution and the staging of seminars as technological assistance for the promotion of economic and social development in developing countries.

UNDP's Project Fields, Number of Projects and Costs (1992)

Field	Projects	Sum of Money (Unit: US$1 million)
(1) Agriculture, Fishery, Forestry	883	1,301
(2) Culture	66	44
(3) Education	184	286
(4) Employment	267	330
(5) Development, Policy, Planning	1,547	1,589
(6) Health	286	389
(7) Housing	147	154
(8) Humanitarian Aid	140	140
(9) Industry	672	866
(10) International Trade and Development Aid	211	165
(11) Natural Resources	437	746
(12) Politics Related	29	11
(13) Population	18	20
(14) Science, Technology	283	348
(15) Social Conditions and Equality	167	224
(16) Transport, Communications	399	701
Total	5,736	7,314

UNDP's activities reach more than 150 countries and regions. Projects target nearly all aspects of economic and social fields including environment protection. UNDP rarely executes projects on its own - about 60% are handled by 34 UN organizations and international organizations that come under the 16 categories of aid and about 25% are implemented by the countries giving direct support. Some 5,736 projects

being promoted with UNDP assistance have been counted up to the end of 1992. Within these 87% have been modules for some 164 countries. On average, funding comes to US$990,000 per project. Some 80% of plan funds go to countries where the national average income is less than US$750 per year.

UNDP's Proportion of Projects Per Region (1992)

Region	Number of Cases (%)	Sum of Money (%)
Africa	32.5	31.5
Arabia	9.2	11.5
Asia and the Pacific	28.2	35.1
Latin America and the Caribbean	22.5	16.2
Europe	3.2	2.0
Multiregional	4.4	3.7
Total	100.0	100.0

Participation in Environmental Matters

Having accepted Agenda 21, UNDP is promoting the "Capacity 21" plan to enable developing countries to strengthen consideration of the environment in development plans. The following are the fields to be strengthened.

- The capacity for forming government policy and legal systems
- Training of key personnel
- System for creating sustainable development
- Mechanisms for creating citizen participation and information and technology exchanges

This programme will be realized through the following.
- Grasping the needs of developing countries
- Grasping in greater detail of the capabilities of developing countries
- Creating lists of cooperating organizations
- Grasping the present state and needs of existing organizations in developing countries
- Strengthening regional encouragement mechanism
- Forming a link mechanism between supply and demand necessary for forming capabilities

Necessary funding for this programme is estimated at US$500 million up to 1995.

Water Related Work

UNDP does not have a "lake and reservoir" category in its field of work, but agriculture, fishing and water resources work takes up 10% or more of all work. A total number of 904 (16%) projects (costing US$1.334 billion [18%]) related to water are being handled. Lakes are important as water sources but ground water is judged to be better from a treatment cost perspective.

In the case of water, UNDP, in joint cooperation with the World Bank, has been implementing a "Water Sanitation Programme" for the last ten years. The aim has been to provide water treatment facilities (for use as drinking water) that can be maintained at regional community level without specialist supervision, but above all else they should be low-cost facilities.

UNDP's water related projects in Asia include the creation of a general development master plan for the Mekong Delta in Vietnam, and a current status-level study of organizations and legal system jointly carried out with the Asia Development Bank and EU to point the way for water resources management in the Mekong basin.

Lake and Reservoir Related Work

UNDP is not involved with very many projects that solely cover lakes. Lakes are important as water sources but, as noted previously, ground water is judged to be better from a treatment cost perspective. At present, UNDP is planning a technology cooperation project (US$500,000) related to the development and environmental management in the vicinity of Lake Erhai with the government of Yunnan Province in China. UNEP is scheduled to cooperate in implementing the project.

United Nations Environment Programme (UNEP)
P.O.Box 30552, Nairobi, Kenya
Tel:+254-2-230800 Fax:+254-2-226890

Work Outline

Since its creation in 1972, UNEP has been active in the promotion of environmental protection and improvement within the framework of the Stockholm Plan of Action for Human Environment. Obviously this includes consideration for integrating environmental factors in the development and management of water resources. Nevertheless, since UNEP deals with the broad question of environmental protection and improvement, it is somewhat difficult to disentangle water activities and their expenditures, particularly since UNEP budget and organizational aspects are not broken down in this manner.

Water Related Work

Water Management issues are dealt with by the Freshwater Unit within the Environmental Management Branch, and Water Monitoring and Assessment issues are dealt with by the GEMS/Water under the Global Environmental Monitoring System Branch. Furthermore, the newly established UNEP International Environment Training Centre (IETC) in Shiga and Osaka, Japan has become an important factor in the management of lakes and reservoirs and their basins. Other departments are involved intermittently in water projects, for example the basin related Global Resources Information Database (GRID) department and the Biodiversity Treaty office.

1. Freshwater Unit

The following are the activities of the Freshwater Unit.

1) Preparation of action plans for the environmentally sound and sustainable development of international freshwater systems - namely, those shared by two or more countries. UNEP has developed in 1985, the Environmentally Sound Management of Inland Waters (EMINWA) programme that the Freshwater Unit does most of its work for.

The purpose of EMINWA is to promote the sustainable supply and use of water (including drinking water supply and inland water ecosystem protection) together with the general analysis and managerial policy making in socioeconomic, political and technological areas related to inland waters and surrounding coastal districts. These will enable the establishment of consensus internationally, regionally and nationally. This work will be carried out in the following three steps.

(a) Diagnostic study

(b) Action plan finalization (including preparation and analysis with relevant government organizations)

(c) Action plan implementation (including determination of doners)

Under the EMINWA programme, in the early part of 1994, the diagnostic study level had been reached at the River Nile, Mekong River, Caspian Sea and San Juan River (bordering between Nicaragua and Costa Rica).

Action plans are at the finalized level for the Aral Sea and Lake Titicaca, and the Zambezi River Action Plan (approved in 1987) and the Lake Chad Action Plan are at the implementation stage.

Also in the EMINWA programme is the Watershed and Coastal Zone Combination (WACOZOCO) programme for basin and coastal region general management and the Ocean and Coastal Area Programme Activities Centre (OCA/PAC) are involved in water environment conservation for island nations. They have set out to combat coastal pollution that originates inland. As a joint project of regional sea programme in east Asia, case studies have been prepared for hydrological and environmental management of basins and coastal areas in southeast Asia.

2) The Freshwater Unit assesses at a regional and global level the current status of water resources in relation to ecosystems and natural resources, land use and human activity, and elucidates and carries out impact assessments on new fields, priority establishment and cause and effect of pollution. The fields being handled include supply of drinking water and environment sanitation, ground water, storage water, wetlands, inflow load from rivers to coastal areas, and nonpoint pollutants.

3) The Freshwater Unit establishes methodologies for managing the impact exerted on water ecosystems by pollution originating in inland regions. These include impact assessments for pinpoint and nonpoint pollutants in inland waters and surrounding ocean regions.

The following are also being carried out in addition to the above three items.

4) Training courses are carried out, such as courses held with the cooperation of ILEC and IOW, eutrophication courses, and nonpoint pollutant related courses.

5) Textbooks are produced, including revision of eutrophication and nonpoint pollutant texts, and production of publications and river water management manuals.

6) Radio programmes and pamphlets are also produced.

The water department's budget for 1990 and 1991 was approximately US$8 million, covering the following activities.

- Preparation of the Lake Chad Action Plan carried out in cooperation with the UN Sudano-Sahelian Office (UNSO)
- Initiation of the implementation of the ZACPLAN carried out in cooperation with SADC
- Preparation of the Diagnostic Study of the Aral Sea carried out in cooperation with UNEPCOM and ILEC
- Training courses on environmentally sound management of shared freshwater bodies and protection of the lithosphere carried out in cooperation with UNESCO, UNEPCOM and the ex-USSR Academy of Sciences
- Promotion of environmentally sound management of lakes carried out in cooperation with ILEC

Earmarkings also include support to (a) the International Training Centre for Water Resources Management (IOW/CEFIGRE) in France, (b) conferences, symposiums and other events related to water resources management. Several studies are related to field projects and mostly executed in cooperation with other United Nations organizations such as UNDP, UNICEF, WMO, WHO and FAO.

2. GEMS/WATER

GEMS cooperates with countries worldwide to acquire - through monitoring - data necessary for rational management and current status assessments of the environment at global, regional and national levels. Monitoring of the atmosphere and water quality is undertaken on a worldwide scale.

Water quality monitoring of freshwater is carried out under the GEMS/WATER project. Not only UNEP but also other

UN organizations and governments (such as WHO, WMO and UNESCO) and domestic research institutes of certain countries (starting with the Canadian National Water Research Institute [NWRI]) are cooperating in this project. The first programme commenced in 1977 with the task of tackling global water issues through a worldwide network. The first phase of the programme was completed in 1990 with GEMS/WATER concentrating on the development of monitoring methods and monitoring services in participating countries. The second phase moved onto the establishment of data assessment of water quality problems, interpretation of international lake flows and water management options, and were formally approved by the UNEP/WHO's GEMS/WATER operation committee in August, 1990.

UNEP is presently being strengthened within the UN, and a plan is under way to raise capabilities in relation to water resources management. As a link to this, there is also a plan to place GEMS/WATER under the management of the Water Unit.

3. Global Resources Information Database (GRID)

GRID is a centre usefully employed in globally covering resources information using remote sensing equipment and the Global Information Service (GIS); however, as the creation of a database covering the whole world is difficult, GRID has recently linked up with EMS in an effort to develop the Environmental Assessment and Reporting System. This system does not just emphasize monitoring but also the provision of data necessary for status assessments. Furthermore, the use of information sources as information is also being stressed. The information content targets biodiversity and water.

4. The UNEP International Environmental Technology Centre (UNEP/IETC)

Osaka Office : 2-110, Ryokuchi-koen, Tsurumi-ku,
Osaka 538 Japan
Tel:+81-6-915-4580 Fax:+81-6-915-0304
Shiga Office : 1091 Oroshimo, Kusatsu, Shiga 525 Japan
Tel:+81-775-68-4586 Fax:+81-775-68-4587

The International Environmental Technology Centre (IETC) is a new institution created at the request of the UNEP Governing Council (Decision 16/34). Its offices at two locations in Japan - Osaka City and Shiga Prefecture - officially opened in April 1994.

The Centre's main function is to promote cooperation to facilitate the transfer of environmentally sound technologies (ESTs) to developing countries and countries with economies in transition. IETC pays specific attention to urban problems, such as sewage, air pollution, solid waste, noise, and to the management of freshwater lake and reservoir basins. IETC is supported in its operations by a Japanese foundation at each location: The Global Environment Centre Foundation (GEC) based in Osaka and handling urban environmental problems, and the International Lake Environment Committee Foundation (ILEC) located in Shiga Prefecture and contributing accumulated knowledge on sustainable management of freshwater resources.

The strategy of IETC is based on Agenda 21 emanating from the UNCED process and pursues a result-oriented workplan revolving around three issues, namely (a) Improving access to information on ESTS, (b) Fostering technology cooperation, partnerships and transfer, and (c) Building endogenous capacity.

As a relatively new institution, IETC will produce specific outputs which will help establish it as a Centre of excellence for the study of EST transfer in its area of specialty. Outputs programmed for 1995 and the 1996/97 biennium include an overview on existing information sources for ESTs ; a prototype database containing information on ESTs ; a quarterly newsletter, a technical publication series and other media materials creating public awareness and disseminating information on ESTs ; Local Agenda 21 documents developed for selected cities in collaboration with the UNCHS/UNEP Sustainable Cities Programme (SCP) ; Action Plans for sustainable management of selected lake/reservoir basins ; training needs assessment surveys in the field of decision-making on technology transfer and management of ESTs ; design and implementation of pilot training programmes for adaptation, application and operation of ESTs, and training materials for technology management of large cities and lake/reservoir basins.

Among proposed projects are :

Sub-Issue I : Improved access to information on environmentally sound technologies (ESTs)

- Survey on information systems related to environmentally sound technologies
- Forum on Caspian, Aral and Dead Sea - Perspectives of Water Environment Management and Politics
- Source book on Alternative Technologies for Freshwater Augmentation in Asia
- Source book on Alternative Technologies for Freshwater Augmentation in Africa

- Source book on Alternative Technologies for Freshwater Augmentation in Eastern and Central Europe
- Source book on Alternative Technologies for Freshwater Augmentation in Latin America and Caribbean
- International source book on Environmentally Sound Technologies for Municipal Solid Waste Management
- Transfer of information on environmentally sound technologies to developing countries and countries with economies in transition
- Support to the "Symposium on the Management of Earthquake Wastes"

Sub-Issue II : Fostering technical cooperation, partnerships and training
- Development of demonstration 'Sustainable Shenyang'
- Development of demonstration 'Sustainable Wuhan'
- Integrating the concepts of environmental risk assessment into the sustainable cities planning model
- Environmental consideration for regional development of Lake Erhai and Xier River Basins, China
- Case studies - technology needs for lake management in Indonesia
- Case studies on technology transfer

Sub-Issue III : Building endogenous capacity
- Design and implementation of a pilot training programme on utilization of environmental technology assessment (ETA) for decision-making on management and transfer of environmentally sound technologies
- Training on "Environmentally Sustainable Cities, An Urban Development Leadership Program" for municipal government officials
- Assessment of training needs for adaptation, application and operation of environmentally sound technologies for urban and lake/reservoir management
- Workshop on ecological engineering and ecosystem restoration training, phase 1
- Workshop on Environmental Risk Assessment for Sustainable Cities

IETC staff currently includes seven internationally recruited professionals, four cooperation staff from GEC and ILEC and seven local support staff members. The Centre is closely coordinating its activities with substantive organizations within the UN system. The Centre also seeks partnerships with international and bilateral finance institutions, technical assistance organizations, the private, academic and non-governmental sector, foundations and corporations. An International Advisory Board (IAB) has been established to provide policy level advice to the Executive Director of UNEP on IETC's strategy and the orientation of its programme.

Example 1. (in preparation) :
Source Book on Alternative Technologies for Freshwater Augmentation in Eastern and Central Europe (A Joint Project with the UNEP Freshwater Unit).

The region of Eastern and Central Europe has sufficient freshwater resources. However, over the last decades, the process of urbanization and industrial development which was taking place without adequate environmental protection measures and efficient production technologies had resulted in a tremendous increase in water consumption, and in the depletion and pollution of surface water. The authorities turned to groundwater but over pumping of the groundwater soon lowered the water table and caused wells to dry up. Most surface waters in Eastern and Central Europe are eutrophic. This is a result of discharging nutrient rich sewage effluent and agricultural runoff into the water courses making water unsuitable for most uses.

The main objective of the project is to prepare a thorough inventory of available technologies for augmenting and maximizing use of existing freshwater resources in Eastern and Central Europe. Data on the capital, operation and maintenance cost, ease of operation and suitability of the technologies will be included in the inventory. Case studies of innovative and cost-effective technologies will be documented. The contents of the inventory will be compiled into the Source Book on Technologies for Augmenting Freshwater Resources in Eastern and Central Europe, in a user-friendly format for professionals in the region (to be computerized at a later stage and made available on Internet).

Example 2. (in preparation) :
Environmental Considerations for Regional Development of Lake Erhai and Xier River Basins, China (A Joint Project with the UNEP Freshwater Unit).

Lake Erhai is a freshwater lake located in the western part of Yunnan Province in People's Republic of China. 117 rivers flow into the lake and there is only one river flowing out of the lake, Xier River, which is connected with the upper Mekong system. The economy in the Lake Erhai area is expected to expand dramatically. The UNEP project aims to (i) prepare an integrated technology needs assessment in accordance with Lake Erhai and Xier River basins development plans, including strengthening of existing institutions to assess, develop, manage and apply new technologies and (ii) assessing the environmental impacts of planned tourism development in the area and proposals for sustainable tourism development. The project is a component of a larger UNDP project for the area.

Lake and Reservoir Related Work

Some 12% of GEMS/WATER's monitoring stations are

located at lakes and reservoirs, but this is not sufficient to find out the water quality status of the world's lakes.

The EMINWA programme deals directly with the Aral Sea, Caspian Sea, Lake Titicaca and Lake Chad. Other lakes dealt with include Lake Kariba on the Zambezi River, Lake Victoria on the River Nile and Lake Erhai on the Mekong River. GRID also cooperates with ILEC in various activities including the publishing of a world lake databook and lake management guideline book and lake environment management training (see ILEC for details).

⬆ UNEP/IETC Building in Shiga

United Nations University (UNU)

Address: 5-53-70 Jingumae, Shibuya-ku, Tokyo 150 Japan
Tel:03-3499-2811   Fax:03-3499-2828

Work Outline

The objective of UNU is to research worldwide issues related to the existence, development and welfare of the human race, and disseminate the results. The UNU functions as a headquarters for activity planning and as an axis for its own Research and Training Centres (RTC) and Research and Training Programmes (RTP) that are scattered throughout both developing and developed countries. UNU is - starting with Helsinki's UNU World Institute for Development Economic Research (UNU/WIDER) - promoting the siting of research and training centres (such as the ones listed below) in regions across the globe. These centres take on the special long-term assignments that existing research organizations find it difficult to handle. Actual research and training activities are carried out as set work provided by existing universities and research organizations that collaborate closely with RTC and RTP.

- **UNU/BIOLAC :** UNU Biotechnology Programme for Latin America and the Caribbean
- **UNU/CESG :** UNU Centre for the Study of Governance
- **UNU/IAS :** UNU Institute of Advanced Studies
- **UNU/IIST :** UNU International Institute for Software Technology

- **UNU/INRA :** UNU Institute for Natural Resources in Africa
- **UNU/INTECH :** UNU Institute for New Technologies
- **UNU/WIDER :** UNU World Institute for Development Economics Research

Participation in Environmental Matters

At present environment issues are substantially taken care of at the UNU headquarters by just the vice-principal and the science planning officer. The science planning officer is in charge of research and coordination work. There are other associates at the headquarters, but not enough to handle all the projects, so outside consultants are used when necessary; the UNU also has external advisers. Characteristic activities of the UNU show a strong academic essence centered around interdisciplinary comparative research.

In the case of the environment, UNU is intermittently involved in part of the HDGC project. For example, in the case of environment impact assessments, there are often problems in making practical use of technologies developed in temperate-zone advanced countries in tropical developing countries, so UNU investigates methodologies to see whether or not these technologies can be revised for suitable use in developing countries. Such a methodology workshop was held in Shanghai, China in June 1993.

Water Related Work

The following are the environment projects that are closely related to water; however, water is not really marked for serious attention in the total programme. Nevertheless, water does play a part in regional environment projects such as the ones in Southeast Asia and south of the Sahara desert.

- **Staging of Minamata International Environment Congress Related to Industry, Environment and Health**

    This conference was jointly held with Minamata city in Kumamoto prefecture, Japan in 1991 to raise, among others, the issue of Minamata disease as a Japanese experience of pollution subjugation.

- **UNU Research and Training Centre on Water and Environment**

    One of the study training centres that UNU is installing is a research and training centre on water and environment that is being prepared in the province of Ontario in Canada. This centre is scheduled to focus on problems related to water quality and health related to freshwater. For example, increased amounts of nitrogen in drinking water, the blood fluke problem, contagious diseases conducted by water and the cost of supplying water have been raised as themes. The idea for setting up the centre in province of Ontario came from researchers at the local McMaster University and the Ontario Provincial Government promised to support the project. Like other RTCs, this center will only function as a coordinating office that is scheduled to make use of seven local university networks.

- **Middle East Water Forum**

    In the Middle East there are water resources shortages - foremost on the River Jordan - that could potentially become the cause of disputes over distribution in the future. For this reason, specialists that are knowledgeable about the Middle East will be brought together to research hydro-politics through the creation of several scenarios. An Asian Water Forum is planned as a follow up to this project.

Lake and Reservoir Related Work

The following are projects related to lakes and reservoirs.

- **Aral Sea**

    The water-level reduction and environment problems of the Aral Sea are being focused on. In 1992, UNU cooperated with GIF to hold a forum in Tokyo. UNU is also collaborating with UNEP's Water Unit in the case of the Aral Sea.

- **Limonolgy Training Course**

    This course was held in Brazil at the end of 1993 for young researchers.

- **Central Eurasian Water Forum**

    This forum, focussing on the Aral Sea, Caspian Sea and Dead Sea, was held in March 1995 with the cooperation of the UNEP International Environmental Technology Centre (IETC), United Nations University (UNU), Japan International Corporation Agency (JICA), International Water Resources Association (IWRA), and the International Lake Environment Committee (ILEC).

United Nations Centre for Human Settlements
(UNCHS, usually referred to as HABITAT)

P.O.Box 30030, Nairobi ,Kenya
Tel:+254-2-621234 Fax:+254-2-624266

Work Outline

This organization is involved in projects related to human settlements and is cored around coordinating and information exchange.

Water Related Work

HABITAT increasingly devotes time to the management of water resources, and many programmes reflect this. The recommendation to designate the 1980s as the International Drinking Water Supply and Sanitation Decade was first made at the United Nations Conference on Human Settlements. Since then HABITAT has continued to call for the protection of scarce water resources and the rectifying of waste and degradation, that has resulted from neglect of effective water resources management. Following the UN General Assembly's adoption of the Global Strategy for Shelter to the Year 2000 and HABITAT's designation as the coordinating agency for the implementation of the strategy, special emphasis has been given to the provision of, among others, water supply and sanitation infrastructure based on an enabling role for governments in order to facilitate and assist communities in gaining access to these services essential for achieving "adequate shelter for all".

HABITAT's work in the area of water resources management is based on three broad categories: 1) a programme of applied research, 2) technical cooperation with member states and 3) the provision of information and training. The activities of each category will aim at implementing programmes pertinent to Agenda 21 of the United Nations Conference on Environment and Development held in Rio de Janeiro, Brazil in June 1992. In these programmes, HABITAT will emphasize the demands of management and the environmental impact on water resources posed by the continued rapid rate of urbanization and associated industrial growth.

HABITAT initiated and developed the theme: Water and Sustainable Urban Development for the International Conference on "Water and the Environment" held in Dublin, Ireland from the 26th to 31st of January 1992. Furthermore, HABITAT is in the process of preparing a book-style analytical publication presenting a global overview of conditions and trends in urban water resources, including case support evidence, and presenting requisite policy measures to improve management of resources. Also under preparation is an action programme publication to serve as guidance for the formulation and implementation of technical cooperation projects to help ensure the continued supply of affordable safe water essential for safeguarding sustainable urban development.

HABITAT, in cooperation with the Asian Development Bank (ADB), is presently initiating a programme to enhance the efforts and capabilities of Asian governments for sustaining national development and productivity through environmentally sound management of water resources for urban use. The programme is expected to lead to regional consultations that will investigate, identify and discuss the underlying environmental and developmental issues concerning the supply and use of water in the densely populated cities of Asia. It is also hoped that the programme will develop a consensus on appropriate strategies and actions for managing water resources in a manner that will ensure their continued and sustained supply.

In implementing the programme of work approved by the United Nations Commission on Human Settlements, HABITAT will, during 1992 and 1993, carry out applied research leading to the production of a variety of reports on infrastructure operation and maintenance including strategic options for their management, methods of financing and recovering maintenance expenses; as well as corresponding guidelines for legal and institutional arrangements. Much of this work will focus on water supply and sanitation infrastructure. In addition, HABITAT continues to expand its present programme of research aimed at providing technical guidance and associated policy frameworks for delivering water supply and sanitation facilities to the urban poor.

HABITAT is an active member of the Water Supply and Sanitation Collaborative Council Global Forum. Following the presentation of the key-note paper on "Urbanization: Water Supply and Sanitation Sector Challenges" at the last meeting of the Global Forum, HABITAT - together with the Italian Government and other bilateral agencies - is currently establishing a working group to identify policy measures and technical means by which basic services can be extended to urban poor communities. Often, present-day constraints go beyond the immediate water and sanitation sector and include such aspects as security of tenure, resource mobilization and infrastructure development financing. Given the inextricable link between these issues and the provision and upgrading of shelter and the fact that, while improved health and environmental protection are often the principal objectives of providing basic services, many of the intervening actions to achieve these objectives must be taken within the context of human settlements planning and construction, new approaches that take implicit account of these relationships are being currently pursued. While the HABITAT/bilateral collaborative applied research initiative will focus on water supply and sanitation, these services should be integrated with other basic services such as garbage disposal and stormwater drainage will also be given emphasis. In view of the fact that garbage disposal services and stormwater drainage facilities are important determinants of urban water and environmental quality, HABITAT is also currently engaged in applied research in these complementary basic services.

HABITAT expects technical cooperation in the provision of solid waste and stormwater drainage services to increase considerably during the present decade, in direct response to the need to prevent, control and reduce water pollution. HABITAT has also produced various other technical publications on a variety of water-related issues.

As an executing agency, HABITAT implements projects funded by the UN Development Programme (UNDP), organizations and funds-in-trust. HABITAT's technical cooperation programme covers all aspects of rural and urban settlements development, from policy formulation and preparation of engineering studies to the construction of infrastructure facilities. The provision of water supply and sanitation facilities often forms an integral component of many of these settlements development projects. The following are projects dealing exclusively with the provision of basic services.

- Planning and preparing of preliminary engineering studies for the first-stage implementation of sanitation systems for Kabul

- Preparing of a feasibility study for the use of sewage farming in Karachi
- Building of capacity for management of water problems in Yangon, Myanmar

At present, HABITAT has a total of 285 ongoing technical cooperation projects in 100 countries with an aggregate annual budget of over US$45 million and additional "Pipeline" projects awaiting funding. Approximately 20 percent of the ongoing projects include elements exclusively related to the planning and construction of water supply and sanitation facilities or components of settlement provision and upgrading.

In addition to the above technical cooperation projects, HABITAT, in cooperation with the World Bank and UNDP, continues its activities under the "Urban Management Programme". Many of these activities are geared towards prevention, control and reduction of water pollution and as such are relevant to improved water resources management. The programme, with its principal objective of galvanizing the contribution that cities and towns in developing countries make to national economic growth and social development, aims to protect the urban environment and promote urban efficiency through appropriate urban policies, programmes, practices and management techniques. The programme is now entering its second phase (1992-96) during which regional networks of experts will be established to take increasing responsibility for the programme's activities including country consultations and related capability building activities.

HABITAT supports the building of national capabilities through human resource development and institutional strengthening for the planning and implementation of water supply and sanitation services. In addition to the in-service training, field visits and seminars arranged under different technical cooperation projects, HABITAT also conducts tailored seminars and workshops on related issues including municipal finance, community participation in service provision and promotion of the role of women, service delivery and upkeep. It is expected that increasing emphasis will, during the present decade, be directed towards the establishment of pollution control monitoring facilities and the training of personnel for this purpose.

International Research and Training Institute for the Advancement of Women (INSTRAW)

Water Related Work

In line with the goals of the International Drinking Water Supply and Sanitation Decade (IDWSSD), INSTRAW developed a programme which aims at promoting and enhancing the involvement of women in global water and sanitation programmes. The Institute's specific role and goals are to highlight the importance of involving women at all levels of planning and implementation of water supply and sanitation projects and programmes, and to strengthen their contribution to the water resources sector through appropriate training programmes.

In 1986, INSTRAW prepared, in cooperation with the ILO-Turin Centre, multi-media training packages on "Women, Water Supply and Sanitation" for use by senior officials in charge of water programmes and projects, development officials, engineers, NGOs and women's organizations. Five national training seminars were organized in Africa (Ethiopia, Kenya, Somalia, Sudan and Nigeria) during 1987 and 1988. Regional training seminars for Asia and the Pacific region were held in Thailand in 1989, and in September of 1992. The modules have been up-dated recently to include the achievements attained so far in response to the goals of the IDWSSD.

The modules consist of a package containing all the information, examples, exercises, audio-visual support material for 1) the trainers to deliver a lesson or conduct training activities, 2) the trainees to analyze, reinforce and apply theoretical concepts learned during training sessions and 3) the professionals to possess self-learning reference material to upgrade their knowledge and skills related to effectively integrating women in water supply and sanitation projects and programmes.

INSTRAW, in cooperation with the French Foundation de l'Eau, prepared in 1989 a community-level training module on "Women, Water Supply and Sanitation", which is complementary to the INSTRAW-ILO/Turin Centre training package on the same subject.

INSTRAW is a member of the Water Supply and Sanitation Collaborative Council, of the Steering Committee for Co-operative Action on Water Supply and Sanitation, and, jointly with UNDP/Prowess, chairs the Inter-Agency Task Force on Women, Water Supply and Sanitation.

World Food Programme (WFP)

Major Fields of Activity

- Use of food commodities as aid for economic social development, and execution of projects
- Action in the case of emergency food shortages
- Promotion of worldwide food commodities safety guarantees

The World Food Programme (WFP) mobilizes food and cash resources for development and humanitarian purposes and delivers food and non-food items to targeted countries. It also provides services to interested governments for food purchases, shipments, overland transportation and the monitoring of distribution. WFP food assistance is an important additional resource that allows governments to expand their activities. WFP assists countries by offering

advisory services to find the appropriate activities within their respective national development plans that require food aid as an investment resource. It includes design, appraisal, implementation and evaluation of WFP-supported projects to ensure that they are soundly executed in an effort to fulfill pre-defined goals. WFP staff work in close cooperation with Government counterpart staff. The United Nations and its specialized agencies such as FAO, ILO, UNESCO and WHO provide WFP with technical assistance as required against payment of the related costs.

WFP assistance is directed to the poorest level of the population in 91 developing countries, where each year some 34 million people receive WFP-supplied food within the framework of development projects alone. This is in addition to millions of refugees and other victims of disasters who receive humanitarian relief assistance.

Nearly two thirds of WFP's total development assistance of $3.2 billion goes to projects that support increased agricultural production, the construction of rural infrastructures, assisting new settlers in agricultural lands or improving urban environments. Activities include some $260 million for catchment area management and $136.5 million for support of irrigation projects. Other rural development activities include increasing the access to clean water for rural people and provision of improved sanitation facilities in both rural and urban areas. The remaining third of WFP's development assistance is used to fund development of human resources, including the provision of basic education, improved

health care and nutrition, and support to various types of training activities.

In relation to humanitarian relief, WFP cooperates with national authorities, FAO and other relevant United Nations agencies and programmes and non governmental organizations in order to carry out emergency food aid. It collects and distributes information on emergency food aid and related logistics; supplies food commodities and, in certain cases, vehicles and equipment, storage facilities and related management services to ensure the smooth and timely distribution of relief to people affected by man-made and natural disasters. Currently nearly half of WFP-provided emergency food aid helps victims of droughts or crop failures.

United Nations Centre for Regional Development (UNCRD)

Nagoya International Building, 1-47-1 Nagono, Nakamura-ku, Nagoya, 450 Japan
Tel:+81-52-561-9379, Fax:+81-52-561-9374

Work Outline

The UN Centre for Regional Development (UNCRD) was established in Nagoya in June 1971 through a signed agreement between the UN and the Japanese Government, with the objective of developing practical skills for the production of regional development planning in developing countries: Asia, Pacific, Africa, Latin America and the Caribbean Islands. Since then, UNCRD - among all the UN organizations - has developed activities as an individual organization, generally functioning in the area of regional development training and study research.

UNCRD belongs to the UN Department of Development Support and Management Services (UNDDSMS, headquarters in New York) and runs on a trust fund supplied by the Japanese Government to the United Nations. The centre is also funded by domestic regional self-governing bodies (mainly one city and three prefectures in the Tokai region: Nagoya city, Aichi, Gifu and Mie prefectures). The current size of the organization is approximately ten UN specialists, ten UN general staff, 12 national experts from Japan, 14 research fellows from developing countries, ten on-loan staff from prefectures and cities in Japan, and 20 secretaries. As nearly all the work is carried out with the cooperation of Japanese domestic and overseas universities, research organizations and other related bodies, the amount of work actually accomplished is far more than the number of researchers would suggest.

At present, UNCRD has study research and training units in seven fields - namely, an Environment Management Unit, a City and Residential Unit, a Regional Business Unit, a Regional Disaster Prevention Unit, an Information System Unit, a Social Development Unit and an Industrial Development Unit. The study research and training related to regional development in developing countries is the central work of the centre, and is fundamentally executed within the above seven fields upon requests from developing countries. Furthermore, the centre has local agencies: the Africa Regional Office (established in Nairobi in December 1991) and the Japan Regional Office (established in Yokkaichi in May 1993).

The following three items are essential to regional development of developing countries: 1) preparation of necessary finance, 2) establishment of a suitable system and organization, 3) development of human resources to implement the first two items. UNCRD is mainly concerned with the third item "development of human resources", and, therefore, this is the nucleus of training activities.

For this reason, UNCRD is completely different from other UN organizations, in that all its staff are specialists involved directly in training rather than just mediating for external organizations and coordinating financial assistance such as providing scholarships and covering the costs for sending people to project sites. This command of technology and knowledge held by the staff has to be updated to meet the changing social situations in developing countries. It is for

13

this reason that UNCRD concentrates on studies and research in combination with training activities. The results of UNCRD's studies and research are always reflected in training material or training is provided for the staff involved with that subject as a means of concluding the relevant study and research. This differs from the pure research for study and research executed by universities and research organizations. In other words, UNCRD's activities show an effective approach that is directly useful for regional development in developing countries.

The direction of training is responding to recent changes in the many aspects of regional development in developing countries. Broadly speaking these changes come under the following two points.

1) Steering toward sustainable development that considers - as an absolute condition - the impact on the environment (including safety).

2) Changing over to a local and regional government centralized planning system from a central authority planning and execution system run by public authority.

Participation in Environmental Matters

In recent years, within the trend of stronger global awareness of the environmental problems facing Earth, there is an increased concentration on tackling environment issues that are linked to the promotion of regional development in developing countries; therefore, the Environment Management Unit of UNCRD is also being broadly strengthened and numerous research and training activities are being promoted. These activities will be implemented with the aim of searching for efficient methods and measures for promoting sustainable regional social development that considers the environment through cooperation with internally and externally related organizations. The acquired results will be widely disseminated among staff of regional development and environment conservation offices in developing countries. The following shows the developments in two central issues.

1) Management of environment resources related to regional development (namely, management of water resources in the area of river and lake basins and forest cultivation for domestic use) is being targeted as a serious issue.

2) Management of the environment (namely, the improvement of garbage disposal in mega-cities and capability strengthening of regional public groups for city environment management) is being targeted as an issue for sustainable city development in Asia.

UNCRD, including the Environment Management Unit, put together and make public the progress and results in their various activities in the following periodic publications.

- **UNCRD Newsletter** (biannual publication with English and Japanese editions)
- **Regional Development Dialogue** (biannual publication in English)
- **Regional Development Studies** (annual publication in English)
- **UNCRD Annual Report** (English and Japanese editions)

Water Related Work

With regard to the management of water resources seen from the Environment Management Unit's perspective of river and lake basins, UNCRD is targeting methods for proposing and executing management plans for water resources that encompass the ecosystems of river and lake basins and socio-economic changes together with the pursuit of a strategy and an organized and systemized framework for raising the efficiency of such methods. The following are the domains of the major issues for study and research.

- Relationships between land use revisions in catchment areas and water resources management in down stream areas
- Conflict management between water utilization departments
- Political measures for the environmental and social impacts that accompany water resources development

With cooperation from the relevant governments and research organizations, UNCRD is studying and researching issues in the Dali and Lake Erhai regions in Unnan province, China, the northern region of Laos and the La Plata River region of South America that focus on the coordinating and managing of water resource uses in areas between the upper and lower reaches of rivers; balancing out the benefit and damage relationship between the main differing uses related to water use; managing catchment area resources through community participation, and studying environmental and social impacts related to water resources development.

Lakes and Reservoir Related Work

UNCRD, in joint cooperation with UNEP and ILEC from 1987 to 1990, carried out case studies on lakes and reservoirs in nine countries worldwide (Lake Biwa, Lake Kasumigaura, Yahagi River, Lake Laguna, Lake Victoria, Broa Reservoir, Sagling Reservoir, Lake Sonkhla and Lake Dianchi). Related workshops under the theme of "water environment management with basin perspective included" were also carried out. As a follow up to this work, related regional workshops and workshops in developing countries were held from 1991 (Philippines in 1990, China in 1991 and the countries in the La Plata basin). Furthermore, the above regional development and environment management plan for the Dali and Lake Erhai regions of China are directly related to the conservation of Lake Erhai.

⭘ Follow-up national training course supported by UNCRD

United Nations Department of Development Support and Management Services (DDSMS)

(Former United Nations Department of Economic and Social Development [DESD] has undergone a transformation and is now known as the above DDSMS. The following explanation includes activities undertaken during the DESD era.)

Water Related Activities

The water programme of the United Nations Department of Economic and Social Development (DESD) comprises the water-related activities of the former United Nations Departments of International Economic and Social Affairs (DIESA) and of Technical Cooperation for Development (DTCD). The programme is implemented through the Water Resources Branch of the Division for Science, Technology, Energy, Environment and Natural Resources. DESD thus deals with both research and coordination, and technical cooperation activities. The Branch functions under a broad mandate laid down by the UN Charter as well as by more specific resolutions of the General Assembly and the Economic and Social Council, and the special instructions of the Secretary-General which created the Department of Economic and Social Development on the 1st of March 1992, and consolidated all the functions and mandates of five previous United Nations departments or centres.

The research and coordination activities of the Water Resources Branch of DESD involves the promotion of system-wide cooperation among the organizations of the UN system concerned with water resources development and management through systematic coordination and joint planning of activities. It also includes the gathering and analysis of information and reporting thereon to the General Assembly and/or the Economic and Social Council through the Committee on Natural Resources. These activities are undertaken in connection with the review by the above-mentioned bodies of the progress made by governments and by the organizations of the system in the implementation of the Mar del Plata Action Plan adopted by the UN Water Conference in 1977. The gathering and analysis of information as well as the preparation of reports are carried out in conjunction with the regional commissions, the specialized agencies, and other organizations concerned.

The Water Resources Branch also serves as Secretariat to the Intersecretariat Group for Water Resources (ISGWR). This body is a coordinating mechanism for system-wide activities established by the Administrative Committee on Coordination in 1979 and subsequently noted by the Economic and Social Council. The Department has two specialists, who work full time in the Secretariat of the ISGWR. Other organizations provide supplementary assistance, as needed.

The bulk of the Branch's programme is, however, directed at technical cooperation activities involving operational projects in the field. The projects cover such areas as the establishment of national water resources institutions, groundwater exploration and development, planning of combined surface and groundwater development, river basin development planning; and they involve resources assessment, water supply and demand management for different uses, various technological and socio-economic studies and research, training and promotion of technical cooperation for development. To backstop its technical cooperation activities, the Branch has five regular programme posts at headquarters, as well as seven technical advisers and four interregional advisers.

Typical Projects Executed by DESD

The typical projects executed by the Water Resources Branch of DESD fall into the following four broad areas.

- Assessment and development
- Planning and management
- Conservation and water law
- Training and capacity building

The Branch conducts hydrogeological and hydrological surveys and offers assistance in rural water development in many parts of the world. It has also carried out a considerable number of groundwater and rural water supply projects throughout the developing world, with particular emphasis on the promotion of appropriate technologies to increase water supply, and adapting them to local conditions. A typical example of the Branch's activities in this area is its project to supply potable water to 130 rural villages in the Sahelian region of Chad. Over a 21-month period, more than 500 boreholes were drilled to tap groundwater circulating within fractured granitic rock, with a 55 percent rate of success in difficult hydrogeological conditions.

Frequently, the most critical need is not technological so much as administrative and managerial assistance, and thus the Branch has often provided support for the establishment of the institutional machinery to plan, operate and monitor water resources. In this area, for example, the Branch is helping the Chinese State Science and Technology Commission to develop a water management model for the water-short, heavily populated North China region. In a break with reliance on traditional water master plans, this model integrates hydrological data with sociopolitical, environmental and economic objectives to develop guidelines for allocating water among different users.

The Branch also assists developing countries in formulating laws and pricing policies which encourage efficient water development and reduce water loss. Advice focuses on the protection of water supplies, the development of sound environmental water policies, introduction of principles in water legislation, identification of pollution sources and promotion of clean-up efforts. The above-mentioned water management modeling project in China, for example, also helped the Government to develop plans and regulations for reducing agricultural waste, controlling groundwater pollution and treating industrial wastewater.

Finally, a key element in the Branch's work is human resources development. This is mainly done through seminars and workshops on all aspects of water use and management, on-the-job training of national staff, and the provision of educational programmes in both water quality protection and efficient water use to local communities. The above-mentioned rural water supply project in the Sahel, for instance, also trained 80 nationals in hydrogeological and geophysical techniques, and educated villagers in pump maintenance and water-related health measures. Another typical example of the Branch's activities in this area can be found in its broad five-year programme with the aim of developing the water resources of various Pacific island countries which, among other things, helped to strengthen the capabilities of national water authorities through training and technical guidance, including the drafting of appropriate legislation.

United Nations Committee for Sustainable Development (CSD)

CSD was established in February 1993 under ECOSOC as a follow up organization of UNCED. CSD's mandate is to monitor implementation status of respective topics of Agenda 21 which is to be reviewed at a special session in 1997. CSD also submit recommendations where appropriate. The status of freshwater supply and quality was examined in 1994.

All of the UN regional economic commissions carry out the following.

- Cooperation for economic social development within designated regions
- Proposals for the maintenance and development of economic relationships between countries inside and outside designated regions, and participation in actual activities
- Execution and support of studies and research for solving economic and technological problems within designated regions
- Collection, arrangement and provision of information related to economic and technological statistics

Economic and Social Commission for Africa (ECA)

Water Related Work

In relation to water resources programmes, ECA concentrates its efforts on the priority needs of the African region as a follow-up to the Mar del Plata Action Plan, which, in turn, is carried out within the context of the Lagos Plan of Action. These efforts are made by the Water Resources Unit, located within the Natural Resources Division of the Commission. The unit is staffed by three specialists. The Commission's work is executed in cooperation and consultation with other UN organizations, such as: WHO, WMO, UNEP, UNESCO, FAO, ADB, DESD and the World Bank. It also works in close consultation with the Organization of African Unity.

Drinking water supply and sanitation is a major part of the Commission's work. The Commission follows up on the progress made by member states towards reaching the goals of the International Drinking Water Supply and Sanitation Decade. In connection with this, the Commission prepared in 1989 a paper on the economic aspects of drinking water supply and sanitation in Africa with particular reference to rural areas. In 1990 ECA prepared a study on conservation and rational use of water resources in selected North African member states. In 1991, the Commission prepared a review of progress in the implementation of the Mar del Plata Action Plan in Africa together with strategies for its implementation in the 1990s.

The Commission also prepared in 1990 and 1991 reports and studies on such subjects as: i) water situation in Africa, ii) status of river and lake basin development in Africa, and is at present preparing technical publications on (a) large scale water transfers and their implications for water resources development in Africa, and (b) case studies on strategies and policies for water resources development in Africa. During 1992 and 1993 ECA intends to publish a directory of water resources specialists in Africa and a study on problems, prospects and strategies for integrated development of water resources of the Nile River.

ECA's activities also involve surface and ground water resources assessment. In the case of groundwater, the work of the commission aims at assisting member countries in the exploration and development of these resources, and at strengthening their related institutional and manpower needs. ECA recently cooperated with UNDESD in updating the national profiles on groundwater for West African as well as Central and South African member states. In the case of surface water, ECA, jointly with WMO, executed a project on planning and development of hydrometeorological networks and related services in Africa. The project aimed at strengthening national hydrological services and networks, and promoting cooperation between countries on assessment of data on surface water resources and on river system operation and management.

With regard to water for agriculture, the secretariat in the early 1980s conducted a study on land and water resources potential for irrigation in Mozambique, Somalia and Tanzania. The study included assessment of existing and potential irrigation schemes and identification, planning, improvement of existing irrigation schemes and strengthening of national irrigation service institutions in these countries.

The Commission actively promotes subregional and regional cooperation in the development of shared water resources in Africa. In this respect, the Commission provides coordination and technical assistance to such subregional intergovernmental organizations as the UNDUGU, Hydro-Tech, OMVS, OMVG, KBO, LCBC, NBA, CILSS, Mano River Union and a host of others. It is also making efforts to promote cooperation among the Nile basin countries and the riparian countries of Lake Tanganyika/Kivu basin with a view to promoting the establishment of intercountry organizations for integrated development of these rivers and lake basins.

ECA periodically stages meetings, seminars and study tours on various issues of water resources development. For example, a Regional Meeting on Socio-economic and Policy Aspects of Water Resources Management was held in June 1986. The goals of the meeting were to assess the progress made and the constraints encountered by countries in water resources management. An interregional meeting on River and Lake Basin Development with emphasis on the Africa region was held by ECA and the former Department of Technical Cooperation for Development at Addis Ababa from 10 to 15 October 1988. The goal was to make a detailed examination of the legal, political, economic and technical aspects of basin development. Some 36 technical papers were presented for discussion which included case studies from Africa and other regions of the world.

ECA is actively involved in promoting information exchange in the field of water resources development in Africa. For this reason ECA has published four issues of a yearly information bulletin entitled 'MAJI' since 1988. It is planned that this will be a recurrent publication in future years as well.

Economic Commission for Europe (ECE)

Water Related Work

ECE has worked hard to promote and strengthen regional cooperation among its member states in the field of water management. The water programme of the Commission is formulated and implemented by senior advisers to ECE Governments on environmental and water problems assisted by the working party on water problems. A number of water-related activities in the field of industry, agriculture, energy production, transport and statistics are being carried out by senior advisers in cooperation with other principal subsidiary bodies of the Commission. ECE has two specialists on water related problems in its Environment and Human Settlements Division. Reports and expertise, provided by Governments at no cost to the Commission, contribute to an efficient programme.

Cooperation in the field of environment and water management has developed into a priority activity of the Commission. It gained substantial momentum by the Final Act of the Conference on Security and Cooperation in Europe (CSCE), the 1977 United Nations Water Conference, the Concluding Documents of the Madrid and Vienna CSCE Follow-up Meetings and the outcome of the 1988 Sofia CSCE Meeting on the Protection of the Environment. The response of the Commission and its member governments to the challenge of sustainable water management by, among others, prevention control and reduction of water pollution as well as rational use of water has been productive in terms of soft-law instruments such as strategies, policy recommendations, declarations, charters and codes of conduct. A legally binding instrument, the Convention on the Protection and Use of Transboundary Watercourses and International Lakes was signed in Helsinki in March 1992.

Significant efforts have been made to strengthen cooperation in the field of transboundary waters. Intensive negotiation and cooperative action have led to a number of ECE policy declarations and decisions in this field. Examples include the 1980 Declaration of Policy on Prevention and Control of Water Pollution, including Transboundary Pollution, and the 1987 Principles Regarding Cooperation in the Field of Transboundary Waters.

A Code of Conduct on Accidental Pollution of Transboundary Inland Waters, adopted by the Commission in 1990, provides guidance to the competent authorities in individual member countries in their task of protecting transboundary inland waters against pollution resulting from hazardous activities in the event of accidents or natural disasters. A first approach was made towards a concept of responsibility and liability regarding transboundary water pollution.

With the commission's support a number of water-related recommendations to ECE Governments have been adopted in particular on: long-term planning of water management (1976); selected water problems in islands and coastal areas with special regard to desalination and ground water (1978); rational utilization of water (1979); economic instruments for rational utilization of water resources (1980); water pollution from animal production (1981); drinking water supply and affluent disposal systems (1982); rational use of water in industrial processes (1985); water management systems (1986); protection of ground waters against non-point sources of pollution (1988); dam safety with particular emphasis on small dams (1989); waste-water treatment (1989) and waste-water management (1991). Recently, the Seminar on Ecosystems Approach to Water Management (1991) elaborated a set of draft recommendations to ECE Governments on ecosystems-based water management as a holistic way of viewing, planning and managing the ecosystems components, promoting sustainment of these components and the environment as a whole.

Other soft-law instruments such as declarations and charters address specific water problems. The 1984 Declarations of Policy on the Rational Use of Water, for example, aims at combating wasteful water use and effectively supporting policies of prevention, control and reduction of pollution in the ECE region. Intense regional cooperation has also been directed towards reaching agreement on common policies for the protection of groundwater resources which are threatened by over-use and the long-term effects of pollution. The adoption of the Charter on Groundwater Management by the Commission in 1989 was the result of these activities.

The prevention, control and reduction of water pollution caused in particular by discharges from industrial and municipal sources ; agricultural methods which rely on the heavy use of fertilizers and pesticides ; run-off from urban and industrial areas including the accidental pollution of soils, unsaturated zones and aquifers ; the percolation of pollutants from sanitary landfills; and wet and dry fallouts of airborne pollutants call for water management policies with broad linkages to policies in other sectors of national economies. The promotion of integrated water management policies necessitates the further strengthening of international cooperation, as stipulated in the 1988 Regional Strategy for Environmental Protection and Rational Use of Natural Resources in ECE member countries covering the period up to the year 2000 and beyond. The implementation of the regional strategy in the field of water is currently being promoted through various cooperative activities, including the application of the ecosystems approach to water management, eutrophication control and the restoration of prime water quality, the prevention and control of water pollution resulting from agricultural production, water-quality criteria and objectives, the protection and use of transboundary waters as well as statistics on water use and quality.

Economic Commission for Latin America and the Caribbean (ECLAC)

Water Related Work

ECLAC undertakes, through the Division of Natural Resources and Energy, activities in the water resources field with the following goals.

- Support efforts by governments for the development and sustainable use of water resources.
- Facilitate cooperation between adjacent countries.
- Improve and coordinate water-related activities being carried out by the UN specialized agencies and other international agencies.
- Implement, within the general aims set out above, the recommendations of the Mar del Plata Action Plan.

The activities for water resources place emphasis on the following areas.

- Review developments in water management policies and programmes in the countries of the region.

- Identify suitable areas for horizontal technical cooperation and the promotion of such cooperation.
- Support activities of Governments to incorporate the environmental dimension into water resources management practices.

Examples of ECLAC Projects

The following are some of ECLAC's typical projects.

- Preparation of a report "Inventory of Water Resources and their Use" on the utilization of water resources in Latin America and the Caribbean.
- Promotion of training in the management of water resource projects and systems.
- Preparation of reports on research projects similar to that produced on the current state of water resources management in the region.

Economic and Social Commission for Asia and the Pacific (ESCAP)

UN Building, Rajadamnern Avenue, Bangkok 10200, Thailand
Tel:+66-2-282-9161 Fax:+66-2-282-9602

Water Related Work

ESCAP has a long history of activities in water resources, focusing in the earlier years on flood control problems, but broadened later on to encompass most aspects of water resources assessment, development and management. Results are widely distributed through UN sales publications, such as "Water Resources Series" (known until 1963 as "Flood Control Series"), with No. 1 appearing in 1951 and in 1991 up to No. 68. Since 1952, ESCAP has also published a quarterly "Water Resources Journal" and since 1982 a semi-annual newsletter, "Confluence". The publications cover a variety of research topics as well as proceedings of conferences, inter-governmental committee sessions, symposiums and seminars organized by ESCAP.

ESCAP was the prime force behind the establishment of the Committee for Coordination of Investigations of the Lower Mekong River Basin (Mekong Committee), which is a model for international river basin cooperation. In cooperation with WMO, ESCAP established the Typhoon Committee and the WMO/ESCAP Panel on Tropical Cyclones to reduce flood damage caused by tropical cyclones. These have their own offices (in Manila and Dhaka, respectively) and receive UNDP and other extrabudgetary support with ESCAP providing technical back-up.

Activities are designed based on the results of periodic surveys carried out as part of the Mar del Plata Action Plan that identified the areas in which countries require support from international agencies. Therefore, in the period from 1992 to 1997, ESCAP will concentrate on assisting member countries in the following.

- Application of integrated water resources management within the context of national economic and social development plans
- Improvement of planning and policy formulation processes, taking into account environmental considerations
- Economic use of water
- Wastewater reuse
- Water quality monitoring and management
- Development and management of water resources in drought affected areas
- Application of microcomputers in water resources development
- Training of technical staff and strengthening of national training institutions
- Dissemination of information on current developments of regional interest, global experience, ideas and techniques applicable to national water resources development programmes in the region

The secretariat will also undertake the following.

- Assessment and inventory of water resources and demands for water in the region
- Promotion of regional cooperation in water resources development through technical cooperation among developing countries (TCDC) and other means
- Coordinating the activities of the interagency Task Force on Water for Asia and the Pacific

ESCAP's natural disaster reduction work will aim to strengthen disaster preparedness and alleviating capabilities of member countries through provision of technical assistance and training of key personnel in the following areas.

- Prediction and early warning of natural disasters, risk assessment of water-related hazards, hazard mapping and land-use planning, hazard monitoring and damage assessment
- Selection of appropriate structural and non-structural measures for minimization of risk to lives, property and infrastructure
- Strengthening or establishment of institutional frameworks for natural disaster preparedness and alleviation
- Development of appropriate guidelines and strategies for application of existing knowledge and new technologies on water-related natural disaster reduction

Advisory services will be provided to member countries on various aspects of water resources development and management as well as on natural disaster reduction.

Economic and Social Commission for Western Asia (ESCWA)

Water Related Work

The main problems of the ESCWA region concern the arid and semiarid climate giving rise to critical limitations in the supply of water to meet the full demand for domestic, agricultural, industrial and other uses. The absence of national water planning and well-designed policies limits the capability of the region to achieve optimum social and economic growth as well as food production. A collective intercountry approach has been limited and no effective regional mechanism exists for this purpose.

Following the regional recommendations from the Water Conference in 1977, ESCWA held a second regional meeting (Riyadh, 1979). Subsequently, in following the recommendations of the Commission in 1980, the possibility of establishing a regional water resources council has been envisaged. An ad-hoc expert group meeting on water security, held by ESCWA in November 1989, once expressed support for the concept. ESCWA is aiming to establish such a council between 1992 and 1993, in an advisory capacity, and with a view to coordinating efforts of the regional organizations and bodies active in the field of water resources.

Hence, the general goals of ESCWA's water programmes are oriented toward promoting and intensifying inter-regional and regional cooperation and coordination in order to conserve, develop and use water resources in the most efficient and economic way. In this regard, appropriate level of emphasis is placed on optimum development and use of conventional water resources and on non-conventional ones, particularly in ESCWA oil producing countries. ESCWA will also follow up and monitor progress achieved in the Mar del Plata Action Plan in the 1990s, and participate in the efforts of the United Nations System in the area of water supply and sanitation.

ESCWA is currently involved in a number of activities such as establishing a regional water resources database, surveying potential areas for regional cooperation and setting-up institutions for this purpose, including a regional water training network, promoting technical cooperation in the field of water resources development and providing assistance for the assessment of water resources within the region. These activities are expected to be supplemented with additional meetings and studies. The latter would cover the areas of institutional arrangements, national water plans and policies, research and training programmes and technical cooperation among member countries.

ESCWA's 1990 to 1991 programme provides two professional staff members within its water programme, which is located within the Commission's Energy and Natural Resources Division. The work involves the following.

- Collection, dissemination and exchange of information among countries of the region
- Drawing-up guidelines for efficient water use
- Promotion of new technologies, such as remote sensing and use of isotopes for water exploration and assessment
- Establishing training network and regional water council
- Seminars on selected problems affecting water resources development and planning in the ESCWA region

World Meteorological Organization (WMO)
Case Postale No. 2300, 1211 Geneva 2, Switzerland
Tel:+41 22 730 81 11   Fax:+41 22 734 23 26

Water Related Work

One of the major purposes of WMO as set out in Article 2 of the WMO Convention is to promote activities in operational hydrology and to further close cooperation between meteorological and hydrological services. The term "operational hydrology" is defined as the "measurement of basic hydrological elements from networks of meteorological and hydrological stations, including collection, transmission, processing, storage, retrieval and publication of basic hydrological data". Thus operational hydrology is strongly inter-related with water resource assessment. WMO's activities are exercised through the Hydrology and Water Resources Programme (HWRP), which assists the Hydrological Services of Members in operational hydrology and in mitigating water related hazards such as floods and droughts. In accordance with the recommendations of the United Nations Water Conference, the overall objective of the proposals made by HWPR for the Decade 1992 to 2001 within the WMO Third Long-Term Plan is: to ensure the assessment and forecasting of the quantity and quality of water resources, in order to meet the needs of all sectors of society, to enable mitigation of water-related hazards, and to maintain or enhance the condition of the global environment.

HWRP is closely linked to other WMO programmes which have important hydrological components, such as the Tropical Cyclone Programme (TCP) and the World Climate Programme (WCP). In addition, a substantial proportion of WMO's technical cooperation is in the field of operational hydrology, funded largely through UNDP. Regional aspects of projects covered by the HWRP are implemented principally by the six regional working groups on hydrology of WMO's regional associations. The HWRP contributes to, or has links with, a large number of other international programmes, in particular those of UNESCO, UNEP, WHO, FAO, and the UN Regional Economic Commissions.

1. Hydrological Water Resources Programme (HWRP)

HWRP is one of WMO's principal programmes, and as well as monitoring in the areas of flooding and water and the environment, it is also developing the Operational Hydrology Programme (OHP) as a management field. UNESCO also has an International Hydrology Programme (IHP); but the differences are that whereas IHP concentrates on research, OHP targets operations. Part of OHP's work is following up on the Mar del Plata Action Plan.

Over a period of some 20 years the HWRP has responded to the changing needs of Members in a world which has seen rapid changes in social and economic conditions, advances in technology, and a growing awareness of the importance of the environment. Accordingly, the proposals contained in WMO's Third Long-Term Plan (1991 to 2001) show an increase in activities at the interfaces between operational hydrology and meteorology, in climate studies and, in particular, in environmental management. The Plan takes account of recent shifts in emphasis towards the study of surface and groundwater quality, and the operational hydrology of urban areas, lakes and reservoirs. It includes the development of the geographical information system (GIS) and studies in response to the accidental release of hazardous pollutants. The programme also comprises areas of activity where greater effort has been called for, such as contributions to the hydrological aspects of the UN International Decade for Natural Disaster Reduction (IDNDR) (1990 to 1999), and the follow-up to the International Drinking Water Supply and Sanitation Decade (IDWSSD) (1981 to 1990).

The following are HWRP's three major functions.

1) Operational Hydrology Programme (OHP)-Basic Systems

This component concentrates on the basic organization and phased development of Hydrological Services. It includes development, comparison, standardization and improvement of instruments and methods for the collection and archiving of water resources information (quantity and quality of both surface water and groundwater), and human resource development. Specific support to the transfer of technology is provided through the Hydrological Operational Multipurpose Subprogramme (HOMS).

2) Operational Hydrology Programme (OHP)-Applications and Environment

The component brings together hydrological activities in support of water-resource development and management, including hydrological modeling and forecasting, and the provision of data for a range of projects, including those for environmental protection. It contributes to various meteorological and climatological programmes of WMO, such as the Tropical Cyclone Programme (TCP) and the World Climate Programme (WCP).

3) Programme on Water-Related Issues

The component contributes to the international programmes of other bodies within the UN family and those of intergovernmental organizations and NGOs through inter-agency coordination and collaboration in water-related activities, including regional projects associated with large international river basins.

2. Operational Hydrological Programme (OHP)

The OHP is planned and executed under sponsorship of the WMO Commission for Hydrology (CHy). Implementation is principally through a system of working groups and individual rapporteurs, who address specific aspects of operational hydrology appropriate to their expertise, through the convening of technical meetings and symposiums, and through organizing training courses.

Specific projects are designed to investigate and compare technology such as instruments, forecasting models and network design techniques. Projects results are published, principally in the series of WMO Operational Hydrological Reports. The essence of these and other activities are summarized in the Guide to Hydrological Practices, currently being updated for its fifth edition, which provides guidance to key subjects over a wide range of conditions including minimum network densities. Agreed standard practice is published in Volume III (Hydrology) of the WMO Technical Regulations.

Working groups on hydrology are also established by the six regional associations of WMO to address some topics covered by the HWRP and others relevant to the hydrological problems of their respective regions. These include, in particular, the following.

- Surveys of the adequacy of networks of hydrological stations, hydrological data transmission and processing facilities, databanks, hydrological forecasting

- Application of WMO standards and recommended practices in hydrology
- Development and promotion of the Hydrological Operational Multipurpose Subprogramme (HOMS)
- Contributions to projects under the World Climate Programme-Water

3. Hydrological Operation Multipurpose System (HOMS)

The Hydrological Operational Multipurpose System (HOMS) is a technology transfer system for operational hydrology that was established in 1981 under the OHP. Its aim is to assist hydrologists, primarily in developing countries, by making available to them technology largely from developed countries, in order to solve their problems.

HOMS is primarily a mainframe database. As developing countries regard practical usage more highly than methodoligies, HOMs follows the same line of thought. Some 2,800 elements are published in 430 books, and GIS and remote sensing are used also. HOMS is provided for in the WMO general budget, and only has one staff and a computer in the headquarters. If possible HOMS would like to install computers in centers in other countries. HOMS is also carried out training for 15 people in Indonesia.

Countries that wish to participate in HOMS designate one domestic location as a HOMS National Reference Centre (HNCR) - 108 countries have done so to date. HNRCs in developing countries tend to coordinate requests for the transfer of technology while those in developed countries more usually make national technology available to users in countries making requests for transfers. The technology available through HOMS is presented in over 400 components - computer software, technical and general guidance manuals, and instruments descriptions covering much of operational hydrology. To the best of WMO's knowledge, between 1981 and August 1990, there were over 2000 requests for the transfer of components. These requests came from some 94 different countries and 14 international organizations. The success of HOMS is a credit to the effective cooperation among the Hydrological WMO Members aided by the Meteorological Services.

4. Databases

The following two computer databases have been established as part of the HWRP. Both databases are regularly updated and important information is published in bookform.

1) The Hydrological Information Referral Service (INFOHYDRO)

This service contains information on national and regional hydrological agencies, networks and data banks of WMO Members (but does not handle actual hydrodynamic data). Information is offered in the form of a book; however, this is scheduled to gradually become an online service. The information includes the following.

- A list of hydrology related organizations in countries and regions
- The hydrology related work of the above organizations
- The world's important river and lake basins
- The number of monitoring stations and their past measuring periods
- Processing and storage status of data collected by countries (including network and databank information)

2) The Global Run-off Data Centre (GRDC)

This centre is in the Federal Institute of Hydrology, Koblenz, Germany (as part of WCP-Water), which holds daily and monthly flow records of selected stations from over 100 countries. Both these databases are regularly updated, and the key information published.

5.   Human Resource Development

Training in hydrology uses a number of different approaches, including: in-service training, training in educational institutions, workshops, seminars, and short-term residency of experts. WMO grants fellowships for study in operational hydrology, and organizes training courses, particularly for hydrological technicians. It also prepares and publishes related guidance and training material. Much of the Organization's support for certain training activities, including international training courses in hydrology, workshops and symposiums, is undertaken in collaboration with UNESCO and other agencies of the United Nations system, and with non-governmental organizations.

6.   Technical Cooperation

The objective of WMO's Technical Cooperation Programme is to assist Members in developing their capabilities and self-reliance to the point where efficient hydrological and meteorological services can contribute effectively to economic and social development. Presently there are three major sources of support, while a smaller effort is channeled through HOMS activities. The sources are as follows.

- The United Nations Development Programme (UNDP)
- WMO's Voluntary Cooperation Programme (VCP)
- Trust Fund arrangements, by means of which assistance is provided by donor countries to specific projects

Other sources, such as the World Bank, the regional development banks, or economic groupings like the Southern African Development Community (SADC), augment the assistance provided. Technical cooperation funds allocated under the regular budget of WMO are very limited, and are used almost exclusively for training and fellowships.

WMO's technical assistance projects are administered by the Technical Cooperation Department, with scientific support and technical backing from the Hydrology and Water Resources Department. The two departments jointly offer, on request, sectorial advisory services in hydrology to UNDP field offices.

International Bank for Reconstruction and Development (World Bank)

1818 H street, N.W. Washington D.C. 20433 USA

Work Outline

The World Bank (WB) together with its affiliated International Development Association (IDA: established in 1960 to support poor countries that cannot pay interest, and up to 1993 has been providing 35 to 40 year long-term, no-interest finance) are frequently referred to as the "World Bank".

Loan Amounts and Ratios (%) in 1992

Departments	Amounts (Unit : US$1million)	Ratio (%)
Agriculture and Rural Development	3,894	17.9
Development Finance	1,025	4.7
Education	1,884	8.7
Energy	4,037	18.6
Oil, Gas, Coal	(980)	(4.5)
Electricity	(3,057)	(14.1)
Industries	789	3.6
Non-project	3,430	15.8
Population, Nutrition, Sanitation	962	4.4
Community Department Management	602	2.8
Small industries	60	0.3
Technical cooperation	196	0.9
Communications	430	2.0
Transport	2,110	9.7
Urban Development	1,377	6.3
Supply Water and Sewage	911	4.2
Total	21,707	100.0

The World Bank, in addition to carrying out some technical assistance and studies on many relevant aspects, provides a "crowning" for resource assessment and pre-investment or feasibility studies, etc., and with others, inside and outside the UN system, makes actual implementation and end results possible through loans and other financing.

Loan Amounts and Ratios (%) of Individual Regions (1992)

Region	Cases (%)	Amounts (%)
Africa	34.7	18.3
East Asia and the Pacific	20.7	25.1
Middle East and North Africa	7.7	6.8
Latin America and Caribbean	20.2	26.1
Europe and Central Asia	6.4	9.9
South Asia	10.4	13.8
Total	100.0	100.0

Participation in Environmental Matters

Entering into the 1990s, the World Bank declared five themes, broader than those conventionally included in environment themes, as environment issues that promised impartial sustainable growth. The five themes are as follows.

1) Alleviation of global poverty
2) Protection of the environment
3) Improvement of education and nutrition, support for sufficient realization of human capacity through family planning
4) Support for debt reduction and economic efficiency
5) Strengthening of public departments

Among the multilateral aid organizations, the World Bank can be said to be a leader in the trend toward global aid, as it has already conclusively financed environment projects, published various guidelines, technical handbooks and other publications, and, notably, developed dynamic activities.

In recent years, the World Bank has been clearly promoting the integration of environmental awareness into its own activities. A comparison of fiscal 1989 and fiscal 1993 shows a thirty-fold quantum leap in environmental lending carried out by the World Bank. The Bank allocates the title "Primarily Environmental Project" to projects with costs and profits for complete environmental conservation action at 50 percent or more of the total cost and the title "Significant Environmental Components Project" to projects with between ten percent and 49 percent of the total cost going to environmental conservation. Fiscal 1992 (1/7/91 to 30/6/92), saw the approval of 19 projects (about US$1.2 billion) for the former and 43 projects for the latter out of 222 approved projects.

Fiscal 1993 (1/7/92 to 30/6/93), saw the approval of 24 projects (US$1.99 billion) for the former and 30 projects for the latter.

The projects are mainly comprised of three types of work - namely, 1) urban and industrial pollution control, 2) natural resources management, 3) environmental institution building. The first type is called the Brown Agenda and has three domains directly linked to cities - energy use and efficiency, prevention of urban and industrial pollution, and management of urban environments. Fiscal 1993 saw seven large-scale projects with funding of US$1.3 billion for water contamination management in Brazil, China, Korea and Turkey, and atmosphere pollution regulations for India and Mexico. The second type is called the Green Agenda and includes management of sustainable water resources and catchment areas. Funding of US$521 million was made available for ten projects, including water resources management and national land conservation for Egypt, India, Pakistan and Turkey.

The World Bank classifies projects with fixed standards, and recipient countries are requested to carry out environment assessments for all projects that have been approved as necessary. Present environment assessments take the form of environmental consideration at both project planning and implementation levels. Screening action probes to find the level of necessity and the degree to which environmental assessment should be executed in order to classify environmental problems by nature and scale in four categories (A, B, C and D). Category A is for projects with diverse and serious environmental impacts (dams, reservoirs and large-scale irrigation); category B is for small-scale development projects; category C is for projects deemed not to need environmental assessment (education, family planning, system development, etc.); category D is for projects where the main concern is the environment. In fiscal 1993, of the 626 projects (approved or under-consideration) 79 are category A, 267 are category B, 235 are category C and 45 are unclassified.

All of the World Bank projects are constantly monitored during the loan period by the staff responsible. In particular, the Activity Assessment Section investigates loan cases to specify patterns and tendencies that appear in order to give advice for future work. For example, six cases, like the Namada River Basin Project in India, were assessed for the 1990 Environment Report.

Example : Lessons from the Narmada River Basin Development Project

The World Bank decided to make loans for the Narmada Project in April 1985. The project was for the construction of a dam, power station and irrigation channel in one of the poorest regions (constantly beset by drought) of western India. The project aimed to provide residential water, agricultural water, industrial water and electricity, as well as providing an employment opportunity. However, in the late 1980s, local residents and international NGOs raised arguments concerning surfacing environment problems and the migration plan in this project. Their argument was built round three points: economic (economic gain and benefit), forced migration, and flooding of forest regions.

In August 1995 the World Bank decided to suspend the Arum III Hydropower Project in Nepal under the similar situation. The World Bank's independent study group report systematically raises the points that perfunctory assessments and non-consideration of human rights and the environment had been tacitly approved up until that time. The report also had the significance of calling for a swift expansion of the viewpoint range that must be acknowledged by those carrying out massive development.

Water Related Work

The World Bank is active in the International Water Resources Office Amalgamation (the Administrative Committee on Coordination). The gamut of financing operations obviously requires close involvement with substantive aspects of the water field, including "own expertise" and building on the work of others, as is done, for example, in cooperative programmes with FAO and WHO to ensure a flow of sound projects for investment financing. The Bank also has a remarkable record of bringing together finance packages so that Bank/IDA resources are stretched by inclusion of other multilateral, bilateral and other sources of financing as well as the (often large) self-financing element of the numerous recipient developing countries.

In the water field, Bank loans and IDA credits are devoted primarily to irrigation, water supply and hydropower development, although support is also provided for navigation, fisheries, and other water development activities. During the period of 1st July 1986 to 30th June 1991, such Bank/IDA financing amounted to US$10.31 billion. It is difficult to isolate the "water" parts of these projects. The repayment periods on Bank loans has varied from 10 to 20 years. All IDA credits have been repayable over a period of 50 years, including a ten-year grace period. The above total includes Bank/IDA financing of US$4.408 billion for water supply and sanitation projects.

Bank/IDA financing for agricultural projects with irrigation or rural water supply components during this period amounted to US$3.635 billion. Many of these projects benefit from additional co-financing from multilateral sources (such as regional banks, IFAD, UNDP), as well as different bilateral sources. Hydropower development (including relevant transmission) during the period, was funded by Bank loans and credits totaling US$1.989 billion.

Typical Projects Executed by the World Bank

While World Bank lending activities are directed primarily towards the design and execution of projects, funds for some technical assistance and studies may be included in the financing packages. Under certain circumstances, when requested by a Government and agreed to by UNDP, the Bank may agree to serve as executing agency for a particular UNDP project. In general, the Bank's response to such a suggestion will depend on the Bank's operational interest in the country, upon the availability within the Bank of the knowledge and technical competence necessary to direct the proposed project properly, and upon the burden which such direction would impose upon Bank staff. Accordingly, the Bank agrees to serve as executing agency only where it has the necessary specialized experience and where, in its judgment, there is no other specialized agency better equipped to administer the particular project. In such undertakings, the Bank organizes and supervises the project execution closely, but normally employs consulting firms to carry out most of the work.

Main projects in recent years for which the Bank has served as executing agency are listed below.

- **Egypt (1985) :** Egypt Water Master Plan (US$675,000)
- **Thailand (1987) :** Thailand People's Irrigation (US$147,900)
- **Africa (1988) :** Africa Region Hydrological Assessment (US$4,385,100)
- **Bangladesh (1989) :** Bangladesh National Master Plan (US$4,252,900)
- **Sri Lanka (1989) :** Sri Lanka Rural Water Master Plan (US$690,000)
- **Bangladesh (1990) :** Bangladesh Flood Action Plan (US$1,015,000)
- **Nepal (1990) :** Nepal Upper Arum Hydroelectric (US$1,312,500)

- **Interregional (1991) :** Urban Sanitation (US$2,506,900)
- **Interregional (1991) :** Community Water Supply (US$2,201,900)
- **China (1991) :** China Low-Cost Rural Water Supply and Sanitation (US$591,000)
- **Nepal (1991) :** Nepal Irrigation Sector Support (US$1,753,100)
- **Africa (1991) :** Sub-Saharan Water Supply and Sanitation Sector Development (US$5,206,100)

Furthermore, in relation to water resources in Asia, the Bank put forward the following five items as a strategy reflecting the results of the Dublin Conference, as there are few approaches to the Asian region that intersect ministries and agencies or point to market economies.

1) Prompt and low-cost action must be taken to prevent an irreparable impact on water resources (for example, designating regions for conservation purposes, including the limitation of industrial activity in groundwater development districts).
2) Make it clear that water is an economic component and improve water resources measures (for example, moving toward appropriate charging for water).
3) Revise the system , for example, a) decentralization of power in the basin units, and b) streamline water supply activities to enable business-base functioning.
4) Improve planning, executing and maintenance in water supply work (for example, use existing facilities to their maximum capacity and always think of the environmental cost and social cost).
5) Strengthen management and analysis capacity for the organizations involved in the decentralization of power (for example, improve information collection and joint systems within or intersecting basins).

Lake and Reservoir Related Work

The World Bank is in the process of starting the Aral Sea recovery programme with the help of GEF and OECD member countries (see UNEP for details). The Bank also has a plan for the development of tourism in the Lake Baikal area which takes into consideration the environment.

Example 1 :

The Aral Sea Programme (in preparation) :

For the relief of the Aral Sea, the World Bank is taking an initiative in promoting the Aral Sea recovery programme. In April 1993 the World Bank convened a meeting attended by donor countries and international organizations as well as basin countries. Donor organizations agreed the World Bank's policy to establish a trust fund for the Aral Sea Programme. The following is the components of the Aral Sea Programme Phase I :

⊙ A house buried under the sand blown from the Aral Sea

Planned Components and Budgets of the Aral Sea Programme Phase I

Projects	Estimated budgets at implementation stage (million US$)	Expected donar agencies at preparatory stage
Programme 1		
Formulation of strategies for water resource management	5.	GEF/NL/EU/UNDP
More hydro-power and water resources by efficient operation of existing dams.	1.0	BITS
Establishment of sustainable use of dams and reservoirs.	1.0	BITS
Programme 2		
Establishment of hydrometeorological data center	19.5	UK/Swiss/EU/UNDP
Database and information management system on water quality and environmental information	8.0	UK/Swiss/EU/UNDP
Programme 3		
Water quality assessment and management	15.0	GEF/NL
Construction of drainage at Amu Darya and Syr Darya	10.0	NTF/PHRD
River improvement of Syr Darya and renovation of a hydro-power station	10.0	ITA/EGY
Programme 4		
Rehabilitation of wetland ecosystem	25.0	NL
Rehabilitation of the northern basin ecosystem	50.0	PHRD
Investigation on the environmental deterioration of the basin	-	UK/NL/DK/UNEP
Programme 5		
Safe water, sanitation, human health at Uzbekistan	18.0	NTF/Swiss/KFAED/NL
Safe water, sanitation, human health at Trkmenistaan	18.0	PHRD/UNDP
Safe water, sanitation, human health at Kazakhstan	25.0	NTF/PHRD/KFAED/
Supply of safe water (mid-term)	-	UNDP
Long-term water supply and waste water management	-	EU/BITS/FINNIDA/ UNEP
Programme 6		
Integrated water resource management at upstream areas	2.0	
Programme 7		
Control system of civil engineering at Amu Darya basin	6.0	
Control system of civil engineering at Syr Darya basin	6.0	
Programme 8		
Institutional capacity building for the executive committee and International Aral Rehabilitation Fund	-	WB/NL/UNDP/ UNEP/EU

NL and NTF, Netherlands; BITS, Sweden; PHRD, Japan; ITA, Italy; DK, Denmark; KFAED, Kuwait

Example 2 :

Comprehensive Treatment Project of Lake Dianchi, China (in preparation)

In Dianchi Lake near Kunming City, the capital of Yunnan Province of China, heavy blooms of the blue-green algae, Microcystis, cover the lake surface almost all the year round, killing 90 % of native waterweed, fish and molluscan species and destroying fish culture industry because of the oxygen deficiency in lake water. Ironically city water supply for 1.2 million residents of Kunming are running short, and the city began to take this hypertrophic lake water as a source of tap water in 1992. The first sewage treatment plant also started working in this summer, but its capacity covers only 10 % of the city's population. To rehabilitate the lake, the World Bank funded projects are going to start .

Comprehensive Treatment Project of Lake Dianchi

		Estimated cost (million RMB)
I.Projects for municipal and industrial point pollution sources		
1	Municipal drainage system	360
2	The second sewage treatment plant	100
3	The third sewage treatment plant	150
4	The north suburban sewage plant and land treatment system	150
5	The east suburban sewage treatment plant	100
6	Extension of the first sewage treatment plant and reconstruction of its sewer (oxidation ditch)	30
7	Municipal refuse disposal plants	72
8	The key industrial pollution sources treatment	10
II. Projects for nonpoint pollution sources		
9	Forest belt around the lake	1.2
10	Renovation of sub-drainage area (engineering) and construction of farmland with less pollution (afforestation)	110
11	Afforestation of the watershed	250
12	Pre-reservoir, pre-pond for sand trap (gravity precipitation) and constructed wetland system	95
13	Small scale sewage treatment system in towns and villages (bio-technology)	100
III. Projects for treatment of Internal Pollution Source		
14	Large aquatic plants restoration in Lake Dianchi	10
15	Water purification with water hyacinth	2
16	Sediment dredging in Chaohai	250
IV. Water resources development and uses		
17	Construction of dike around the lake continuously	33.1
18	Treatment of the Tanglangchuan River	100
19	Sustainable water in Songhuaba Reservoir with water in Lake Dianchi to irrigate the farmland in Songhuaba Area	7
20	Treatment of the Panlong River	16
21	Flood control, lake protection and turning sewage into water resource engineering	280
22	Extension of No.4 Water works	6
23	Water taking pipe from Songhuaba Reservoir to No.5 water works	18
24	Suburban water supply system reconstruction	120
25	Diversion works	520
V. Scientific research and monitoring		
26	Scientific research and monitoring system	73
Total		RMB 2,953.3

1US$=10 RBM

This World Bank funded project is expected to start in 1996 and will take about seven years. The total budget will reach US$ 300 million (US$ 150 million by loaning from the world bank, and 150 million by counterpart contribution). Redemption is to be made by ordinary and special accounts of Kunming City, water charges, pollution charge from factories, ordinary account of Yunnan Province, and probably national budget.

⊙ Construction of a dike in Lake Dianchi to confine polluted water

Global Environment Facility (GEF)

GEF Secretariat 1818 H street, N.W. Washington D.C. 20433 USA

Work Outline

GEF is an international funding institution established in 1991 to deal with global environment action that is conventionally difficult to support. Therefore, GEF - which goes beyond the World Bank's usual finance framework - is an integrated system using several types of funding mechanisms for global environment conservation, and directs funds from developed countries to developing countries and manages such work. At present GEF is set up and operates as a satellite of the World Bank, and receives cooperation from UNDP to execute projects and UNEP for technical advice on planning. GEF's office is in the World Bank in Washington DC, USA.

GEF does not handle all global environment problems, rather it is initially sticking to the following four areas of work. At the 1992 point of time, the amount of money and projects related to biodiversity occupied nearly half of the work. In recent years, desertification prevention has also been added. Among these, "International Waters" and "Biodiversity" come under the water related fields.

GEF experienced a pilot scheme in operation from 1991 to 1994. The following are the three kinds of work GEF can carry out.

- Investment projects that have been approved by the World Bank

- Technology cooperation projects that have been approved by UNDP
- Small-scale gratuitous funding cooperation for work to be carried out by NGOs at community level in developing countries

Activity Fields and Budget for the Initial Three Years
(Unit :US$1 million)

Field	Number of Activities	Amount of Budget
Biodiversity (habitat reduction and mining of natural resources)	54	303.5
Global warming (use of fossil fuels and destruction of forests)	43	296.0
Pollution of international waters (oil pollution and accumulation of waste)	13	121.9
Ozone layer conservation (chlorofluorocarbon emissions)	2	5.7

At a meeting for participating countries held in Geneva in March 1994, GEF's initial three - year period was brought to a close, and it was relaunched as an orthodox international organization. After its revision, GEF will be provided with funds of about US$2 billion for the next three years. The USA will contribute US$430 million and Japan will contribute US$410 million. Developing countries have strongly criticized the relaunch (developing countries' opinions were ignored before the decision on funding, in addition to which, there is a lot of waste in the organization). The following are the revision items made clear in March 1994. In other words, a conference made up of 30 countries was convened as a mechanism to decide expenditure destinations and operation methods with all the countries involved being evenly represented to reflect the opinions of developing countries in decision making.

Lake and Reservoir Related Work

In the case of lakes and reservoirs, GEF's international waters pollution criteria is limited to just lakes and reservoirs that include international river basins - lakes and reservoirs inside the border of just one country are excluded from the criteria. On the other hand, many of the world's lakes, reservoirs and wetlands are treasure troves of biodiversity, so GEF's first and second period items that take up the case of biodiversity are related to lakes, reservoirs and wetlands. The following examples explain: 1) pollution of international waters and 2) to 5) biodiversity.

Example 1 :

Water Hyacinth Control in East Africa

The water hyacinth (foreign species originating in South America) in East Africa first appeared in Lake Kyoga (Uganda) and the following year it appeared in Lake Victoria. The problem with water hyacinth is that the amount of water evaporation increases due to the water in the plant evaporating, and there is a reduction in dissolved oxygen and nutrient salts. This chronic water hyacinth problem also causes a reduction in biodiversity of animal and plant life along with the cultivation of snails that act as a medium for schistosomiasis and insects that act as mediums for malaria, filariasis and encephalitis. For this reason, a five-year GEF project to monitor and control chronic outbreaks of water hyacinth was approved in 1993. Execution of the project will be headed by the World Bank and UNEP and covers Kenya, Uganda, Tanzania and Rwanda. The biological control of water hyacinth is also scheduled for test runs in this project. (see FAO for details)

Example 2 :

Environmental Management of Lake Victoria

The World Bank and UNEP - with the participation of FAO - intend to commence the "Lake Victoria Environment

Management Project" in 1994. This is a GEF project covering Kenya, Tanzania and Uganda with a US$20 million budget over four years. This project aims at: a) promoting the creation and execution of projects by national governments related to fishing management, lake and reservoir pollution, and land use in wetlands and basins, and b) the strengthening of necessary resources management systems. As a result, it is hoped that each country's investment projects and projects involving development and management of resources in the Lake Victoria basin will yield greater benefits. (see FAO for details)

Example 3 :

Prevention of Pollution and Worsening Environment in Lake Tanganyika

This project is being executed by GEF and UNDP under the cooperation of FAO, and covers Burundi, Tanzania, Zaire and Zambia with a budget of approximately US$10 million.

Example 4 :

Protection of Biodiversity in Lake Nyasa (Malawi)

This is a World Bank and GEF project that is scheduled to commence in the very near future, and covers Malawi, Mozambique and Tanzania with a budget of US$5 million.

Example 5 :

Protection of Biodiversity in East Africa

FAO is the executing organization for this project financed by UNDP and GEF. The project - having already commenced - covers Kenya, Uganda and Tanzania with a budget of US$10 million. The project in Kenya is scheduled to concentrate on the protection of Lakes Nakuru, Naibasha and Elementaria in the Nakuru region. In Uganda, the project will concentrate on the protection of the Sango Bay wetland on the west shore of Lake Victoria.

Other wetland protection projects include the protection of wildlife biodiversity in the Danube River delta wetland (US$6 million) and protection of biodiversity in the eastern wetlands of Uruguay (US$3 million). Also, there is a move toward the protection of biodiversity in the Caspian Sea.

Food and Agriculture Organization of the United Nations (FAO)

Via delle Terme di Caracalla 00100 Rome, Italy

Work Outline

FAO promotes investment for improvements in agriculture and agricultural land and improvements in water resources and livestock in order to raise the standard of nutrition and living for the people of many countries. In addition to this, FAO also works to provide technology transfers to developing countries, carry out studies and research related to agriculture, and tackle sea and freshwater fishing issues.

Project Numbers and Funding Ratios (%)

Field	Project Numbers (%)	Funding (%)
Natural Resources	11	15
Cereals	24	22
Livestock	11	11
Research & Technical Development	3	2
Rural Development	12	14
Nutrition	4	1
Information & Analysis for Food & Agriculture	2	2
Food & Agriculture Policies	7	5
Fishery	10	9
Forestry	13	16
Others	3	4
Total	100	100

Project Numbers and Funding Ratios (%) of Individual Regions

Region	Project Numbers (%)	Funding (%)
Africa	40	42
Asia & the Pacific	24	21
Latin America & the Caribbean	14	8
Arabia	12	14
Europe	3	1
Multiregional	7	14
Total	100	100

By the end of 1992, some 2,157 projects (US$2.235 billion) were being implemented. Regionally, some 40 percent of the projects and budget are concentrated in Africa.

Water Related Work

Water is, of course, a basic requirement of agriculture, and agriculture accounts for some 80 percent of water consumption. Water is also a key element in FAO's fisheries and forestry activities. FAO activities and staff configuration are thus far more extensive than the expression "Water for Agriculture" conveys. FAO is an organization working in major water utilization fields with activities in most aspects of water resources development and conservation, including a variety of cooperative programmes. Within the investments and support made by FAO between 1966 and 1987, a total of 44 percent was water related (irrigation 31%, forest related 9%, fishing related 4%).

Expenditures in 1990 to 1991 for water-related activities totaled US$10.5 million from the regular budget. Financial allocations (mostly from UNDP and trust funds) for relevant field projects amounted to US$50.4 million. The details appear in the FAO Programme of Work and Budget, in which the Major Programme, "Agriculture" has three sub-programmes under the heading of Natural Resources, with US$6.12 million for the regular programme and US$16 million for corresponding field projects. The three sub-programmes cover assessment and planning; water development and management; conservation and reclamation.

Under the Major Programme "Fisheries", the sub-programme Inland Water Resources and Aquaculture has US$4.004 million in the regular programme and US$8 million for corresponding field projects; it includes pollution control and many publications are produced under this programme. The Major Programme "Forestry", sub-programme Conservation and Wildlife has US$220,000 in the regular programme and nearly US$30 million in field projects dealing with watershed management, erosion and sediment control, and soil and water conservation. Major Programme "Legal", has US$200,000 in the regular budget and US$150,000 in the field project budget devoted to collection and dissemination of information on water legislation; legal studies and guidelines; organizing training activities; and assisting governments and river basin committees in drafting water laws and regulations.

The above programmes are carried out through the FAO's Departments of Agriculture, Fisheries and Forestry, and the Legal Office. Water-related work is perhaps most visible in the Land and Water Division of the Agriculture Department.

That Division has some l6 officers dealing with various aspects of water resources. It also has a land and water development officer in each of the four regional offices. There is also the affiliated World Food Programme (WFP), which receives considerable back-stopping from FAO technical experts.

Altogether, FAO has 36 professionals at its headquarters and regional offices assigned on a permanent basis to water problems, plus about l20 in field projects on contracts for one year or more and 40 on consultancy contracts.

FAO's Investment Centre cooperates in the field of investment project preparation with multilateral financing institutions, mainly the World Bank, but also the International Fund for Agricultural Development (IFAD), the regional development banks, and the United Nations Capital Development Fund (UNCDF). Under its various programmes and with back-stopping by FAO's technical divisions, the Centre aims primarily at assisting governments in formulating well-prepared, high priority projects which the borrowing countries have the capacity to implement and which can attract external capital resources. Since 1964, 847 projects formulated with Investment Centre assistance in 116 countries have been approved by financing institutions, for total investments of US$41.7 billion, including US$21.5 billion from external sources and the balance from recipient countries. Some 133 of these projects, with total investments of US$11.5 billion including external loans of US$5.8 billion, were for irrigation and drainage and many more include land and irrigation components. While most external funding comes from the World Bank/IDA, some 50 percent of IFAD projects and UNCDF agricultural projects are prepared with Investment Centre assistance. The Centre has a multi-disciplinary staff of nearly 100 specialists including eight engineers. 60 percent of the staff is assigned to the FAO/World Bank Cooperative programme and 40 percent to the Investment Support Programme which operates with other financing institutions.

The following are typical irrigation and water-related projects executed by FAO from 1982 to 1991.

- **Resources Surveys for the Planning and Development of Irrigation and Drainage Schemes**

    These surveys are carried out through training and support to national institutions. There is still considerable emphasis on the assessment and use of groundwater for agricultural development, illustrated by projects in Laos, Greece, Libya, the Lake Chad Basin and the Near East Cooperative Projects.

- **Resources Management in Drainage and Reclamation Projects**

    These include the Control of Waterlogging and Salinity, in particular in the arid region of China and in projects in Peru, Ecuador, Panama, for the improvements of existing irrigation schemes.

- **Utilization of Sewage Water for Agriculture**

    Attention is also given to the use of sewage water for irrigation making use of modern irrigation technologies such as micro irrigation.

- **FAO International Action Programme for Water and Sustainable Agricultural Development (IAP-WASAD)**

    Its main objective is to assist developing countries in planning, developing and managing water resources on an integrated basis to meet the present and future needs for agricultural production. In meeting this objective, the IAP-WASAD will assist national governments and regional institutions in setting priorities concerning the use of water and land resources for agricultural development, in updating their current policies and strategies, and developing and implementing programmes to translate their policies and plans into action. The UN system will play a catalytic role in the implementation of the Action Programme by creating greater awareness of the importance of integrated water and land development, responding to specific requests to member governments for technical cooperation and assisting in mobilizing bilateral and multilateral donor support for technical assistance and investment for development.

- **Development of Integrated Information Databases and Management Systems in the Field of Water Conservation, Irrigation and Drainage**

    Assistance to national institutions for the development of such databases and management systems continues. Typically, such systems involve conventional and real-time data collection, databases resident in a computer network and computer-supported management routines, with an increasing role for satellite-based data collection, GIS-type databases, and automated microelectronic monitoring instruments. A typical case is a project for development of the computer application capability of the national service dealing with irrigation, drainage and groundwater in Costa Rica.

- **Integrated Rural Development Projects Based on Rainwater Harvesting and Application of Water and Soil Conservation Techniques**

  Typically, such projects target the less favoured rural populations and rural women and have a strong extension and demonstration component supported by food for work and credit programmes. A typical case is a project for rainwater harvesting and rural development in southern Honduras.

- **Transfer of Management Responsibilities to Farmers**

  Several projects are concerned with this kind of transfer like the Technical Assistance to the Irrigation Projects of the High and Medium San Francisco River and the Technical Assistance to the State Public Irrigation of Sergipe and others are under development in Mexico and Colombia.

- **Training of Extension Agents and Workers and Field Staff in Water Management**

  This is also a subject that is receiving major attention. An innovative methodology has been developed and fully tested in Indonesia through two field projects worth over US$10 million.

- **Technical Cooperation Projects**

  Finally, there is the FAO Technical Cooperation Programme (TCP), within the regular programme resources, intended to enable the rapid implementation of small but critical interventions at country level. It has served as a pilot to many larger projects by identifying and defining the lines of approach, as in Ethiopia for future irrigation studies; in Swaziland to help the Government decide on multi-purpose hydropower and irrigation developments and in Malawi and the People's Democratic Republic of Yemen to assess the feasibility and cost of reclaiming flood-damaged irrigation schemes.

Lake and Reservoir Related Work

FAO devotes a massive 42% of its efforts to Africa. The reason Asia does not receive much attention is that Asia is relatively developed in comparison with Africa. In the case of lakes and reservoirs, FAO mainly handles the management of inland surface fishing, concentrating on production, regulations and environment conservation. In the case of lakes, FAO is involved in - as well as the Lake Victoria related project

shown below - a medium-scale project promoting fishing in four countries in the vicinity of Lake Tanganyika and work on Lake Volta. Furthermore, FAO, together with USAID, supports fish breeding workshops for SADC's Lake Kariba.

FAO commenced the "Nile Project" from 1990 as a link to promoting resources management in agricultural production in the Nile basin. The following are FAO's contribution and support in recent years for implemented projects related to the Lake Victoria basin. All of these include an environmental essence.

- **Monitoring, Forecasting and Simulations for the Nile Basin**

  This was implemented between 1990 and 1991, and became the base of the FAO Nile Project. Something was needed for monitoring, forecasting and simulations of the Nile basin, and decisions were needed on what kind of new technology would be of practical use, so the basin's nine countries gathered and proposed - through workshops - 35 projects related to the White Nile basin.

- **Early Warning and Food Information System in IGADD Countries**

  Through financial support of US$6 million from Italy (that continued up to 1993), food protection was strengthened for IGADD countries (Djibouti, Ethiopia, Kenya, Somalia, Sudan and Uganda).

- **Remote Sensing System for Early Warning in Eastern and Southern Africa**

  This system - mainly monitoring precipitation and life forms using remote sensing - is an early warning system for maintaining food supplies. The system has already been installed in Nairobi and staff are being trained. Japan will offer finance.

- **Strengthening of Agricultural Meteorology Departments for Global Information Early Warning Locust Control System**

  This activity - within the FAO's Global Information and Early Warning System (GIEWS) - is expected to be useful for harvest forecasts by automatically accumulating, processing and analyzing data from meteorology and agricultural meteorology. The second-phase project of this activity is supported by US$1.35 million from Belgium, and is scheduled to continue intermittently until 1993.

- **Water Hyacinth Control in East Africa** (see GEF for details)

  From the viewpoint that monitoring and controlling of chronic water hyacinth growth in East Africa is necessary, this project was approved in 1993 as a five-year GEF project. The work is overseen by the World Bank and UNEP, and covers Kenya, Uganda, Tanzania and Rwanda.

- **Water Resources Management Policy and System for the Lake Victoria Region**

  This project was approved in 1993 with the aim of bringing harmony to the policies of countries in the Lake Victoria region from the point of view that water resources management policies of individual countries in the Lake Victoria region need to be strengthened and cooperation from the Nile region countries is necessary. Italy is supplying the finance for this project that covers Kenya, Uganda and Tanzania.

- **Support for Establishing Lake Victoria Fishery Commission**

  This project was approved in 1993 with the aim of establishing a fishing commission made up from shoreline countries in order to manage national fishing in Lake Victoria.

- **Monitoring, forecasting and Simulating for the River Nile in Egypt**

  This project is carried out with USAID finance as a link to Egypt's irrigation management system project. The objectives are: to strengthen the monitoring capacity of water resources for the Nile basin and estimating capacity for inflow volumes to the Aswan High Dam Lake through remote sensing; to still more accurately manage water, and to simulate impacts on the Nile basin due to natural and manmade changes. The first phase related to the Blue Nile basin was completed in 1993 and the second phase is scheduled to take place between 1993 and 1995. (see USAID)

- **Hydraulic Assessment for Africa South of the Sahara Desert**

  This project was carried out between 1987 and 1993 by the World Bank as multilateral support. Hydraulic capabilities in African countries south of the Sahara Desert are far from satisfactory. The work consists of: 1) data collection and processing, and confirmation of publishing status, 2) confirmation of lacking parts in current network (including facilities, technology, accuracy and training), and 3) gapfilling, raising of data quality, recommendations to improve regional hydraulic-related capabilities. However, Kenya did not participate in the project.

The following projects are in the preparation stage.

- **Operational Water Resources Management and Information System**

  In the case of the upper reaches of the White Nile and the upper reaches of the Blue Nile, the Sobato/Atobara Rivers and the mid-reaches of the Nile, the system will start with a basin plan, and aim at the fair common ownership of the Nile River.

- **Landcover of East Africa Using Remote Sensing**

  With US$5 million worth of finance from the Italian Government, 1:250,000 and 1:500,000 landcover maps will be made using remote sensing and geography information system, and landcover - map - making capabilities will be raised in the countries concerned.

- **Environment Management for Lake Victoria** (see GEF for details)

  The World Bank and UNEP, with the acquired participation of FAO, will start the "Lake Victoria Environment Project" in 1994 that targets Kenya, Tanzania and Uganda. This is a four-year, US$20 million GEF project.

- **Information System Work for Water Resources Monitoring Plan in Lake Victoria**

  In Lake Victoria, that spreads across Kenya, Tanzania and Uganda, the environment is deteriorating due to industrial development and increased human population on the shoreline. In order to manage the lake completely, information related to volume and quality of water resource and water demand is necessary. To obtain this, the capabilities of the relevant countries' organizations and people involved need to be improved in the areas of monitoring, planning and water resources management. This project will attempt to provide these organizations with the know-how for using the latest technology - such as, remote sensing, automatic measuring of the environment, and geographical information databasing, together with support for planning, and contributions for equipment. Japanese funding cooperation is scheduled to provide about ¥250 million over five years from May 1994 through trust funds to FAO.

United Nations Educational, Scientific and Cultural Organization (UNESCO)

(UNESCO/IHP) 1 rue Miollis, 75732 PARIS CEDEX 15 France

Work Outline

UNESCO is fundamentally involved in the following fields.

- Cooperation for the promotion of mutual understanding among people and thoughtful free interaction through the mass media
- Cooperation in the development of education activities
- Furthering and disseminating knowledge through human interaction, the exchange of published material in education, culture and science fields

UNESCO's programmes in the natural science field are : Man and Biosphere Programme (MAB), inter-country programmes for marine science committees, the International Hydrology Programme (IHP), and the International Geology Programme.

Water Related Work

UNESCO's activities in the field of water, which have been developed since 1950, are focused on the improvement of the capacity of Member States to assess, plan and manage their water resources through the improvement and utilization of scientific knowledge concerning the water resources system itself and its relationship to human activities and the natural environment through the adequate training of specialized manpower and education of the general public.

UNESCO carries out the following activities in its normal programme.

- UNESCO stimulates and coordinates studies concerning the assessment, development, conservation and management of water resources. This is done through the development of methodologies, the holding of symposiums, the issuing of publications, etc. About one hundred specialists from all over the world cooperate in this effort.

- Develops a better scientific understanding of the impact of human activities that influence hydrological and ecological systems, especially those resulting from climate change.
- Provides decision-makers with the necessary information in succinct, properly contracted formats as a basis for sound environmental management of water resources.
- Promotes the development of education and training in the field of water sciences and water engineering. This activity results in guidance material for the training of specialists and technicians and in the actual training of approximately 500 specialists and technicians per year through courses organized or sponsored by UNESCO.
- Assists its Member States in increasing their capacity to assess their water resources and manage them, in particular through the strengthening of their (applied) research and educational infrastructures.
- Promotes and supports technical cooperation among developing countries at the regional level.

1. International Hydrological Programme (IHP)

The International Hydrological Programme (IHP) is coordinated by an Intergovernmental Council, which reports to the UNESCO General Conference, and is a long-term programme focussing on the scientific and educational aspects of hydrology and water resources management. The programme is based on an interdisciplinary approach to these aspects. The IHP occupies a central place within the whole UNESCO water-related programme. IHP started off as IHD (executed from 1965 to 1974), only becoming IHP in 1975, and is now in its fifth term (1990 to 1995).

The main responsibility for the execution of the programme, as determined by the General Conference with the advice of the Intergovernmental Council for the IHP, rests with the Division of Water Sciences. There are five professionals in the Division and, in addition, five regional hydrologists and up to two associate experts (administratively included in the five UNESCO Regional Offices of Science and Technology), one water engineer in the division of Operational Programmes, and two other water resources specialists working in the Division of Ecological Sciences.

The total regular programme budget available to the Division of Water Sciences for the period 1990-1991 is about US$2.3 million. In addition funds are obtained from UN (UNDP and UNEP) sources (about US$8 million), and from Funds-in-Trust (about US$1.5 million). To this amount, a further US$2 million should be added from the regular programme and US$1 million from extra-budgetary funds administered by other divisions of UNESCO, including relevant activities such as scientific information exchange and public information.

The 1990 UNESCO Conference adopted 44 projects in the following three fields as the programme for 1990 to 1995.

1) **Hydrological Studies**

Some 15 projects with five themes (relation between atmosphere, landmass and water system, relation between climate changes and hydrology, relation between hydrology and water quality, the function of snow and ice in water circulation, and hydrological problems) will be executed.

2) **Water Resources Management for Sustainable Development**

Some 17 projects with five themes (methods for water resources assessment and hydrological planning; scientific and technological water-related information and mapping system; assessments of social and environmental factors and prediction of human activities in relation to freshwater system; relation between integrated water resources development and political decisions, and international water system management) will be executed. Within these projects, ILEC is cooperating in the Integrated Comparative Study on the Great Lakes.

3) **Education, Training and Technical Transfers**

Some 12 projects with five themes (education and training for top technologists, university education, post-graduate training, intermittent education, and public education and information) will be executed.

IHP functions through domestic committees in 150 member countries and supervising agencies for IHP, and it has formed the world's most integrated water-related network. Also, the five regional offices of the science and technology of the UNESCO and the five regional centers for training and investigation cooperate with IHP. Moreover, there are 32 strongpoints for training and 42 important regions for activities, and cooperation is also received from many international NGOs. Much of the technology that can be used in IHP's activity fields is for water in temperate zones. As little of this technology can be used in arid or tropical zones, there is a plan to build a humid tropics centre in Panama; IHP would like to build such a centre in Southeast Asia, but a financier is needed. IHP's programme for 1993 has the following fields.

- Hydrological, scientific and microbiological mechanisms of toxicant transfer in rivers, reservoirs and lakes
- Hydrology studies and water resources management in tropical and temperate regions with heavy rainfalls
- Water-related information and culturalizing system development - especially, descriptive information
- Standard education materials for hydrology

IHP's attention on education focuses on courses for post-graduate students. More than 30 courses have been held in various countries. Finance comes from the budgets of relevant governments, with IHP only providing about US$15,000 (approximately 10%) for each course. Japan has held the following courses centered around the hydrosphere science research laboratory of Nagoya University.

Examples of IHP Training and Courses in Japan

- Lectures and seminars on Asia's precipitation and water resources
- Lectures and seminars on hydrosphere's substance circulation and water quality
- Inspection tours of dams, retarding basins, flood control channels, drainage plants, and measuring facilities
- Observation of integrated field hydrology
- Indoor hydrology tests on bare-land evaporation
- Measuring observation of evaporation water loss and land moisture, and observation of test basin
- On-site inspection tours of research facilities for water quality conservation
- Lectures on hydrology observation and out-flow models
- Lectures on and inspection of precipitation forecasts using radar
- Inspection tours of meteorological satellite facilities

Typical Projects Implemented by UNESCO

- Improvement of National Capabilities for Solving Domestic Water Problems

    This project foresees the strengthening of the National Institute for Hydrology in India by building up an indigenous capacity to master the country's water problems. A similar project is under preparation in Thailand.

- Education Material Development and Local Staff Training

    With a view to training local personnel and to developing systematic guidance material for other countries, UNESCO has organized a larger number of regional training courses for technicians and their supervisors, particularly in Africa, Asia and South America. A network of 32 postgraduate courses cater to high-level hydrologists in developing countries.

- Integrated Management of Small Earth Dams in Burkina Faso

    This project on the "Integrated Management of Small Dams in Earth" in Burkina-Faso, funded by OPEC, was executed by UNESCO and completed

in 1991. The objective of the project was to train technicians and engineers in the field of rehabilitation of small earth dams , and in the management of the available water resources. A local multi-disciplinary team was established at national level to deal with these activities, and guidance was prepared for the optimal use of existing dams.

2. International Geosphere-Biosphere Programme (IGBP)

This programme - promoted by UNESCO in cooperation with scientists from around the world - also includes research of hydrosphere environment assessment of a global scale.

3. World Heritage Convention

There is movement toward registering Lake Tonle Sap in Cambodia as designated land under the World Heritage Convention which comes under UNESCO. There are local moves to also register Lake Baikal, but this will probably not be realized in the near future because of the lake's environment problems.

World Health Organization (WHO)

20, Avenue Appia, CH-1211 Geneva 27, Switzerland
Tel:+41 22 791 21 11   Fax:+41 22 791 07 46

Important Activity Fields

- Supervision and Coordination of International Health Work and Support of Health Work in Countries
- Execution of Epidemiological and Statistical Work

Water Related Work

WHO's interest in water-related activities, goes back to the very beginning of the Organization. In 1949 the WHO Expert Committee on Environmental Sanitation recommended that water supply and sanitation be the main element of the organization's environmental health programmes in recognition of the fact that safe water in adequate quantity and appropriate sanitation were essential to health. Over the last forty years, the organization has been engaged in the promotion of health through programmes and projects designed to provide better water supplies and waste disposal as well as facilities for pollution control in most countries of the world with emphasis

on the unserved poorer people of developing countries. Most of this work is overseen by the Division of Environmental Health. WHO also has a Technology Transfer Programme Office, which manages to work efficiently with a tight budget.

During 1992 and 1993, WHO's financial allocations for water-related activities, including regional and country work as well as global and interregional projects, came to US$24 million from the regular budget and US$13 million from other sources. Resources for headquarters activities from the units primarily involved in water supply and sanitation are estimated at US$4.75 million for the same period.

Technical cooperation is provided through staff assigned to countries, as well as through staff from the Regional Offices and headquarters. Besides the regular WHO staff, the Organization also employs consultants and temporary advisers on short-term contracts and for specific assignments. In some cases, the Organization utilizes contractual services and sub-contract arrangements. There are approximately 50 professional staff working on water and sanitation activities within the Environmental Health Programme of the Organization, mainly in programme and project activities at regional and country levels.

1. Division of Environmental Health

There are approximately 30 staff in the headquarters of the Division of Environmental Health. There are regional offices in the six regions divided across the globe - for example, the West Pacific EHC (formerly PEPAS) office in Kuala Lumpur, that functions on a US$2.5 million budget. The office concentrates on cultivating human resources through training (for example: training of technologists for drainage treatment plants); especially, the exchange of knowledge between different fields. The division shows great concern for city water, handling water resources management under a separate project to monitoring. The division has technical information concerning the environment sanitation field, which it puts out as an integrated reference bibliography list.

2. International Drinking Water Supply and Sanitation Decade (IDWSSD)

As one of the main organizations concerned, WHO was a spearhead for the International Drinking Water Supply and Sanitation Decade (IDWSSD), which ended in 1990, and has played a leading role in the planning and initiation of strategies and programmes to continue and accelerate efforts through the 1990s. Through its Unit for Community Water Supply and Sanitation, WHO provided the Secretariat for the Interagency Steering Committee for Cooperative Action for the IDWSSD, composed of the organization of the United Nations system active in all aspects of water supply and sanitation. WHO will continue this function through the 1990s for the Steering Committee for Water Supply and Sanitation, the extension of the Decade Committee. Additionally, the Organization has provided the secretariat support to the ESA Collaborative Council established at a Global Consultation at The Hague, Netherlands, 1988, and which expanded into the broader based Water Supply and Sanitation Collaborative Council at a Special Meeting in New Delhi, in September 1990.

The Organization cooperates with member countries by supporting them in implementation of their water supply and sanitation programmes within the framework of water resources and environmental planning and management. Throughout the 1980s, the organization received a series of mandates from the World Health Assembly and its six Regional Committees to intensify its cooperation programmes with member states and to strengthen its cooperation with other UN and external support agencies. The latest World Health Assembly resolution in 1989 placed particular emphasis on expanding activities during the 1990s, through extending the Decade framework until the year 2000 and the strengthening of WHO's role in support of national programmes.

3. Typical Projects by WHO

The following information includes typical activities relating to water development being carried out by the Organization under three areas of emphasis.

- Expansion of sustainable community water supply and sanitation services
- Promotion of health-related linkages with water resources management
- Development of improved environmental technology

Under these headings the main outputs of the programme are as follows.

(a) technical assistance to countries
(b) information and guidelines
(c) sector coordination
(d) external support coordination in the areas of institutional development, human resources development, monitoring and evaluation, policy development, water related diseases control, water resources protection, technology development and improved operation and maintenance

The following are more specific examples to the type of projects in which WHO is involved at global and regional levels.

- GEMS/WATER (see UNEP)
  GEMS is a collective effort of the world community to acquire, through monitoring, the data needed for assessment and rational management of the environment at global, regional and national levels. GEMS, a UN-wide system to which many organizations and national institutes contribute, began in 1977 as the first programme of its kind to add new global issues of water quality through a global network. The first phase of the programme ended in 1990. A UNEP/WHO GEMS/WATER Consultations Meeting held in St. Petersburg in August 1990 formally

approved GEMS/WATER, second phase, shifting the previous emphasis from monitoring methods and the development of monitoring services in participating countries to interpretation of data and assessment of water quality issues and global trends, and the formulation of water management options. These are needed to assist governments and international bodies to develop and manage freshwater resources in an environmentally sound and sustainable way.

In the future, GEMS intends to promote assessment - namely, to find out why water quality has changed, and in what ways it has made an impact on people. Moreover, GEMS has started a study on information from several countries to find out what each country knows about water. However, under the current GEMS/WATER system, the networks hands are full from extending itself from monitoring to assessment, so environment management goes just about untouched. Nevertheless, GEMS is looking to also start monitoring using bottom sediment and bio-indicators. In the case of ground water, GEMS is also scheduled to publish a ground water monitoring guidebook in cooperation with the British Geological Survey.

- **Pan American Sanitary Engineering and Environmental Center (CEPIS)**

    CEPIS, American region, operates under the sponsorship of WHO, with extra budgeting funds (IDB, IDRC etc.) and support from the Government of Peru. It cooperates with countries of the American Region in the planning and implementation of environmental health programmes, by providing assistance in training, research and information enclosed. The Western Pacific Regional Center for the Promotion of Environmental Planning and Applied Studies (EHC, formally PEPAS) and the Eastern Mediterranean region's Center for Environmental Health Activities (CEHA) perform corresponding funding, while in 1991 a European Center for Environment and Health was established as a consequence of the First European Conference on Environment and Health in 1989.

- Environmental Health Centre
  (WHO/EHC [former name : PEPAS])

The following are fields covered by EHC.

　　＊ Community water sanitation

　　＊ Urban environment
　　＊ Environment impact assessment
　　＊ Urban solid waste
　　＊ Food safety toxic residues

EHC concentrates on the theme of safe drinking water in undeveloped countries and toxic substances in food and lifestyle modes in semi-developed countries. EHC also handles work in individual countries and on a multilateral level. In the past EHC put emphasis on executing projects but now it concentrates on giving technical advice. In relation to water, EHC is implementing a project using a lagoon to provide drinking water for the island state of Kirivati.

In the past, EHC published a newsletter to publicize its work; however, at present this is not being published. The reason for this is that there is a shortage of staff, which would lead to a poor-quality newsletter - something EHC does not want. So, instead, a computerized list of networks related to EHC is kept and staff in each field have the responsibility of updating the list. A network index can be obtained from EHC.

In relation to lakes and reservoirs, EHC is interested in eutrophication, and is carrying out a study on Miyun Reservoir, a water source for Beijing in China and carried out a study on Lake Laguna in the Philippines.

- UNDP Funded Activities

    WHO continues to implement projects funded by UNDP particularly at country level while acting in cooperation with UNEP, UNICEF selected ESAs on projects at inter-country, regional and global level. These projects include activities related to both water supply and sanitation, pollution control and source protection, human resources and institutional development, and community participation.

- Drinking Water Quality Level

    In 1984, WHO Guidelines for Drinking Water Quality were produced. Since 1990, work has also started on a revision of these Guidelines with emphasis on review of microbiological inorganic and organic chemicals including pesticides and disinfectants and their by-products. It is planned to up-date the revision of the Guidelines by June 1997.

International Atomic Energy Agency (IAEA)

P.O.Box 100, A-1400 Wien, Austria
Tel:2360/2030

IAEA encourages and supports research and development for the peaceful use of atomic energy as well as organizing and executing compensation measures for the removal of atomic energy used in the military.

Water Related Work

The IAEA's water-related activities include programmes for promoting and supporting development of nuclear technology for hydrological applications in water resources assessment, development and management; in crop water use and soil-water-plant relationships and nuclear desalinization. A substantial part of the programme concerns also the transfer of proven nuclear technologies in the above fields to the member countries and support for research and training.

The work directly related to nuclear applications in the water resources sector is carried out by the Division of Physical and Chemical Sciences (Isotope Hydrology Section). This work covers isotope and tracer methodologies in groundwater (including geothermal waters), surface waters, sediment transport and sedimentation studies. The joint FAO/IAEA Division of Nuclear Techniques in Food and Agriculture is involved in nuclear techniques related to crop water use efficiency studies. The Division of Nuclear Power is involved in programmes related to nuclear desalinization. Nuclear analytical techniques for environmental pollution studies (including aquatic environment) and research in marine environment (IAEA Marine Environment Laboratory, Monaco) is part of the work carried out in peaceful nuclear applications by the Department of Research and Isotopes.

The Isotope Hydrology Laboratory of the Agency provides analytical support for its field projects being carried out through technical cooperation projects and serves for the global basic isotope data collection programmes. This laboratory also provides quality assurance on analytical techniques for isotope measurements of water samples through international intercomparison studies and provides internationally accepted standards in this field for calibration purposes.

The Agency's work in the water sector is coordinated with UN organizations, such as UNESCO, WMO, UNEP and WHO through various joint programmes.

Examples of IAEA Projects

The activities carried out through regular programmes of Technical Cooperation, provide main mechanisms for transfer of technology to member states. During the current two-year period 1991/1992, technical cooperation projects (supported by 55 agencies) in the isotope hydrology field were carried out in 40 Member States. The total funding allocated from the regular budget for these projects is about US$1.4 million per annum. The majority of these projects are applied isotope field investigations both in groundwater and surface water studies (including sediment transport and sedimentation investigation). Strengthening the analytical capabilities of existing materials and laboratories involved in isotope hydrology applications and provision of assistance in up-grading the equipment is also among the goals of some of these technical cooperation projects.

Direct financial support to applied and theoretical research in nuclear applications in the above fields aims at the development of new methods or improvement of existing techniques. At present, 48 research projects, involving a total financial support of about US$150,000 per annum, is being implemented with various institutions in the member states in the field of isotope hydrology.

Furthermore, Coordinated Research Programmes on specific isotope methods related to the water resources sector are being implemented by the Agency through participation of selected national research institutions. The training courses (international, regional or national) being regularly organized by the agency provide an effective way of developing manpower in Member States. Meetings and symposiums organized at regular intervals provide a forum for exchange of information, which usually leads to publications for a wider dissemination of information.

United Nations Industrial Development Organization (UNIDO)

As one of environmental projects, UNIDO is investigating air and water deterioration of central region of Romania, river of which is seriously polluted by heavy metals from industries.

Organization for Economic Cooperation and Development (OECD)

2, Rue Andre-Pascal, 75775 Paris CEDEX 16, France

Work Outline

The Organization for Economic Cooperation and Development (OECD) is an international cooperation organization involved in economic work between advanced industrialized nations, and at present it has 25 member countries. One of OECD's major objectives is to contribute to the total economic growth of developing countries.

Contribution to Environment Matters

As a reflection of the heightening concern over worldwide environmental problems in the late 1960s, the OECD's Environment Committee was established in July 1970 (this was partially reorganized and renamed the "Environmental Policy Committee in March 1992) to professionally investigate environmental problems that had been handled by science policy committees up to that point. The Environmental Policy Committee is used to investigate problems that are thought to be important after member governments have proposed plans on environment policies. If warranted, the results of such investigations receive an OECD decision or recommendation at council. Other committee activities include the public announcement of results from studies and research in report form. For example, economic policies around the world are increasingly having to tackle the environment problem barrier, thus, the effective inclusion of environment policy in economic policies has become a major issue. The OECD Environmental Policy Committee promotes case studies on the failures and successes of agriculture, forestry, wetlands and transport fields to find out how environment policy can be integrated with economic policy.

Furthermore, in recent years, environment issues have been cross-referenced from a variety of viewpoints in other OECD committees, which has meant an increase in joint work with the Environmental Policy Committee. The following are some examples.

1) **Creation of Guidelines for "Development Assistance" and "The Environment"**
   (Development Assistance Committee)

   Notably, OECD concentrates on the strengthening of environment consideration in development aid.

In 1985, 1986 and 1989, it gave advice to member countries about the strengthening of environment consideration in development aid projects. Approximately, every five years, cabinet-level meetings are held by the Environmental Policy Committee. At the cabinet meeting in January 1991 - as part of the environment conservation strategy for the 1990s - it was agreed that environment aid for developing countries would be strengthened and positive action taken against environmental problems on a global scale. The committee also puts together guidelines and collections of good examples for environment impact assessments in development projects.

2) **Staging "Environment and Development Joint Committees"**

3) **Creation of Guidelines for "The Environment" and "Trade"** (Trade Committee)

   OECD accepted the final settlement of the Uruguay Round, and it proposed that the environment be raised as an important item in addition to joint policy, investment and labour standards as the theme for the next round.

4) **"The Environment" and "Tax System"**
   (Tax Committee)

Water Related Work

At present OECD does not have any projects directly related to water or lakes and reservoirs; however, it published a report covering wetlands in 1992. Also, the OECD-backed study on the mechanism of eutrophication carried out by R. A. Vollenweider has had an extremely large influence on eutrophication research and action for the world's lakes and reservoirs.

North Atlantic Treaty Organization (NATO)

Lake and Reservoir Related Work

NATO held a workshop in Central Asia in May 1994 to tackle research needs related to environment destruction in the Aral Sea as a link to international cooperation. Moreover, NATO gave financial support to INTAS (a one-week symposium for about 50 invited participants being planned for May 1994 by the Baikal International Center for Ecological Research (BICER).

Asian Development Bank (AsDB)
P.O.Box 789, 1099 Manila, Philippines
Tel:+63-2-711-3851 Fax:+63-2-631-6816

Work Outline

The Asian Development Bank (AsDB) is a development aid organization that targets the promotion of economic development in Asia and the Pacific region. Its main functions are: 1) investment finance for socioeconomic development in developing countries, and 2) technical assistance for construction and execution of development projects. Finance for 48 projects approved in 1994 amounted to US $ 3,687 million. AsDB's member countries in Asia and the Pacific regions total 39 countries including Japan, China, Indonesia, Thailand and the Philippines. Outside of these regions, there are 16 member countries including the USA, UK and Germany. Up to 1993, AsDB had 641 specialists and 1,253 assistants, and an Environment Section with 12 specialists and 16 assistants.

Contribution to Environment Matters

(Thoroughness in Environment Studies)

AsDB's loaning is mainly for infrastructure development (communication, 35 %; energy, 24 %). However, it is shifting the target to social problems, including environmental conservation, poverty, education and WID. Regarding environment, emphasis is laid on environmental consideration in all development project, as well as promotion of environmental conservation projects.

AsDB classifies all environment aid projects into three categories (A, B, C). Projects that are thought not to have any environmental impact are obligatorily classified as category C, and the other categories are obligatorily applied in accordance with the environmental impact of projects: category A is for environmental impact assessment and category B is a simple environment evaluation. Category criteria is based on the World Bank's criteria. Of the 77 projects approved in 1993, 13 fell in the A category, 49 in the B category and 15 in the C category.

AsDB considers the environment at every level of project implementation - namely, from the conception of the project through creation, investigation, approval, contracting, execution and retrospective assessment. EIA and IEE are carried out by recipient countries and AsDB checks these assessments. The execution methods for EIA are as follows.

- Recipient's affiliated research organization executes assessment.
- Consultant is hired to execute assessment.
- Recipient receives AsDB technical assistance to execute assessment. (Normally, advanced-nation consultants hired by AsDB receive information from recipients to execute assessments.)

To assure the quality of EIA, AsDB - as well as providing the previously described technical assistance - trains and holds seminars for government staff and consultants of developing countries cooperating in environmental impact assessment to raise their capability level as a link to the following environmental technical assistance.

(Promotion of Environmental Technical Assistance)

AsDB not only carries out onerous finance cooperation but also gratuitous technical assistance. As shown in the following chart, these are widely classified into three sections: 1. cooperation for creation of projects, 2. advice to developing countries, 3. cooperation for regions made up of numerous countries. Up to now in the environment field, the majority of cooperation comes under item 2., such as training of environment administration staff, drafts of environment related legislation, or drafts of environment impact assessment guidelines. This kind of technical assistance is carried out through consultants, and the budget per case is several hundred thousands of US dollars.

- **Project Preparatory Technical Assistance**

  * Establishment of Environment Agency Regional Network (Indonesia)
  * Metro-Manila Vehicle Exhaust Regulations (Philippines)
  * Environment Rehabilitation (Thailand)

- **Advisory and Operational Technical Assistance**

  * EIA Procedure Strengthening (Mongolia)
  * Hai-he Basin Environment Management (China)
  * Toxic Chemicals Integrated Management Plan (China)
  * Shoreline Resources Management (Malaysia)
  * Environment Regulation Study for Hydrocarbon Development (Thailand)
  * Establishment of Environment Unit in Ministry of Public Works (Thailand)
  * Environmental Management of Coal-fired Power Stations (Indonesia)
  * Organization Strengthening for Biodiversity Conservation (Indonesia)
  * Strengthening of Ministry of Industry's Industrial Pollution Management Capacity (Laos)
  * Lake Phewa Environment Conservation Study (Nepal)
  * Workshop Related to the Environment Facet of Thermoelectric Power Stations (India)
  * Strengthening of Environment Protection Organizations (Marshall Islands)

- **Regional Technical Assistance**

  * National-level Regional Information System for Environment Planning and Management
  * Hindu Kush Himalayas Regional Information System and Network
  * Economic Analysis of Environment Impact in Development Projects

Water Related Work

AsDB has a strong interest in water. It, with the cooperation of HABITAT, is currently commencing a programme to maintain development and manufacturing in Asian countries through sound environment management of water resources to be used in urban locations. This programme is expected to create and implement appropriate strategies for water resources management in order to achieve an inquiry function that studies and investigates basic environment and development issues related to water supply and demand, and reliably carry out intermittent and sustainable supply in the mega-cities of Asia. AsDB, in joint cooperation with UNDP and EU, is also carrying out preparation studies in the organization and legal system for water resources management in the Mekong basin. Work in joint cooperation with AIT and UNEP/GRID also includes factors related to action and water in the South China Sea region. This work is also scheduled to use GIS and remote sensing for monitoring.

Lake and Reservoir Related Work

AsDB is involved with very few projects that are concerned with the major issues of lakes and reservoirs or their basins. The following are examples of the kind of projects it is involved in.

- AsDB encourages the making of regional master plans to study the relationship between environment and development - AsDB has supported the production of the regional master plan for the Lake Sonkhla basin of Thailand (including salinity barrier construction efficiency analysis).
- AsDB financed (US$6.68 million [domestic funding of US$529,000]) the Lake Batoo basin management and recovery test project (land conservation and erosion prevention) executed by the Philippines Environment and Natural Resources Ministry from 1981 to 1990.
- AsDB carried out a study of Lake Phewa in Nepal in 1992.

The Committee for Coordination of Investigation of the Lower Mekong Basin (Mekong Committee)

Work Outline

The Mekong Committee was established by ESCAP (formerly ECAFE) as an intergovernmental body (Vietnam, Cambodia, Laos and Thailand are the basin countries) targeting water resources development in the lower Mekong basin. Since being established, the committee has executed numerous Mekong projects, including power generation, irrigation, improved water transportation and freshwater fishing. At the time of establishment, the committee attracted a lot of attention as a model case of regional international cooperation; however, due to prolonged violent upheaval in the region, all work other than basic activities, such as water quality monitoring, was stopped, but in recent years activities have taken off again.

The committee's budget is supported by UNDP, funds provided by member countries and cooperating countries, and proportionally large support from UNDP. Up to the end of 1986, 25 countries, 13 UN organizations, five international organizations, and three foundations have supported the Mekong Committee. By 1989, the activities of the committee's office had reached the scale of about US$7 million, with personnel expenses occupying three quarters of the running costs. There are approximately 100 office staff, and 22 specialists other than member-country specialists. In addition to UNDP's assistance during the 1980s, other major contributers include Australia, EU, Holland, Sweden and Switzerland.

In recent years, the following environment-related projects have been implemented for the Mekong basin (see Chapter Two for details). Initially scheduled water resources development projects (such as the construction of a big dam on the Mekong River) have fallen into difficulties as there has been a remarkable leap in antagonism over advantages and disadvantages between the basin countries.

Examples :
- Research of organization and legal system related to the fair distribution, use, conservation and development of water resources in the Mekong basin
- Creation and management of directory of wetlands in the Mekong basin

- Water quality monitoring network in the Mekong basin (second phase)
- Furnishing environmental consideration for development plans
- Controlling the danger of land erosion, sedimentation and flash flooding
- Status assessment and management of the Mekong basin through a classification system for the basin
- Establishment of a national park following the course of the Mekong River (all of the basin should be covered starting with Laos and Thailand)
- Fishing in reservoirs of the Mekong basin
- Management of marine resources in the region
- Study of commercially important fish species in the lower Mekong basin
- Study on impact exerted by water resources management on marine resources
- Funding of environment training
- Planning of water resources training
- Planning of water contamination control training

Lake and Reservoir Related Work

Lake Tonle Sap on the lower Mekong basin is useful as a natural flow volume adjuster and flood alleviator. There are plans to construct embankments to increase this usefulness, and a study was carried out with support from, among others, India during the initial period of the committee.

Asian Institute of Technology (AIT)
G.P.O. Box 2754, Bangkok, 10501, Thailand
Tel: +66-2-529-0100

Work Outline

The Asian Institute of Technology (AIT) was founded in 1957 as an international post-graduate institute backed by countries around the world, and is located some 40 km north of Bangkok in Thailand. The institute offers post-graduate and doctorate courses for those who will realize academic leadership in developing countries, and has the intention of becoming the centre for research on the relevant regions. In other words, technology transfers and the cultivation of talented people will be emphasized as well as the usual post-graduate objectives - namely, a major objective of the institute is to prevent a "brain drain". Countries assist by: 1) sending lecturers, 2) contributing facility equipment, 3) offering scholarships to students. Japanese contributions add up to about ten percent.

Contribution to Environment Matters

Currently AIT is comprised of four courses in civil engineering, environment, resources, development, leading technology and business. The environmental engineering programme annually accepts approximately 35 post-graduate students, and approximately ten lecturers supervise the students research work. The current environmental engineering programme started out as a public hygiene engineering course in 1964.

Water Related Work

Class courses in the environmental engineering programme include "industrial effluent control" and "water management".

International Centre for Integrated Mountain Development (ICIMOD)

G.P.O.Box 3226, Katmandu, Nepal
Tel:+977-1-525313 Fax:+977-1-524509

ICIMOD is a centre aimed at regional development of Hindu Kush-Himalayas ranges through seminar, publications and training. Eight countries (Afghanistan, Bhutan, India, Nepal, Bangladesh, China, Myanmar, Pakistan) surrounding the Himalaya Mountains are members of the Centre. Special attention is paid to environmental management of highlands, in particular basin management such as erosion prevention. Risk management of glacial lake break up and environmental management of the Arun River Basin are among topics of publication programme.

Southeast Asian Fisheries Development Centre (SEAFDEC)

Zulueta St., Binangonan, Rizal 1903 Philippines
Tel:+63-2-924-5511 Fax:+63-2-924-5511

Work Outline

Japan, Malaysia, Philippines, Singapore, Thailand and Vietnam are members of the Southeast Asian Fisheries Development Centre (SEAFDEC) - a regional treaty organization tackling research of appropriate technology and the training of fish breeding technologists related to the promotion of fishing, and the collection, publishing and analyzing of information related to the above. The training section is in Thailand, the sea fishing research section is in Singapore, the sea fishing resources development and management section is in Malaysia, and the fish breeding section is in the Philippines. The Philippine fish breeding section is comprised of three stations, the main station is in Iloilo City on Panai Island, the sea fish breeding station is on Guimaras Island, and the freshwater fish breeding station is in Binangonan in Rizal State that faces onto Lake Laguna. By sending specialists, JICA has been supporting for many years the activities of SEAFDEC, including freshwater fish breeding.

Lake and Reservoir Related Work

SEAFDEC has a strong interest in appropriate fish breeding as excess breeding has caused severe eutrophication in lakes and reservoirs in Southeast Asian countries.

✦ Lake Laguna suffering from exessive fish-pen aquaculture

Asian Productivity Organization (APO)

Work Outline

The Asian Productivity Organization (APO) was founded in 1961 and has 17 Asian member countries with the headquarters in Tokyo, Japan. APO concentrates on human development and oversees improvements in business and production technology.

Water Related Work

Industrial pollution prevention training under sponsorship of the headquarters is executed by the Japanese productivity headquarters with the cooperation of the Ministry of International Trade and Industry. Each year this training course (which also includes water conservation activities) accepts about 20 technologists from Asian countries.

The Regional Environmental Centre for Central & Eastern Europe (REC)

Miklós tér 1, 1035 Budapest, Hungary
Tel:+36-1-250-3401   Fax:+36-1-250-3403

Work Outline

The Regional Environment Centre for Central & Eastern Europe (REC) was founded as an international NGO under an agreement between the USA and Hungary ; later on, Holland and Denmark entered the agreement, and at present other countries contributing large amounts of finance - such as Japan and the EU have entered. The Budapest headquarters comprises 30 staff and the regional branch office comprises six staff. Of these people, half are Hungarian, a quarter are European, and the other quarter are American. Countries targeted for action include Romania, Poland, Hungary, and Slovenia. The three Baltic nations are not yet included, nor are the other republics of the former Soviet Union. The question of whether or not Macedonia will be included is being discussed at present. There is a move to create a centre for technology transfer as part of REU's development. Material types are limited, and REU gives the impression of a center that has just been started up. Nearly all applications for aid are being answered, but strengthening is still needed in many areas.

The following are the major activities.

● Small-scale Aid for NGOs

In the midst of political mayhem in Central and Eastern Europe, the national governments of these regions are unable to implement environmental policies; moreover, under the socialist system, citizen involvement was not allowed. Numerous cases of financial aid are being carried out for the many environmental NGOs that have emerged in these countries; however, the amount of aid per case is small. Nearly all the budget (ECU10,000) is being directed to this field (research assistance is not being carried out).

● Flexible Response to Special Problems

REC feels that it is important for the people involved (such as local representatives) to meet and exchange opinions, so aid for staging meetings is also a major funding item.

● Regional Offices

Poland, Slovenia, Bulgaria, Romania all have REC offices, and information exchanges between headquarters and regional offices are being promoted.

● Case Introduction and Information Exchange

Work such as the introduction of specialists is being carried out.

Water Related Work

In relation to water, REC is focusing its support on a water quality information system for the Danube River (INFODANUBE) and the conservation plan for the Danube delta at the Black Sea. In addition to this, REC is also continuing its support for the development of an information system for the Hungarian Water Research Centre (VITUKI). This system is being realized under cooperation with the Brussels Danube Environment Plan, and the US Environment Protection Agency (EPA). JICA is also contributing to this work.

Example : INFODANUBE

The INFODANUBE project is for collecting environment information on the Danube River as a REC activity in the information field. INFODANUBE is financed by Fulbright in the USA, and the Bulgarian Science Academy collects the information for it. Information is placed on one floppy disk as a Dbase type database which can be freely copied. The contents includes: 1) related organizations names, names of directors of each organization, sections to be contacted in governments, names of study and education organizations, related NGO databases in Europe, and 2) monitoring data (life forms and science data) for the Danube River collected within the framework of the Bucharest Statement.

Lake and Reservoir Related Work

REC does not have any projects related to lake and reservoirs, but it is paying attention to the pollution problems in the three lakes of Macedonia.

The International Institute for Applied Systems Analysis (IIASA)

A-2361 Laxenburg, Austria
Tel:(0-2236) 71521 Fax:(0 2236) 71313

Work Outline

The International Institute for Applied Systems Analysis (IIASA) was established as an international non-governmental research organization in Vienna through the advocacy of the USA and Soviet Union during the cold war in 1972. IIASA carries out research to contribute to policies for the solving of problems related to national borders. The research and development takes the form of system analysis to deal with worldwide problems, such as energy, water resources, waste and ecology problems. In recent years the Institute has been concentrating on various global environment problems, population problems, and the move to market economies. The Institute also has a wide network made up of global research centres, researchers and government decision makers, and permanent researchers take the role of coordinators to promote research work. At present, some 15 countries - including European states and Japan - have domestic IIASA commissions. The Institute functions under finance, trusts and aid from countries worth Austrian schillings 137 million; however, functioning in recent years has been particularly tough.

Contribution to Environment Matters

The environment has become the main focal point of IIASA's attention. The following are its research fields.

- Global Environment Changes and Impact on Biosphere
- Chemical Pollution in River Basins
- Global Atmosphere Pollution
- Global Environment and Development
- Global-scale Use of Energy and Climate Changes
- Forest Resources
- Water Resources
- Toxic Substances and Europe's Environment
- Strategies for Climate Changes

Water Related Work

As the chemical pollution in the River Rhine has improved relatively over the past 20 years, IIASA is analyzing the reasons and process, and is also contributing to policy decisions for other river basins. IIASA, under the cooperation of WMO and UNESCO, has developed a large-scale model to simulate river basin reactions to climate changes, and is making practical use of this information in European and African river basins.

Lake and Reservoir Related Work

At present, IIASA does not have a project that deals just with lakes or reservoirs, but in the past it handled the simulation research of water pollution in Lake Balaton in Hungary.

Ramsar Convention Bureau

Rue Mauverney 28, CH-1196 Gland, Switzerland
Tel:+41-22-999-0170 Fax:+41-22-999-0169

Work Outline

The Ramsar Convention Secretariat was established to carry out international coordination and necessary action for the Ramsar Convention, which was set up to promote the conservation and wise use of wetlands. The Ramsar office is located in the IUCN building, and functions with a staff of ten or more.

The Ramsar office's budget is provided by member countries. For example, in fiscal 1992, the budget was approximately Swiss Francs 3.3 million; about half of this was for work expenses. In the case of the Ramsar Convention Meeting, held once every three years, the country holding the meeting bears the cost directly, and organizations give support for participation expenses of representatives from developing countries. The Fifth Ramsar Convention Meeting (1993) was given such support by organizations including AIDAB, CIDA, Denmark's Ministry of Foreign Affairs, France's Ministry of Foreign Affairs, Germany's Environment and Nature Conservation and Nuclear Safety Ministry, Japan's Environment Agency and Ministry of Foreign Affairs, Holland's Ministry of Foreign Affairs, Norway's Ministry of Foreign Affairs, Swiss Ministry of Foreign Affairs and Ministry of

Environment and Forestry, Swedish Ministry of Foreign Affairs, British Ministry of Environment, American Department of the Interior, UNEP, and UNESCO.

Lake and Reservoir Related Work

Lakes and reservoirs are defined as being a type of wetland under the Ramsar Convention. About half of the wetlands registered as being important in 654 locations in 81 countries (as of March 1994) are lakes or reservoirs.

One of the jobs of the Ramsar office is the promotion of international cooperation for wetland conservation. The office carries out the following activities while cooperating with other conventions and NGOs such as IWRB, IUCN and WWF.

- Mediating for the conservation of transboundary wetlands
- Promoting training
- Cooperating with other conservation organizations - making multilateral aid organizations (such as bilateral aid organizations, international development banks and OEUD) aware of the necessity to conserve wetlands
- Creating wetland conservation funds
- Maintaining an internationally important wetland list and a list of wetlands on the verge of being critically damaged
- Supporting wetland policy decisions in each country - supporting the dissemination of wise-use concepts through the support of case studies related to wise use
- Promoting the establishment of wetland nature conservation areas

The following are future priority activity fields.

Basic Fields
- Maintain wetland registration list.
- Cooperate with related NGOs to monitor registered lakes and reservoirs that need external aid.
- Lay down guidelines for conservation and management of registered wetlands.
- Support the wise use of wetlands through the establishment of wetland policies in individual countries.

Priority Fields
- Promote the training of wetland managers by collaborating with cooperation organizations such as IWRB and AWB.
- Promote the conservation of transboundary (two countries) wetlands and the life forms that live there.
- Complete wetland conservation fund for aiding the realization of small-scale wetland conservation projects by developing countries (Japan contributed ¥10 million in 1993)
- Strengthen publishing activities for wetland lists, newsletters and yearly reports.
- Make public in various forms the wetland conservation experiences and research results of member countries.

Medium-term Priority Fields
- Increase Ramsar registered wetlands.
- Strengthen monitoring and management of conservation areas.
- Work on member countries to prepare wetland directories for individual countries.
- Frequent staging of regional meetings.

The World Conservation Union (IUCN)
Rue Mauverney 28, CH-1196 Gland, Switzerland
Tel:+41-22-999-0001 Fax:+41-22-999-0025

Work Outline

The World Conservation Union (IUCN) is a union of characteristically different groups such as national and governmental organizations and NGOs, and is currently comprised of 11 countries, 57 states, 92 government organizations, 46 international NGOs, 452 domestic NGOs and 34 cooperating organizations. The union's headquarters is in Switzerland, and has four regional offices, 13 offices in separate countries, and 17 project offices. The headquarters has 136 staff and the 34 offices have 400 staff between them. The objectives of IUCN are to preserve the repleteness and diversity of the natural world and bring about the appropriate, sustainable and fair use of natural resources by mankind. Since its establishment in 1948, the union has led the world over the past 40 years in the field of nature conservation and protection of species threatened with extinction through publications such as the "Red Data Book". Also at present the IUCN has a committee comprising six fields: ecology, education and dissemination, environmental legislation, environmental strategy and improvements, national parks and reserves, and species preservation, and more than 3,000 specialists cooperate.

Lake and Reservoir Related Work

(See the activities of IUCN Wetlands Programme for Asia in Chapter Two for details)

IUCN's freshwater-related work revolves mainly around the Wetlands Programme. The IUCN Wetlands Programme is one of the world's biggest organizations involved in wetland conservation and coordinates IUCN activities related to wetland ecology management. The core action of the Wetlands Programme is on-site work for establishing methodologies for wetland management in developing countries.

The Wetlands Programme coordinates activities related to the conservation and management of wetlands; in particular, it concentrates on tropical wetlands being frequently used by communities. The Wetlands Programme values the ecological biodiversity of wetlands, while developing on-site projects for sustainable use of wetland resources, and implementing these with the help of wetland researchers, managers, government decision makers and related domestic/overseas NGOs.

The IUCN Wetlands Programme is also active in publishing wetland policies (including lakes and reservoirs) - representative of these are the wetland by continent publications (including "Africa Wetlands Directory" and "Asian Wetlands Directory") published with the help of UNEP, WCMC, IWRB and WWF. Some of these are translated into the relevant local language like Thai or Vietnamese. Moreover, the "Lake Baikal: on the brink" publication is published as a link to the IUCN Eastern Europe Programme.

At the IUCN Wetland Project Review held in July 1992, it was recognized that freshwater wetlands and coastal wetlands management is rapidly becoming more and more important as a form of wetland conservation for the 1990s, and as such the capacity of this field should be raised. IUCN Wetlands Programme is receiving financial support from many of the major organizations in Europe and the USA including FINNIDA, NORAD, SIDA, DCA, and USAID.

IUCN established a Wetlands Programme office in Bangkok, Thailand in 1991 to support and strengthen the wetland conservation action of South Asian and Southeast Asian member groups. Up to now, IUCN's method has been to support the staging of domestic workshops to find the order of priority for carrying out action. Workshops have been held in Vietnam (May 1992), Bangladesh (November 1992), and Nepal (March 1993). At the Vietnam workshop, concern was expressed about the IUCN Mekong delta wetland, and IUCN is closely cooperating with the Mekong office concerning the wetland problem. IUCN functions as a government advisor in Laos, and offers support in Cambodia through a newly established office.

Furthermore, at a more general level, IUCN aims at effectively conserving wetlands, and supports national governments in the creation of domestic wetland strategies. For example, support for wetland conservation in Nepal and Bangladesh is carried out along the lines of IUCN conservation strategy for individual countries.

World Wide Fund for Nature (WWF)

Work Outline

The World Wide Fund for Nature (WWF) was founded in 1961 and is the world's biggest citizens nature preservation group. WWF has a worldwide network including committees and cooperating groups in 28 countries and support groups in other countries. WWF International's headquarters are located together with IUCN in Gland, a suburb of Geneva in Switzerland.

WWF worldwide membership reaches some 4.2 million, and its budget is ¥28 billion. WWF's ultimate objectives are to halt the rapid worsening of the natural environment, recover those things that have been destroyed, and establish harmony between mankind and nature for a future way of life. WWF's mission is to: 1) protect biodiversity (saving life forms from extinction), 2) sustainable use of natural resources (avoid overwhelming destruction), 3) prevent environmental pollution and the wasteful use of energy resources.

Up to now, WWF has protected life form species - for example, WWF has thrown its weight behind the move to protect the Bengal tiger, African elephant, mountain gorilla and giant panda, and in recent years it has broadened its scope to protect the ecology systems that support valuable life forms.

Water Related Work

Conservation of ecology systems - these being a focal point in WWF's work - includes the conservation of tropical rainforests, maintenance of bogs and wetlands, and the protection of coral reefs. Furthermore, in the case of Asian wetlands and water-related matters, the WWF headquarters and the committees of countries are involved in the following projects (see Chapter Two for details).

WWF Headquarters
- Philippines Wetland Conservation Programme

WWF UK
- Wetland Training, Studies, Assessments (for Regions) (Joint Cooperation with ODA)

- Wetland Planning and Management (for Regions) (Joint Cooperation with ODA)

WWF USA
- Nature Conservation Debt Swapping Plan for Philippines

WWF Malaysia
- Malaysia, Selangor Coastal Fish Breeding
- Malaysia, Selangor Action Plan for Northern Peat Wetland Forest
- Malaysia Socioeconomic Evaluation of Wetland Plants (1st and 2nd phase)
- Freshwater Study for Malay Peninsula

WWF Hong Kong
- Vietnamese Translation of Wetland Directory
- Training Trip to Maipo Reserve in Hong Kong for Staff Related to Conservation of Hong River Delta in Vietnam

(See World Wide Fund for Nature Japan for details)

World Resources Institute (WRI)
1750 New York Avenue, NW., Washington, D.C. 20006 USA
Tel:+1-202-393-4048

Work Outline

The World Resources Institute (WRI) was established by G Speth in Washington DC in 1982 as a non-profit think tank specializing in global environment issues. In recent years, WRI has a very large influence on identifying the problems affecting the global environment at an international dimension. WRI studies, researches and makes policy statements for the following issue: "How will human beings' basic demands be fulfilled and economic growth achieved without losing natural resources or environment that is essential to human living conditions, economic activities and international stability?" WRI is also technically supervising and assisting developing governments and NGOs to test out sustainable management of natural resources.

The core items of WRI's work are as follows.
- Items that make an impact on economic development and poverty and starvation measures that accompany deteriorating natural resources.
- Items not yet approved within the system for problems newly generated in the environment and energy field on a global scale.

The following are important activities.
- Austere review of environmental conditions through the World Resources publication (biennial) published with cooperation from UNEP and UNDP
- Cooperation in establishing IPCC for work in global warming
- Cooperation in proposing and establishing the Global Environment Fund (GEF)
- Advocacy of green GNP
- Research covering biodiversity conservation and cooperation action planning, starting with the Global Biodiversity Strategy
- Technical supervision assistance through the International Development and Environment Centre (affiliated to WRI) for developing countries and NGOs to be able to create plans for resources management by themselves
- Working on a scenario for global sustainment in the year 2050.

Water Related Work

WRI, in cooperation with UNEP and UNDP, biennially publishes World Resources, which has a chapter on "water". For example, a lot of work went into freshwater resources items (water volumes and water quality in rivers) that amounted to 19 of the 383 pages that appeared in the 1990/91 report, and the 1994/95 report focused on oceans. However, on the whole, special attention is not given to water resources problems. The reason for this is that WRI focuses on environmental problems that have not been systematized - WRI acknowledges that international organizations and national governments have already formed systems for dealing with water resources problems and urban problems.

Worldwatch Institute

1776 Massachusetts Ave., N.W. Washington, D.C. 20036 USA
Tel:+1-202-452-1999   Fax:+1-202-296-7365
Email wwpub@igc.apc.org

Work Outline

The Worldwatch Institute is a NGO located in Washington DC, and - unlike the issues the WRI policy think tank specializes in - it is developing education activities at citizen level. The institute puts together the environmental conditions of the world and biennially publishes the data in World Watch.

In "The Last Oasis", published in World Watch in 1992, the global lack of water resources from the 1990s heading into the 21st century is emphasized as an environmental problem - namely, an extremely important issue in international politics. Also, water-related articles are published in World Watch magazine, such as the Aral Sea problem and decrease of ground- and river-water in the world.

Water Related Work

Monitoring and Assessment Research Centre (MARC)

The Old Coach House, Campden Hill, London W8 7AD, UK
Tel:071-376-1577   Fax:071-937-5396

Work Outline

The Monitoring and Assessment Research Centre (MARC) is a cooperating organization for UNEP, and was founded before UNEP. MARC has 12 staff with the office head being a staff member of UNEP. The centre is not only located inside but also receives a massive contribution (use of building and library, etc.) from London University. The majority of MARC's work is in joint projects with the likes of UNEP and WHO, and much of the centre's business revenue is acquired through such work. The editing of the "Environmental Data Report" (UNEP's official environment yearbook) - a joint biennial publishing project with UNEP - is MARC's most important work. MARC - in cooperation with WHO - puts together Food Contamination and Human Exposure publications in relation to human health.

Water Related Work

MARC's specialty is traditionally the biology field, and, therefore, concentrates on bio-monitoring. As far as developing countries are concerned, this is not expensive and does not require elaborate facilities. A course covering bio-monitoring has been held in Harare, Zimbabwe, and one is being planned for Ecuador.

Lake and Reservoir Related Work

MARC does not have a project that solely deals with lakes and reservoirs but it hopes to contribute to the management of lake basins through the above environmental diagnosis work.

International Water and Sanitation Centre (IRC)

(Formerly : International Reference Center for Community Water Supply and Sanitation)

Work Outline

The International Water and Sanitation Centre (IRC) aims to supply technical information related to appropriate technology for developing countries in the fields of water supply, sanitation facilities and environment. IRC is a non-profit, independent organization that receives assistance from the Dutch Government, UNDP, UNICEF, World Bank, and WHO.

Water Related Work

Situated in The Hague in Holland, IRC is designated as a collaborating centre for WHO in the fields of drinking water supply and sanitation facilities, and continues to be effectively active. Notably, IRC is heavily involved in work for the regional and urban low-income sector with the idea of achieving citizen participation, sanitation education, female involvement, maintenance management, facility rehabilitation, and environmental management. IRC also has many good publications; in particular, small-scale appropriate technology for water supply. IRC puts out technical information in series form. Notably, the technology series can be said to have become necessary reading for anyone involved in projects directed at developing countries. Anyone with an interest in appropriate technology for drinking water supply will find many useful pieces of information in these books.

International Office for Water (IOW/CEFIGRE)

Department of International Cooperation, BP 113 Sophia Antipolis - 06561 VALBONNE Cedex - France
Tel:92-94-58-00   Fax:93-65-44-02

Work Outline

At the Mar Del Plata Conference held in 1977, there was a call - mainly by developing countries - for training facilities related to water, and the international water resources management training centre (CEFIGRE) was founded with France and UNEP as its nucleus. CEFIGRE was established in 1977 in a science park (Sophia Antipolis) in the suburbs of Nice in France and is an international organization funded by France and other European nations as well as receiving cooperation from UNEP. In 1991, the centre underwent a reshuffle, became a department (International Cooperation Department) of the International Office for Water (IOW), and now mostly handles training activities.

IOW also has database and basin management departments. At present, IOW has NGO status in France, but carries out work without change as an international organization. Germany also makes a large contribution to the office. However, IOW is self-supporting, and as UNEP and national governments provide income through assigned work, public finance is tough.

Water Related Work

CEFIGRE's work mainly involves training as well as case studies like the Zambezi River and Nile River. But research is not the centre's objective, work connected to training is. Notably, the educating and training of senior government officials in the following fields are the major concern, and up to now, more than 3,000 people have been accepted for training.

- Water Resources
- Water Supply and Sanitation for Cities
- Water Supply, Sanitation and Irrigation for Rural Areas
- Environment Management

Political and legal system facets are mostly used in training partly because the centre does not have the facilities to hold technical training courses. Due to circumstances at the time of establishment, CEFIGRE has maintained very close relations with UNEP's Water Unit, and oversees river-related training executed within the EMINWA Programme of the Water Unit. In recent years, the centre is making an effort in basin development and urban environment management (90% of work occupies these two fields); in particular, there are strong requests for assistance from East Europe. Even as a water training centre, CEFIGRE handles urban waste as this is inseparable from drainage water treatment.

Training activities are changing from a system where trainees from developing countries are invited to the French centre to a system where instructors and educational materials are sent to developing countries to hold on-site training in order to concretely meet requests. This has occurred because of questions about expenses and results and because aid organizations have stopped sending trainees to courses held in France. Formerly, the training course catalogue was sent worldwide and trainees were gathered for training; however, this has come to a halt.

Lake and Reservoir Related Work

In the case of lake and reservoir management, several types of training that focus on basin management are offered.

International Waterfowl and Wetland Research Bureau (IWRB)
Slimbridge, Gloucester GL2 7BX, UK
Tel:453-890624   Fax:453-890697

Work Outline

IWRB has 40 years of history as an international NGO working to protect wetlands and waterfowl. The headquarters are in the UK with a staff of 17. Some 41 member countries and numerous citizen groups participate in and various international NGOs - starting with IUCN - cooperate in the bureau's work. The British government makes a major contribution through financial aid as do the governments of other countries and citizen groups.

Lake and Reservoir Related Work

The following come from the bureau's targets for 1993 to 1995.

- Creation of a list of each countries wetlands
- Creation of database related to wetlands
- Strengthening of collaboration with other cooperating organizations

The bureau carries out training about three times a year. Participants are advertised for through the IWRB network. The period of training is usually one week and about 13 people participate.

Asian Wetland Bureau (AWB)
Institute of Advanced Studies, University of Malaya, Lembah Pantai, 59100 Kuala Lumpur, Malaysia
Tel:+60-3-7572176   Fax:+60-3-757-1225

Work Outline

The Asian Wetland Bureau (AWB) is an international NGO that aims at protecting wetlands (including lakes) and their resources in the Pacific region. Several dozen people work in the headquarters in Kuala Lumpur in Malaysia and sub-offices located in Indonesia, India and the UK. AWB is affiliated with the International Waterfowl and Wetland Research Bureau (IWRB) and Wetlands for the Americas (WA). The bureau collects a broad cross section of information, including wildlife protection, and plans development, management and countermeasures for wetlands in countries and regions through collaboration with other international organizations and the staging of specialist meetings.

Lake and Reservoir Related Work

AWB is affiliated with national governmental organizations, and acts as a mediator through aid action for organizing domestic systems and accumulating specialist knowledge in countries. AWB's work consists of the following five themes.

1) A general survey of the status of wetland protection in regions
2) Assistance for regional and domestic wetland action planning
3) Publication of information in various forms
4) Assistance for sustainable management of wetlands by local groups
5) Liaison for international organizations and

conventions that have accumulated experience overseas

AWB has already completed many projects. These include on-site studies on nearly 150 coastlines and island wetlands covering more than 10,000 km of coastline. AWB - in cooperation with the governmental organizations of Malaysia, Philippines, Thailand, India and China - created wetland directories of each individual country, and using these, it completed an Asian wetland directory. AWB carries out a large and diverse number of studies for classifying regions that should be conserved in the Asian region. The bureau has also helped Sumatra, Malaysia, Philippines and China with management of their reserves. AWB holds over 40 training courses related to wetlands, has developed training materials in Asian languages, and has published more than 100 reports and single manuscripts. The AWB newsletter "Asian Wetland News" is published biannually with various reports and opinions related to wetland protection and management. These activities are a very important part of AWB work.

Sub-branches have become independent, and develop their own activities. For example, the Indonesia sub-branch became independent, and is carrying out the following work.

- Training of on-site staff involved in PHPA wetland management
   (This involves the development of a programme to acquire support from citizens in regard to the wise use of PHPA together with wetlands.)
- Value of wetlands, development impact on wetland ecology systems, and the study and research on the problems that accompany the conversion of wetland to farmland
- Commencement of on-site work related to the sustainable use of wetland ecology systems
- Guidelines for environmental impact assessment, staging of workshops for integrated management policies, and support for wetland policy planning in individual countries
- Support of Indonesia's participation in the international agreement of the Ramsar Convention

International Association on Water Quality (IAWQ)

1 Queen Anne's Gate, London SW1H 9BT, UK
Tel:+44-171-222-3848 Fax:+44-171-233-1197

Work Outline

IAWQ was formerly known as IAWPRC but changed its name as it became involved in areas outside of the water sector - as well as working to reduce water contamination, it also takes on the responsibility of management. IAWQ publishes material, holds meetings with members and specialists carrying out activities. The association is thinking of strengthening the activities of its specialist group. It is considering high-tech technology, low-tech treatment, management and control.

IAWQ is also positive in technology transfer to developing countries. In June 1995 IAWQ convened a conference on environmental problems of the Back Sea.

International Limnological Society (SIL)

(Editor of SIL News) Mary J. Burgis, London Guildhall University, Old Castle Street, London E1 7NT, UK

Lake and Reservoir Related Work

SIL is an organization that carries out pure technological activities related to limnology, publishes academic magazines, and holds a world conference and regional conference once every three years (example: East Africa Great Lakes Conference in 1990). SIL also assists the participation of researchers from developing countries in these meetings and lake conservation training; however, the scale of this assistance is small.

International Society of Ecology (INTECOL)

Lake and Reservoir Related Work

The International Society of Ecology (INTECOL) holds an international wetland conference once every three years, and 52 countries (900 people) participated in the fourth conference held at the University of Ohio in the USA in 1992.

A broad range of problems from water quality preservation through to infectious disease vectors with special emphasis on using ecological techniques for Wetland conservation were discussed. Engineering type debates rarely take place. The fifth conference is scheduled for September 1996 at Perth, Australia.

International Association for Hydraulic Research (IAHR)

Water Related Work

IAHR was founded in 1935 as an organization for the world's researchers and technologists in the field of hydrology. The headquarters are in Delft in Holland. IAHR's aim is to construct a wide ranging network from the dual approach of basics and practical applications. The majority of work

revolves around normal association activities such as holding meetings and workshops and publishing academic magazines. The association also cooperates with UNESCO, WMO and UNIDO for the "International Decade for Disaster Prevention". IAHR has cooperated closely with the IHP Programme for many years (dispatching of instructors, etc.).

International Water Resources Association (IWRA)

Water Related Work

The IWRA was founded by Ven Te Chow in 1972 from the stance that the exchange of interdisciplinary knowledge and technology (including not just specialist fields but also engineering, socioeconomic and ecology fields) is necessary for thorough management of water resources. IWRA deals with a broad range of water issues (such as socioeconomics, ecology and environmental impact) in the association

magazine. A specialty of the association is that members abundantly include not just researchers but also government officials and technologists.

The association stages a world conference once every three years with participation from some 1,000 people; moreover, it is one the main backers involved in staging conferences. IWRA cooperates with many UN organizations and NGOs - for example, IWRA cooperates in the translation of IHP reports.

International Commission on Irrigation and Drainage (ICID)

48, Nyaya Marg, Chanakyapuri, New Delhi 110021, India
Tel:+91-11-301-6837 Fax:+91-11-301-5962 Email:icid@sirnetd.ernet.in

Work Outline

ICID is a government-based international organization related to science and technology and has an overseeing role in the fields of irrigation, drainage, flooding and river improvements. Through integrated research related to land and water resources in these fields, ICID promotes development and diffusion of science and technology in the

fields of engineering, agriculture, economics and sociology. ICID was established in 1950, and as of 1989, this international organization's membership included 81 of the world's leading countries. ICID also has a deep manpower connection with the International Water Resources Association (IWRA).

Lake and Reservoir Related Work

ICID is concerned about the environmental problem in the Aral Sea basin. In September 1993, the ICID chairman and the Uzbekistan cabinet minister for water resources management linked up through memos related to the water shortage in the Aral Sea and the deteriorating environment problems that have caused the water shortage. Based on this link up, a special session of cabinet ministers from the five Aral Sea basin nations was held within the ICID international business committee meeting held in Varna in Bulgaria on the 19th of May 1994.

International Congress of Large Dams (ICOLD)

Bureau Central, 151, Boul. Haussmann, 75008 Paris France
Tel:+33-1-40 42 68 24 Fax:+33-1-40-42-60-71

Lake and Reservoir Related Work

The International Congress of Large Dams (ICOLD) - through the staging of meetings and material publication - targets promotion and development with international cooperation in technology for planning, constructing, maintenance and management of large dams, which in turn target power generation, flood control, water works, water for industry and water for agriculture. ICOLD was founded in 1928. As of 1989, the congress had 78 major countries as members, and has domestic committees in various countries. In the case of dam lakes, organizations with the responsibility of management are clearly defined, and these organizations are ICOLD members, which also function as an information network.

North American Lake Management Society (NALMS)

P.O.Box 5443, Madison, Wisconsin, 53705-5443, USA
Tel:+1-608-233-2836   Fax:+1-608-233-3186

Lake and Reservoir Related Work

NALMS objective is to promote understanding of lakes, ponds, reservoirs and their basins as ecological units. By promoting the protection, restoration to original state and management of these water areas, NALMS intends to promote lake and reservoir management, citizen education and information exchanges related to assistance. Furthermore, the society gives advice related to lakes and reservoirs to citizens and businesses, and promotes research for the management of lakes, reservoirs and basins. NALMS publishes a high-quality research magazine related to the management of lakes and reservoirs, and makes a thorough job of staging international symposiums; however, the majority of members attending these symposiums are from North America. In 1995 NALMS opened an Email forum "Lakes-L" on Internet for exchange of lake management information and views. This is accessible from developing countries.

 Canada

Canadian International Development Agency (CIDA)

200 Promenade du Portage, Hull, Quebec, K1A 0G4 Canada
Tel:+1-819-994-3924 Fax:+1-819-953-3348

Work Outline

CIDA was established in 1960 to more efficiently dispose of increasing aid activities, and is under the jurisdiction of the Canadian Minister for Foreign Affairs. CIDA carries out the following work.

- Preparation and execution of bilateral aid planning (finance aid and technical cooperation)
- Inspection and advice on the execution status of the above plans
- Public cooperation programmes
- Assistance for citizen groups active in the aid field
- Cooperation for international organizations
- Food aid

Aid takes the form of bilateral assistance, and breaks down to roughly one third of the total amount for UN organizations and international organizations, about one third for direct bilateral aid, and the remaining one third is for NGOs and research organizations. Within the direct bilateral aid, 48 percent is for African countries, 32 percent is for Asia, Oceania and Europe, and 16 percent is for American countries. Of the 109 recipient countries, 51 (47%) of the countries are African, 23 (21%) of the countries are Asian, Oceania and European, and 35 (32%) of the countries are American. In the case of Asia, CIDA is tending to reduce its aid as Asia is at an overall development level. CIDA exchanges personnel with JICA ; one JICA staff is working at CIDA, and changes work every several months to better understand the total structure of CIDA. CIDA also sends staff to JICA in the same way.

Environment Related Work

Canada announced the "Canada Green Plan" in 1990 as an action plan targeting sustainable development. The following four points are the key to freshwater management in this plan.

(1) Monitoring to assess current status of water quality and volume

(2) Information managing to correctly direct government policy

(3) Scientific researching to understand the workings of the ecosystem

(4) Technology renewing to promote prevention of and recovery from pollution

International cooperation also follows along these lines. The Canadian Office for Training and Environment (COTE) was established within the plan to give developing countries training opportunities. COTE is an organization spread between not only the Environment Agency but numerous other ministries and agencies, and receives cooperation from CIDA with regard to aid.

Lake and Reservoir Related Work

CIDA's programmes do not target lakes by themselves, but makes a contribution to freshwater from the viewpoint of sustainable utilization of resources. Aid for the following example - "The Technical Cooperation of the Development and Protection of the Nile Basin" (TECCONILE) - is greatly used for conservation of Lake Victoria. Moreover, small-scale aid is positively carried out - for example, assistance was given for the creation of an education booklet on mangrove forest preservation by a NGO in Malaysia.

Example :

Aid for The Technical Cooperation of the Development and Protection of the Nile Basin (TECCONILE)

TECCONILE - a technical cooperation committee to promote conservation and development of the Nile basin - was established in January 1993 by ten basin countries (Egypt, Sudan, Ethiopia, Eritrea, Kenya, Uganda, Tanzania, Rwanda, Burundi, and Zaire). CIDA has continued to be at the centre of assistance for TECCONILE from the point it was established; however, this assistance has been accompanied by cooperation difficulties among the basin countries as they each have different interests.

In the 1960s and 1970s, a hydrometeorology programme was developed mainly by UNDP and WMO with the aim of collecting hydrologic data necessary for water resources management, and TECCONILE inherited and developed this programme. TECCONILE has many action plans, and the core of these are included in the following plans connected to the management of Lake Victoria.

- Water supply support study for Lake Victoria
- Policy coordination between the countries in the Lake Victoria region
- Sedimentation monitoring
- Analysis of lake changes due to pollution
- Water quality analysis involving joint laboratory facilities
- Policy coordination in individual countries for prevention of pollution

- Impact study on unrestricted wetland resources
- Integrated basin management

Furthermore, CIDA - as a link to the above, and targeting general water resources development in the Nile basin - assists the staging of the "Nile 2002 Conference (1993 Aswan, January 1994 Khartoum, and February 1995 Arusha).

Environment Canada

Water Related Work

Environment Canada carries out training for facility improvement so that developing countries can implement new treatment technology within the "Water and Drainage Technical Training Programme" which is part of the international cooperation of the "Canada Green Plan" announced in 1990. An important factor is that training is not just carried out in Canada but also in the countries of the trainees.

Canada, in collaboration with the Chinese Research Academy of Environmental Sciences, conducted a joint research on lake pollution in 1991-1993. A joint research on water quality criteria and standards for water pollution and waste water treatment.

National Water Research Institute (NWRI)

P.O.Box 5050, Burlington, Ontario, L7R 4A6 Canada
Tel:+1-905-336-96440 Fax:+1-905-336-4582

Work Outline

NWRI is Canada's largest research organization with the task of researching freshwater problems. The Institute currently has 750 staff, of which 190 are researchers, and is a world-class facility as a freshwater research institute. Research activities lead to the emergence of knowledge and technology in the area of sustainable water resources development for Canada and the world. Lately, in particular, the institute has been involved in studies and research of acid rain, toxic waste and the overgrowth of water plants.

Lake and Reservoir Related Work

NWRI was initially involved in fishing issues, and concentrated on pollution of the five Great Lakes together with water quality research, but has gradually come to be involved in general ecology research. Some 200 members of the NWRI staff (40%) come from other organizations. The Institute is applying its resources to the problem of eutrophication. Other recent work has also included pesticides and other toxic pollution. As the work that one organization can carry out is limited, NWRI often collaborates with other organizations (universities and research organizations). A major project is the unraveling of the ecosystem as the Institute intends to apply itself to the subject of ecotoxicology. NWRI continues to carry out a polluted basins cleanup project in five to six locations covering groundwater pollution, paper manufacturing water drainage, mining water drainage, and petrochemical water drainage.

In the case of international cooperation, NWRI has been fulfilling an important role in UNEP's GEMS/WATER network since the middle of the 1970s by supervising the arranging of data (including lake and reservoir data) collected from global monitoring stations. This cooperation is funded from the budget on the Canadian side, and five staff devote themselves to this work. The results of this kind of cooperation have led WHO to approve NWRI as a cooperating centre for surface and ground water quality. Moreover, it is hoped that NWRI will also be designated as a GEMS/WATER cooperation centre by UNEP. And as there are numerous examples of developing countries mishandling monitoring data, NWRI has developed an environment information system software (RAISON) which has become the official GEMS/WATER software and is being disseminated among developing countries.

In the case of bilateral cooperation, NWRI is focusing on rapidly developing nations such as Brazil, Russia and China, and promotes thorough bilateral cooperation with countries including Germany, Scandinavian countries, France and the USA; however, cooperation with Japan is limited. Within the Japan and Canada Environment Agreement, NWRI wants to transfer the RAISON software to Japan using funds from the Canadian budget. The Institute is also cooperating with REU and EUE in Budapest, and is concentrating on information transfer in training.

▆▆▆▆▆ USA

United States Agency for International Development (USAID)

Work Outline

USAID comes under the umbrella of the International Development Cooperation Agency (IDCA), and is an integrated aid organization involved in non-military aid. In recent years Japan's aid amount has become larger than the USAID's, but in the case of personnel numbers, the agency has the largest total staff of 11,507 (in 1988) - 2,261 in the headquarters, 9,246 in overseas offices (2,643 of these are Americans). A feature of USAID is that each country's office is staffed by 100 people, so that extremely detailed projects can be carried out.

Foreign Assistance Expenditure Budget

	(Fiscal 1990)
Multilateral Aid	US$1.935 billion
Bilateral Aid	US$7.571 billion
(Food Aid)	US$1.301 billion

American foreign aid was initially destined for postwar reconstruction in Europe in the mid-fifties, shifting to Asia in the 1960s; however, regional distribution was transformed with by far the largest proportion of aid being redirected to Egypt and Israel for political reasons after the first oil shock in the mid-seventies.

Distribution of Economic Assistance
in Individual Regions   (Fiscal 1990)

Africa	:	US$	28.9 million
Asia	:	US$	13.4 million
Europe and Middle East	:	US$	2,866.9 million
Central & South America	:	US$	1,093.9 million
Whole World	:	US$	7.7 million
Total	:	US$	4,010.8 million

As US aid cannot be extended further due to economic reasons, the US Government is developing a new overseas aid system to narrow down aid to limit USAID to the objective of providing sustainable development. USAID is also setting about the task of strengthening the organization to become more efficient so as to fulfill the objective of promoting sustainable development overseas so that countries can surmount natural and manmade disasters by themselves.

Another feature of America's aid is that a large amount of power is given to local offices in budget distribution as part of the move towards the decentralization of power. The essence of this is the establishment of foundations as a collaborating organization for NGO action aid in developing countries, then funding in the form of a finance package is made to these foundation, and distribution is entrusted to the local foundation, so that small-scale detailed aid can be carried out.

Water Related Work

In the case of water and sanitation fields, USAID focuses on slum and squatter districts in rural areas on the outskirts of cities. The following shows a fragmentary view of aid action in USAID's water field.

- USAID supplied aid of US$300,000 (US$100,000 to ASEAN countries and US$120,000 to the Philippines) for a basin project (establishment of basin management and system) executed from 1984 to 1988 by the Philippine Ministry of Environment and Natural Resources together with a Philippine University (Los Banos Campus).
- USAID, together with FAO, has assisted fish breeding workshops of SADC at Kariba Lake.
- USAID, in cooperation with FAO, carried out a monitoring, forecasting and simulations on Egypt's Nile River in a project linked to Egypt's irrigation management system project. The aims of this project are to strengthen water resources monitoring on the

Nile River using remote sensing, strengthen forecasting of inflow volume to the Aswan Dam Lake to increase accuracy in water management, and simulate the impact exerted by natural and manmade changes in the Nile basin. The first stage of the project was completed on the Blue Nile basin in 1993, and the second stage is scheduled to be carried out during 1993 and 1995.

USAID has also become involved in recent years in wetland conservation of the Niger delta that had been supported by German cooperation from 1984.

USAID is carrying out a sustainable forest management project in Bolivia (from 1993 to 1999, worth US$15 million) as a biodiversity conservation project that concentrates on water and land conservation.

Water and Sanitation for Health Project (WASH)

WASH is a USAID project with the objective of providing technical assistance for planning, executing and assessing projects in the water and sanitation field. Slum and squatter districts are spreading in the outskirts of cities in developing countries. The safe supply of drinking water and the appropriate disposal of excrement and household waste in these districts are priority problems within the environmental problems of developing countries. As USAID is focusing on slum and squatter districts in rural areas and city outskirts, so WASH is focusing on special issues in the outskirts of cities.

WASH is affiliated to USAID's "Water and Disease Vector Control Division". USAID does not directly carry out this work but acts as a consultant. Since WASH was commenced in 1980, US$30 million has been invested in the project up to 1987. WASH II started in 1988.

(WASH Study and Information Centre)

This centre was established in 1980, and has 22 staff that arrange material such as publications, reports and materials of various countries in relation to the water and sanitation sector of developing countries. The centre also analyzes information and provides materials upon request. The centre has 5,000 reports and 1,500 organization material files. The centre's information is offered in the form of pamphlets, reports, manuals, technical manuals, slides, films, videos, software, and posters. The centre receives more than 150 requests for information each month, and usually responds to requests within five days.

National Aeronautics and Space Administration (NASA)

Water Related Work

NASA has created a global environment information system called SEASON, which includes water resources information.

United States Fish and Wildlife Service, United States Department of the Interior

Washington DC 20240 USA
Email:op@enterprise. nwi. fws. gov
NWI Home Page:http://www. nwi. fws. gov

US Fish and Wildlife Service maintains the National Wetlands Inventory (NWI) over Internet. Anyone with access to the Internet may contact to NWI's server via anonymous ftp and download the data. Information on Wetland digital map, fauna and flora, references on wetland values etc. are made available.

Sweden

Swedish International Development Authority (SIDA)

Information Secretariat, S-105 25 Stockholm, Sweden
Tel:46-8-728-51-00   Fax:46-8-673-32-61

Work Outline

SIDA was established in 1965 under direct control of the Ministry of Foreign Affairs as a unitary aid organization with the purpose of making more efficient implementation of various forms of Swedish aid. Bilateral technical aid is received from NIB (an international aid bureau), bilateral financial aid is received from the Ministry of Finance, and the conciliatory aid for humanity aid and multilateral organizations is received from the Ministry of Foreign Affairs. SIDA's work is completely related to ODA - creation and implementation of original policy plans for financial cooperation and technical cooperation. Note that all loans have become gratuitous loans from 1979 onward, so new loans are not being executed at present. The aid criteria focuses on the poverty level and the democratization of recipient countries.

Some 400 people work in the SIDA headquarters, approximately 100 people in overseas offices and another 350 or so consultants are employed. About 40 percent of the aid budget is received from UN organizations and the World Bank, the remaining 60 percent comes from bilateral aid. SIDA is also involved in numerous joint activities with other organizations. Currently, however, aid recipient countries are restricted to 22 and publications are having to be reduced due to budget reductions.

Breakdown of Aid Amounts
(Unit : Swedish Krona million)

Africa	2,715
Asia	995
Latin America	550
Democracy and Human Rights Aid	550
Disaster Emergency Aid	810
Aid through NGOs	735
Special Programmes	350
Others	600
Total	7,305

SIDA - through long years of experience - has seen many failed projects (for example, electric pumps used for water supply) cored around facility preparation, and have thus come to realize that it is difficult to achieve results through just training and technical cooperation. In future, SIDA will concentrate on system preparation and the strengthening of self-help. To achieve this, the authority is considering that greater emphasis must be given to disseminating education. For example, in SIDA's campaign project related to health and public sanitation, time will be devoted to informing people of the causes and results of disease.

Water Related Work

SIDA is the largest of the Scandinavian aid organizations, and for that reason it is involved in various projects dealing just with water. Of the total budget of about US$1 billion, US$30 million was directed to water-related projects. Sections in SIDA in charge of forestry, agriculture and fish breeding also handle water issues, and there are 31 staff related to water included in these sections. Projects related to sustainable use of water resources include integrated basin management in Southern Africa, shore protection planning (flood plain management), and water resources management in arid regions.

As action related to water, SIDA concentrates on countries south of the Sahara Desert (Botswana, Tanzania, Kenya, Ethiopia, Zimbabwe and Uganda) for regional drinking water supplies in Southern Africa. In particular, SIDA takes seriously the lack of water in Zimbabwe and Zambia. SIDA also devotes itself to training - the authority handles the majority of training in Africa. SIDA also has lengthy project experience in Central America (Nicaragua, etc.) and Asia (India, etc.), but Europe is not targeted. The following are some of the numerous activities undertaken in Thailand and the Mekong basin.

- Diffusion Action for fish breeding in Northeast Thailand (scheduled to be spread to Laos)
- Important action for forest conservation in Vietnam
- Support of IUCN Wetland Programme
- Research of competition in water use in rural and urban areas and the competition in irrigation water and household water use in Tamil, India

Apart from the above, SIDA carries out the following international cooperation in Asia.

- Management of sulfuric acid soil in Vietnam (Mekong delta)

- Creation and management of directory for wetlands in lower Mekong basin
- Water quality monitoring network for lower Mekong basin (second stage) (joint cooperation with UNEP)
- Inclusion of environmental consideration for various development projects (Mekong basin)
- Control of soil wash away, sedimentation and flooding (Mekong basin)
- Environment training fund (Mekong basin)

In addition to these, SIDA also supports the attending of meetings, and thoroughly carries out readily noticeable aid work.

Example :

Support for Stockholm Water Symposium

As people are becoming more concerned about environmental degradation of the world's water resources, SIDA started annually staging the Stockholm Symposium from 1992, with the aim of recommending methods for analyzing and conquering problems. The symposium is also used as a platform for awarding the "Stockholm Water Prize" to individuals or organizations that have contributed to water environment conservation. At the 1992 symposium, SIDA, with cooperation from BITS, footed the participation expenses for 61 people from 32 countries.

Centre for International Technical and Educational Cooperation (CITEC)

Royal Institute of Technology, CITEC, S-100 44 Stockholm, Sweden
Tel:+46-8-790-9654 Fax:+46-8-2033716

Work Outline

CITEC is an influential cooperation organization closely linked with SIDA that executes SIDA projects.

Water Related Work

CITEC is starting to devote more energy to fields related to water resources management. The following are examples of work entrusted from SIDA.

- Monitoring in the Mekong basin
- Supporting the Mekong bureau (sending staff, environment financing)

- Water resources development in southern India
- Social impact study of reservoir construction in Sri Lanka
- Practical remote sensing training course for environment impact assessment and monitoring
    (This course held at the Bangladesh Technical Engineering University in 1991 aimed at being useful for flood control and drainage.)

Lake/Reservoir Related Work

CITEC is involved in work in Nicaragua (Lake Managua) with finance from SIDA.

Danish International Development Agency (DANIDA)

Ministry of Foreign Affairs, Department of Information, Asiatisk Plads 2, 1448, Copenhagen K., Denmark
Tel:+45-33-92-00-00   Fax:+45-33-92-07-10

Work Outline

DANIDA is an aid organization under the jurisdiction of the Danish Ministry of Foreign Affairs, the majority of countries targeted for aid are African countries - approximately 20 countries are receiving aid. Increasing the number of countries receiving aid at the moment is difficult because of public finance reasons.

Water Related Work

There are some 200 technology-related staff in the DANIDA headquarters, roughly 30 of these staff are involved in water-related work. A breakdown shows that six staff are involved in drinking water, five staff in agriculture, and the other 20 or so staff in manufacturing. In addition to these staff, many external consultants are used, which raises the figure of water-related people to a total of about 200.

Lake/Reservoir Related Work

DANIDA supports various water resources management projects, such as the revitalization project for the Pasig River that links Lake Laguna and Manila bay in the Philippines, and the creation of a master plan for water quality monitoring and water resources management in Lake Victoria in Uganda.

The agency is also involved in the same kind of work in Tanzania.

Denmark is also carrying out a status study and management in Cambodia (first stage) and fishing promotion in the Mekong reservoir, although details are unclear.

Finland

Finnish International Development Agency (FINNIDA)

Department for Development Cooperation, Ministry for Foreign Affairs, P.O.Box 176, 00161 Helsinki, Finland
Tel:+358-0-13-41-61   Fax:+358-0-13-41-63-75

Work Outline

FINNIDA was established in 1961 as an aid organization under the jurisdiction of the Finnish Ministry of Foreign Affairs. There are some 100 technology-related staff in the FINNIDA headquarters, roughly 20 of these staff are positioned in embassies. The following are the agency's aid principles.

1) Adhere to UN actions.
2) Keep in line with Scandinavian countries.
3) Attain the level of Nordic countries through action starting with bilateral aid.

To ensure effective aid, FINNIDA has trimmed its operations down to aid for about 20 countries mainly in Africa. One third of the aid amount is for multilateral aid, and about half of this is directed to Africa. FINNIDA's largest problem is its tough financial situation, the aid budget for 1991 shows a turning point toward a reduction trend, and by 1993, the aid amount had become 40 percent of the 1991 budget. Note, though, that 95 percent of the aid amount comes from gifts.

Regional Ratio of Bilateral Aid Amount

Region	Regional Ratio (%)
Africa	47.8
Asia	22.7
Latin America	6.6
Europe and the Pacific	7.5
Others	15.4
Total	100.0

Water Related Work

As the Baltic Sea is a brackish sea area with a low salinity concentration, FINNIDA is highly involved in brackish water projects, and possesses leading technology in specific fields, such as disposal technology for drainage water in pulp plants. In the case of water environment support, FINNIDA has a long record of results mostly in Africa.

Lake/Reservoir Related Work

FINNIDA, through FAO, is assisting (US$6 million over four years) fishing management in Lake Tanganyika and is assisting in environmental action for biodiversity protection in the same lake. The agency is also in the process of proposing a Cambodian wetland project (Lake Tonle Sap). The agency is supporting the IUCN wetland programme. Cooperation is also received from Finland's Kopio University, a school strong in the fishing field. FINNIDA adheres to the cooperation agreement it has with IUCN to offer finance for conservation of wetlands (including lakes and reservoirs) in Central America, Southern Africa and Asia, and supports wetland conservation of Hadejia (a flood plain in Nigeria) through NGO funding. Action being carried out in southern African countries through SADC has been suspended.

Norwegian Agency for Development Cooperation (NORAD)

P.B. 8034., 0030 Oslo, Norway
Tel:+47-22-31-44-00   Fax:+47-22-31-44-73

Work Outline

NORAD was established in 1962 as an aid organization under the jurisdiction of the Norwegian Ministry of Foreign Affairs, and functions in line with Japan's JICA (technical cooperation) and OECF (financing cooperation). The agency had 225 staff as of 1992, and 31 of them were working in local NORAD offices. Of the total aid amount, about 30 percent is provided through UN and international organizations including UNESCO, UNEP and the World Bank, the remainder is bilateral aid. Half of the 26 recipient countries are concentrated in Africa (mostly eastern and southern Africa) - about 60 percent of the bilateral budget is directed to this region. South Asia and Central America are also main action regions. NORAD intends to commence aiding Czech, Russia, Hungary and Baltic nations.

Water Related Work

NORAD is not involved very much in aid activity that concentrates on freshwater. The agency fully understands the importance of the water problem in Africa, etc., but does not have the resources to do anything. In the case of Central America, NORAD cooperates with SIDA to support the CATIE wasteland programme, and wetlands are priority within that work.

Lake/Reservoir Related Work

An example of NORAD work is the plan for assisting the Ugandan national wetland programme. The wetlands in the vicinity of Lake Victoria occupy 12.5 percent of Ugandan land, and as these wetlands are extremely important to the Ugandan economy and social activities, the Ugandan Department of Environment Protection (DEP) acquired financial aid from NORAD and technical aid from IUCN to initiate the Uganda National Wetland Plan. In 1992, the aid organization changed to DGIS, and the second stage of the project was commenced. Within this, an education campaign has been implemented to promote wetland management through the participation of the local society, and evaluation of and sustainable use of wetlands, in order to use wetland resources for various objectives such as wetland studies, training, directory creation, planning and fishing.

Norwegian Institute for Water Research (NIVA)

P.O.Box 69, Korsvoll, N-0808 Oslo, Norway
Tel:+47-22-18-51-00 Fax:+47-22-18-52-00

Work Outline

Norway has four research organizations for handling individual environment fields - NIVA, water; NILU, atmosphere; NINA, nature; NIDA, urban. Of these, NIVA targets the water environment. In the past, this institute was a state-run organization, but, in 1986, it gained independence, became a foundation, and functions as an NGO. The institute's revenue source is bolstered by about 20 percent from the Ministry of Environment, and the other 80 percent is provided by contract work. Some 60 to 70 percent of contracts come from the Ministry of Environment. NIVA has a staff of 190 (90% of them are scientists) with two officials from the Ministry of Environment and three officials from the Research Council. NIVA is comprised of freshwater, ocean, environmental technology, analysis laboratory and general affairs departments, and has three branch offices. The budget is approximately Norwegian Krona 110 million, and ten percent of this is directed toward international projects. Developing countries targeted for action include Central and East Europe, Tanzania, Nicaragua and Sri Lanka.

Water Related Work

Acidification of lakes has been a major freshwater environmental problem in Norway from the past. This is important from the point of view of biodiversity, but other than this there are no major pending problems. Putting lime in the lakes to prevent acidification is the sole countermeasure, however, nothing is done for unused lakes in mountain regions. As commercial lake fishing is not carried out, only sports fishing suffers from the lack of fish. Meanwhile, since records of water quality in the oceans started in 1988, NIVA has transferred its focus from freshwater to seawater. The institute also has an interest in global warming.

Germany

Deutsche Gesellschaft für Technische Zusammenarbeit (GTZ)

Work Outline

The Development Aid Body and the Developing Counties Promotion Company were amalgamated in 1975 to form GTZ as an organization entrusted with the task of executing technical cooperation in developing countries from the German Ministry of Economic Cooperation. GTZ is a large concern in which the number of staff sent to on-site locations has risen to 1,541. Furthermore, there are some 1,300 staff in the headquarters, about 350 contracted consultants, and about 5,000 people employed at on-site locations. At present (end of 1992), 2,260 projects are progressing in 126 countries. Of these, GTZ staff are directly involved in about 30 percent. The number of countries receiving aid are: about 40 percent in Africa, about 30 percent in Asia and Oceania, about ten percent in Europe, and 20 percent in Latin America. As for the amount of money, bilateral aid accounts for 85 percent of the total amount (37% Africa, 26% Asia & Oceania, 20% Europe, and 16% Latin America).

Lake/Reservoir Related Work

Examples are fragmentary, however, one case shows that GTZ assisted in the publishing costs for a Portuguese version of ILEC's "Lake Environment Guidebook" for Brazil in 1993. In Sudan an attempt was made to make fuel bricks from water hyacinth though it was not economically successful.

Once again, the facts are not clear, but the German Ministry of Foreign Affairs has been supporting wetland conservation in the Inner Niger delta in West Africa and an overall management plan for the Logone flood plain in the Cameroon since 1984. Also, GTZ is cooperating with an Argentinean University to collect and analyze shore data from Lake Nahuel Huapi in Argentina. In the case of the eutrophication problem in Lake Valencia in Venezuela, GTZ is cooperating in the analysis of sediment.

The UK

British Overseas Development Administration (ODA)

Lake/Reservoir Related Work

British ODA is supporting wetland conversation through the WWF in the Kafue plain and the Bangweulu basin of Zambia. ODA is also involved in the following action in the wetlands of Asia.

- UK and Indonesia Tropical Forest Management Programme (Sub Project 5): Developing conservation and practical application model to reconcile conservation with the deep-rooted local use of the Danau Centrum Wildlife Reserve in West Kalimantan (ODA)
- Wetland training, status studies and assessments (targeted regions) (ODA/WWF-UK)
- Planning and management of wetlands (targeted regions) (ODA/WWF-UK)

Holland

International Development Cooperation Agency of the Netherlands (DGIS)

Environment Related Work

Holland provides three percent of overseas development aid to environment fields. Holland can be said to be an artificial environment itself, and at a glance many of the peat excavations of hundreds of years ago look like natural ponds. For this reason, there is a strong feeling in Holland that nature cannot be preserved without human management. The core of DGIS's assistance is for global environment issues - such as biodiversity reductions and global warming, improvement of management capacity for natural resources in developing countries, and the search for policies that involve the sustainable use of resources. DGIS also shows a strong interest in the status of indigenous people and women.

Lake/Reservoir Related Work

Holland traditionally makes a large effort to support aid related to water, and as many of the people are surrounded by water, especially, wetlands rich in biodiversity, they feel very strongly about water issues. The wise use of wetlands is also taken seriously as this is linked to the emancipation from poverty. DGIS has achieved results in many wetland conservation projects, and the following are some examples; notably, work focuses on wetlands in densely populated areas.

- Support of environmental impact assessment on mangrove wetlands in Nicaragua and Ecuador
- Support through IUCN of wetland conservation in countries in West Africa
- Management support of the Logone flood plain in Chad (rice over-cultivation)
- Support of conference staging for the Ramsar Convention office's wise use of wetland project
- Support of training facilities in Cameroon and Kenya
- Support of flood plain facility installation for Bangladesh

- Support of wetland policy preparation in Uganda and Sri Lanka

In the case of these projects, training and education are the core activities, as the aim is to raise wetland management capacity and involve local citizens in recipient countries. DGIS not only carries out on-site training but has also established a wetland training centre in Holland to offer training based on Holland's long experience in flat bog management. (Facts are unclear, but Holland has been supporting a programme promoting regionally rooted fishing management in reservoirs in rural districts in Thailand.)

Example 1 :
Assisting Uganda National Wetland Plan Formulation

As the wetlands in the vicinity of Lake Victoria are of extreme importance to the Ugandan economy and social activities, the Ugandan Department of Environment Protection (DEP) acquired financial aid from NORAD and technical aid from IUCN in 1988 to initiate the Uganda National Wetland Plan. In 1992, the second stage of the project was commenced under financial assistance from DGIS. Within this, an education campaign has been implemented to promote wetland management through the participation of the local society and evaluation of and sustainable use of wetlands in order to use wetland resources for various objectives such as wetland studies, training, directory creation, planning, fishing, gardening and harvesting.

Example 2 :
Improvement of Management and Conservation of Wetlands in Indonesia (first stage, Sumatra)

DGIS puts a lot of emphasis on researching the state of wetlands, and thus carried out a status study on Indonesian wetlands (worth US$1 million) in cooperation with the Indonesian Ministry of Forestry (PHPA) and AWB, the bureau that actually carried out the study. However, the programme has been suspended due to worsening relations between Holland and Indonesia.

Switzerland

Swiss Directorate of Development Cooperation and Humanitarian Aid (DCA)

Water Related Work

DCA supports IUCN projects in Africa and South America as a link to the IUCN wetland planning aid programme. DCA also provides finance for the management of coastal wetland in Guinea-Bissau. Facts are unclear, but the following are plans under Swiss aid.

- Fishing community work in Nam Ngum basin in Laos (second stage)
- Assessment and management of Mekong basin

France

Lake/Reservoir Related Work

Work content is unclear, but France seems set to support a Lake Tonle Sap development plan in Cambodia. France has also sent three advisers to the Venezuelan Ministry of Environment and Natural Resources, and two of these advisors are in charge of Lake Maracaibo and the other is in charge of Lake Valencia. The latter is overseeing the establishment of a wetland office and data disposal and operations.

Italy

Lake/Reservoir Related Work

In the case of water resources management in Lake Victoria and the Nile basin, Italy is carrying out financial cooperation through FAO, and seems to be set to support management of Lake Albert and Lake George on the border between Uganda and Zaire.

European Union (EU)

Water Related Work

EU is carrying out a preparation study in joint cooperation with ADB and UNDP to find out the actual state of organization and the legal system being used for water resources management in the Mekong basin. EU is also supporting wetland conservation in the Mauritania National Park, and developing a fishing study project in Lake Victoria worth US$10 million.

Australia

Australian International Development Assistance Bureau (AIDAB)

Work Outline

AIDAB is strongly involved with geographically close ASEAN countries and is also devoting time to assistance of NGOs. From 1991 to 1992, finance of Aus$59.5 million was directed to Australian NGOs, and a further Aus$7.1 million was offered to overseas NGOs. However, the core of this finance was 39 percent for emergency aid and refugee aid, 14.9 percent for bilateral aid through NGOs, and 15 percent for AIDAB/NGO cooperation programme, while only 0.9 percent was directed to NGO environment activities.

Water Related Work

The following activities are related to wetland conservation in Southeast Asia.

- Production of guidelines for developers (regional work)
- Moving toward a management programme for resources rooted in daily use of the local society of Lake Nawjan in the Philippines
- Moving toward sustainable waterfowl protection in migratory route areas of East Asia (regional work)
- Study of migratory routes in East Asia and establishment and coordination of protection zone (regional work)

In addition to the above, the Australian Nature Conservation Agency (ANCA) is supporting the preparation work for an action plan related to migratory waterfowl that migrate across East Asia and Australia. Some of the executing organizations are unknown, but the following are the kind of activities that Australia cooperates in.

- Water resources training in Cambodia (partial responsibility for finance)
- Forestry based development in the Long Xuyen Quadrangle in the Mekong delta in Vietnam
- Water resources training for Mekong basin

Russia

Centre for International Projects (CIP)

Work Outline

CIP was established in 1981 during the era of the former Soviet Union as an executive organization under control of a UNEP/Soviet Union Commission. The Soviet Union collaborated with UNEP and other international organizations, and CIP functioned as the aid organization to carry out projects related to the effective use of the environment and natural resources. Such finance was provided in Russian rubles to UNEP's headquarters; however, as rubles can not be used in projects of other countries, the entire Soviet contribution ended up being restored to CIP activities. In approximately the ten year period up to 1991, 350 or more projects - such as training courses, symposiums, and meetings - were executed. Some 5,000 or more scientists, specialists and international organization representatives from overseas participated in these projects, and more than 500 results were published. Moreover, more than 100 research and training organizations within the Soviet Union cooperated in some form or other.

The breakup of the Soviet Union and the following economic difficulties just about brought CIP's activities to a standstill for a while, but, in 1993, UNEP entrusted CIP with the task of holding a GEMS/WATER conference in Moscow, and thus activities were resumed. However, there are no clear details about the current scale and content of work.

Water Related Work

A look at 1991 shows that about 40 training courses and meetings were held as UNEP projects, and within these, five projects were related to freshwater conservation - namely, the second and third Aral Sea rescue action plan creation aid meeting; training course for micro biological dissipation of mineral pollution from water used in industry; world lakes and reservoirs databook editing meeting; and international science meeting for protection management of groundwater.

Lake/Reservoir Related Work

Of the above projects, the Aral Sea rescue action plan creation aid meeting and world lakes and reservoirs databook editing meeting were for lakes and reservoirs, and both were carried out with the cooperation of ILEC. The latter project was carried out to record lake and reservoir data in the World Lake Databook.

Environment Agency

1-2-2 Kasumigaseki, Chiyoda-ku, Tokyo 100 Japan
Tel:+81-3-3593-3351

Promotion of global environmental conservation through international coordination is one of emphasis points in the Japanese Environmental Basic Law which was enacted in November 1993. Environmental Agency's international cooperation to developing countries is mainly made through JICA (refer to JICA). The Agency is also positing its own cooperation through international organizations, bilateral agreements and regional meetings.

Water Related Work

1) Investigation

To collect basic information for international cooperation, the Environment Agency is promoting investigation on the environmental status and socio-economic background of respective developing countries. The followings are examples of water-related projects aiming at developing countries.

- Investigation on lake environmental conservation measures of the world
- Investigaion for promotion of water quality conservation in developiong countries (Philippines 1993, Indonesia 1994)
- Investigation for formulation of wetland conservation plan (Philippines 1989-93, Thailand 1994-)
- Investigation of biodiversity in wetlands (Malaysia 1992-)

2) Dispatch of environmental experts

In 1994 the Environment Agency recommended and dispatched total 108 environmental experts (50 from national government , 20 from local governments, 35 from private firms, and 3 from universities) through JICA.

3) Training

In 1994 JICA offered 22 regular and 12 ad hoc environment-related traing courses, among which the Environment Agency coordinated the following ones:

Regular group training courses
- Environment Policy
- Environmental Technology (Water quality conservation)
- Environmental Technology (Air quality conservation)
- Environmental monitoring (Water quality)
- Nature conservation and management (from 1990)

- Lake water quality conservation
- Environmental Impact Assessment
  Ad hoc group training courses for 1994
- Seminar on the Ozon layer conservation measures
- Seminar on the global warming
- Environmental conservation in Brazil (Solid wastes)
- Environmental conservation in Brazil (Air quality and water quality)
- Conservation of wetlands and migratory birds
- Industrial environmental measures in Eastern Europe
- Environmental conservation in Korea
- Middle-east environmental seminar
- Environmental conservation in central Asia

In addition to group training, the Environment Agency accepted 20 individual trainees.

4) Project-base technical cooperation

In 1994 the Environment Agency cooperated with JICA in the preliminary study of environmental centers in Mexico and Chili. Biodiversity conservation projects in Indonesia and Madagascar.

5) Regional cooperation

The environmental Agency holds regional meetings such as "Eco-Asia '94 (a ministerial meeting in Asia and the Pacific region)". Among discussion topics were : needs for sustainable development, roles of local governments, follow-up of CSD and biodiversity conservation.

6) Bilateral cooperation through environmental cooperation agreements

Japan has bilateral environmental cooperation agreements with Russia, P.R.China, and S.Korea. Moreover, environmental components are included in bilateral science and technology agreements with Russia, Canada, Germany, China and Korea. The first joint committee between Japan and Russia was held in January 1994, and the committee came to agreement on 17 joint-research projects. Ecological conservation of Lake Baikal is among them. The agreements with China and Korea put emphasis on the acid rain monitoring. In view of rapid increase of SOx emission in East Asian countries, the Environmental Agency is taking initiative in establishing an acid-rain monitoring network of the region.

National Land Agency

1-2-2 Kasumigaseki, Chiyoda-ku, Tokyo 100 Japan
Tel:+81-3-3593-3311

Water Related Work

The National Land Agency is concerned with international cooperation related to water resources by committing itself to meetings between Japan and China and meetings between Japan and the USA based on the Japan-US Environmental Protection Agreement concluded in 1975.

The Japanese and Chinese annually hold meetings about water resources with both countries taking turns to host the event. At the 7th conference in 1991, the main themes were: 1) integrated work on numerous water resources development facilities; 2) conservation measures for groundwater; 3) eutrophication prevention measures for lakes and reservoirs. In the case of the Japan-US Environmental Protection Agreement, the National Land Agency is the chairman on the Japanese side for projects related to measures such as river runoff conservation. In addition to this, the agency participates in the International Conference on Large Dams, the Japanese and Chinese meetings for rivers and dams, the International Irrigation and Drainage Congress and meetings for the International Water Service Association for the Asian and Pacific region.

Ministry of Foreign Affairs

2-2-1 Kasumigaseki, Chiyoda-ku, Tokyo 100 Japan
Tel:+81-3-3580-3311

Contribution to Environmental Matters

At the United Nations Conference on Environment and Development held in Rio de Janeiro in June 1992, Japan made clear its intention to greatly expand and strengthen environmental overseas development aid by setting targets from ¥900 billion to 1,000 billion; also, the official Development Assistance Principles (30 June 1992) was established by cabinet decision in order to realize effective and efficient aid. Environment considerations have become one of the items for serious thought, and, as such, four principles emerged from the above decision :

1) Environment and development coexistence
2) Avoiding the use of military services
3) Sufficient caution concerning the tendency to heavily invest in the military from the viewpoint that funds should be distributed toward reasonable priority resources for economic and social development
4) Sufficient consideration about the development of democracy and basic human rights

Bilateral aid is carried out through JICA and OECF (see OECF, JICA for details). Multilateral aid is contributed to respective United Nations organizations and international organizations directly from the Ministry of Foreign Affairs. The Ministry of Foreign Affairs stands second after the USA in terms of contributing (US$8 million in 1992 and US$10 million in 1993) to environment funds for the United Nations Environment Programme (UNEP). In addition to this, the ministry is contributing approximately US$2 million per year as a trust fund for the UNEP International Environment Technology Centers (UNEP/IETC) established in Shiga and Osaka. Furthermore, among the contributions to United Nations organizations (other than UNEP) and government related organizations, contributions are being used in the field of water environment, the FAO Lake Victoria Project (see FAO for details), for example. However, funding channel details could not be classified.

Apart from the above, the Ministry of Foreign Affairs established the first small-scale gratuitous finance cooperation programme for direct aid to NGOs in developing countries. This programme covers grass-root aid requests from developing countries, such as development of human resources training, elementary training, health and hygiene, regional development and water supply. With Asia (33.8%) and Africa (30.2%) as the core, 258 cases of cooperation - totaling some ¥999.6 million - were made to 54 countries and one region during fiscal 1993. The scale of this cooperation has expanded 3.4 times since the systems introduction in fiscal 1989.

The followings are example of water-related small-scale grant :

- Construction of a village water supply tank (Ghana) 700,000 Yen
- Construction of a canal clean-up campaign center (Indonesia) 7,000,000 Yen
- Environmental Pollution Prevention Plan (Palestine) 6,500,000 Yen

Lake and Reservoir Related Work

Even though the number of projects is small, the ministry is targeting lake and reservoir conservation within bilateral aid work through OECF and JICA (see JICA, OECF for details). Furthermore, a large amount of the trust fund for the UNEP International Environment Technology Centre (UNEP/IETC) is intended for lake and reservoir conservation (see UNEP for details). Among the examples of small-scale gratuitous cooperation, WWF Kenya - in association with the OECF and JICA related Kenyan Great Nakuru Water Supply Project - acquired some small-scale gratuitous aid from the Japanese embassy and used this to purchase water quality testing equipment, which it is using for test work (see OECF for details).

Ministry of Education

3-2-2 Kasumigaseki, Chiyoda-ku, Tokyo 100 Japan
Tel:+81-3-3581-4211

As well as cooperating in the work of UNESCO, the Ministry of Education is contributing to global research cooperation for lakes and freshwater through research grants for international researches.

- Global Environmental Change with emphasis on Asia and the Pacific Region
- IGBP
- Arctic Region Global Environmental Study

Ministry of International Trade and Industry

1-3-1 Kasumigaseki, Chiyoda-ku, Tokyo 100 Japan
Tel:+81-3-3501-1511

Contribution to Environmental Matters

The ministry is advancing international cooperation for the prevention of industrial pollution of water and air under the Green Aid Plan. An example is the useful effort being made by the Agency of Natural Resources and Energy to prevent air pollution such as acid rain by promoting a project to install and monitor efficiency of a simple desulphurizing device at a coal-fired power station in Taiyuan, Shanxi province, China.

To dispatch pollution control specialists, MITI inaugurated "International Environmental Adviser System" in 1994. To facilitate technology transfer to Asian region, The APEC Symposium on Environmental Technology cooperation is scheduled in 1995.

Water Related Work

Water Hope 21

The ministry - through the Environmental International Cooperation for Water Resources (Water Hope 21) - is cooperating with developing countries in the area of water environment conservation. Due to economic and technological problems in developing countries, like Thailand and Indonesia, pollution problems are surfacing due to insufficiently treated waste water and pollutants that are being discharged or dumped into rivers, lakes and reservoirs. For example, water contamination is critical in rivers, such as the malodorous Chaiya river mouth in Thailand and the Surabaya river in Indonesia, which are being used as water supplies for major cities.

In view of the situation, part of the above work is to try and make a portable version of an excellent waste-water disposal unit used in the disposal of organic waste that was shown at Aqua Renaissance '90 as equipment that would be suitable for developing countries. At the same time the ministry is developing the appropriate technical skills in developing countries (see below), as well as planning the prevention of water contamination and gas emissions that cause the greenhouse effect.

1) Develop an easy-to-operate-and-maintain, low-cost, waste-water disposal system that sufficiently

disposes/reduces water contaminating substances such as organic materials in wastewater drainage. Specifically target research measures for extremely toxic organic wastewater.

2) Establish methods to drastically curb methane gas emissions into the atmosphere and sludge build-ups that cause pollution problems.

3) Establish methods that greatly reduce construction and running costs in comparison with current methods.

4) Establish methods for easy operation and maintenance.

As the aim of this work is to develop technical skills in each country according to the situation in each particular country, it is expected that the number of countries applicable will increase. Work has commenced on a five-year basis in Thailand (1992 to 1996) and in Indonesia (1993 to 1997).

Ministry of Posts and Telecommunications
1-3-2 Kasumigaseki, Chiyoda-ku, Tokyo 100-90 Japan
Tel:+81-3-3504-4411

International Volunteer Saving Account

As a measure to financially support NGOs, the Ministry of Post and Telecommunications inaugurated this saving account in 1991 (20% of interests of the account goes to the support). By the end of fiscal 1993, the number of accounts reached 13.79 million. In fiscal 1994, total 2.36 billion yen was allocated to 261 projects in 56 countries. Many of the projects are for support of women, children, refugees and local people. Production of text material for water conservation, well digging, and construction of simple tap-water system are among water-related projects.

Ministry of Construction
2-1-3 Kasumigaseki, Chiyoda-ku, Tokyo 100 Japan
Tel:+81-3-3580-4311

Contribution to Environmental Matters

In December 1992, there was an inquiry from the minister of construction to the subcommittee dealing with the environment, and the reply was published in June 1993. Based on this, on 13 January 1994, an outline for environment measures (including the items below) was announced as a fundamental way of thinking for "the environment" as a matter to be internally targeted in the construction administration.

1) Recognize that the foremost work of the construction administration is the making and conserving of the environment - namely, internal targeting of "the environment" in the construction administration.

2) Adopt the following three items as a doctrine for environmental measures in national land formation: "creation and succession of the environment", "environment conservation" and "countermeasures for global environment problems".

3) Implement schemes for environmental plans and thorough environment impact assessments as a promotion plan for environment measures; together with the promotion of seven leading projects: environmentally friendly housing, ecological cities, the construction of numerous natural-type rivers, ecological roads, public buildings that are friendly to the environment, the reuse of treated sewage water and natural ecology observation parks.

4) Fulfill a promotion structure for environment measures through technology development and environment education.

5) Anticipate era changes and gather and offer environment information together with follow-up support to complete projects.

The following are scheduled projects related to the environment from the Ministry of Construction's fiscal 1994 International Cooperation Project.

● **International Geography Information Improvement Study for the Global Environment** (¥16 million)

This study is overseen by the Geographical Survey Institute. In order to accurately transfer the necessary foundation technology for producing world maps to the technologists in developing countries, the institute works with developing countries on model projects based on the "International Geography Information Improvement Manual" (produced in 1993) and produces a collection of practical examples for the manual.

- **Aid Promotion Work for Environment Measures** (16 million Yen)

    When a developing country is at the inquiry stage of a project, specialists in the environment field from Japan are despatched to supervise and give advice on the application of Japanese technology related to environment impact assessments.

- **West Lake Environmental Upgrading Plan** (Hanoi, Vietnam)

Water Related Work

The following is a list of the majority of water-related technology cooperation projects that the Ministry of Construction has been involved with through JICA in recent years. Although most of the list is concerned with water resources development and flood control, there are some examples of sewage treatment cooperation and lake and reservoir water quality conservation work. Furthermore, the ministry - as part of its environment measures outline - is intending to carry out meticulous support for research and development of appropriate sewage disposal technology for developing countries. To this end, the Infrastructure Development Institute-Japan was commissioned to carry out a study over three years from 1990, so that the ministry could put together a developing-country oriented manual on city drainage and polluted water disposal technology.

Examples of Water-related Technology Cooperation that the Ministry of Construction cooperated (mostly through JICA).

Indonesia

* Erosion Control Technology Centre Project
* Dam Safety Assessment Centre
* Emergency Flood Control and Water Resources Development Plan Study for city and environs
* Water Resources General Development Plan
* Water Resources General Development Plans
* Warenjo Multi-purpose Dam Construction Work Location Study

* Volcanic Erosion Control Work Location Study
* South Sumatra Regional General Development Plan
* Jakarta City Drainage and Sewage Processing
* Northern Sumatra Regional General Development Plan
* River Riparian Engineering Seminar
* Water Corporation Establishment Plan
* Quake Resistant Hydraulic Structure Design Seminar
* Erosion Control International Symposium
* General Disaster Measures Study

Philippines

* Specific Region City Water Supply Safeguard Planning Study
* Pinatobo Volcano Sludge Control Plan
* Flood Forecasts and Warnings Seminar
* Flood Prevention Planning and Disaster Recovery Seminar
* Agano River Basin Flood Control Plan Study
* Irogu Hirabangan River Basin Flood Control Plan Study
* Manila Water Supply Action Plan Study

China

* Jilin Fengman Dam Repair and Reinforcement Plan Study
* National Water Damage Prevention Supreme Command Automation System
* Han River Mid/Down Stream Flood Forecasts and Warning Plan Study
* Guaninge Dam Construction Work
* Lake Tai Water Quality Improvement
* Lake Poyang Water Quality Regulation Protection Measures Study

Nepal

* Nepal Flood Control and Erosion Control Centre Project
* Internal Water Documents Improvement Plan Study
* Upper Karnari River and Mahakari River Water Resources Development Plan Study

Korea

* River Environment Management
* Hangang River Related Medium to Small Rivers Environment Improvement Plan Study

Malaysia

* Nationwide River Mouth Management Plan Study
* Penang Island Water Supply Relief and Drainage Plan Study
* Klantang River Basin Flood Control Plan Study

Kenya

* Nationwide Water Resources Development Plan Study
* Dam Construction Plan Study

Honduras

* Tributary Basin Flood Control and Erosion Control Plan Study
* Flood Control and Erosion Control Seminar

Thailand

* Bangkok Water Quality Improvement Plan

* Phuket Sewage and Drainage Improvement Plan Study
* Southern Thailand Disaster Recovery

Zambia

* Nationwide Water Resources Development Plan Study

Ecuador

* River Basin Water Resources Development Plan

Tanzania

* Erosion Disaster Engineering Seminar
* River and Water Resources Development Plan Study

Tunisia

* City Drainage Measures Plan Study

Morocco

* Basin Dam Construction Plan Study

Oman

* Dam Engineering

Turkey

* River Flood Forecast and Warning System Plan Study

Bangladesh

* Northwest Regional Flood Safeguard and Drainage Plan Study

* Dhaka Metropolitan Flood Safeguard and Rain Water Drainage Plan Study

Venezuela

* Apure River Imp
* Landslide Forecast and Warning System
* River Basin Erosion Disaster Plan Study

Brazil

* Itajai River Lower Basin Flood Control Plan

Nigeria

* Nationwide Water Resources Development Plan Study

Egypt

* Weather Changes and Water Management Seminar

Bolivia

* Le Paz City Water Contamination Measures Plan Study

Britain

* Flooding Measures Formation Study

Nicaragua

* Volcano Disaster Recovery Plan

Water Resources Development Public Corporation

5-3-3 Akasaka, Minato-ku, Tokyo 107 Japan
Tel:+81-3-3584-1251

Water Related Work

The Water Resources Development Public Corporation's overseas technology aid is generally classified as participation in bilateral technology exchange conferences and international conferences, dispatching of staff overseas (short-term or long-term specialists) through JICA, and the acceptance of trainees.

1. International Conferences

a) Bilateral Periodical Technology Exchange Conferences

The following are bilateral technology exchange conferences currently being held at periodic intervals. Japan and Korea Technology Exchange Conference, Japan and China Water Resources Exchange Conference, Japan and Korea River and Water Resources Development Technology Cooperation Conference, Japan and China River and Dam Conference, and Japan and France River, Lake and Reservoir Water Management Seminar

b) International Conference Participation

Participation from 1963 in the International Congress on Large Dams (see ICID for details)

Participation from 1964 in International Commission on Irrigation and Drainage (see ICID for details)

2. Sending Staff Overseas

a) Dispatchment of Long-term Experts by JICA

As many as 26 people were dispatched for a total of 630 months up to the end of fiscal 1992 as JICA long-term specialists. The following are overseas dispatching circumstances for staff in fiscal 1992. Venezuela (river engineering), Kenya (irrigation), Myanmar (irrigation technology), Thailand (irrigation)

b) Short-term Overseas Dispatching (fiscal 1992)

24 cases, 27 people, 296 days

3. Accepting Trainees

The acceptance of overseas trainees is to basically offer the opportunity of viewing the public corporation's facilities. In fiscal 1992, 29 people, 123 cases, were accepted through JICA and 17 people, 89 cases, were accepted from other organs, making a total of 46 people, 212 cases, that were accepted as trainees related to water resources development technology.

Japan International Cooperation Agency (JICA)

Shinjyuku-Mitsui Building, 2-1-1 Nishi-Shinjyuku, Shinjyuku-ku, Tokyo 163-04 Japan
Tel:+81-3-3346-5311

Work Outline

JICA's technological cooperation takes the form of trainee acceptance (groups, individuals), individual specialist dispatching, overseas youth cooperation unit, project methodology and technology cooperation, development studies, and provision of straightforward materials. Development studies are often carried out with the financial cooperation and assistance of OECF.

Contribution to Environmental Matters

JICA set up an environment office in 1989 to strengthen international cooperation in the environment field. In 1993, an environment and women section was set up to deal with issues such as women in development (WID) and poverty. Also, the agency produced an environment consideration guideline to be generally applied to JICA aid work. The following shows the annual increase in actual cooperation in the environment field.

JICA's technology cooperation budget in the environment field (fiscal 1985 to 1992)

1985	¥4,445 million
1986	¥5,404 million
1987	¥6,214 million
1988	¥8,113 million
1989	¥10,033 million
1990	¥13,240 million
1991	¥13,102 million
1992	¥17,407 million

JICA's environment related projects are unfolding in regions across the globe. There are many projects in Asia, but not so many that they become a regional bias. Furthermore, there is a broad spectrum of cases, and in recent years the

Number of people/projects involved in JICA's technology cooperation for the environment (fiscal 1991)

Field	Trainee(s) (group training)	Expert(s) Dispatch	Cooperation Volunteers	Comprehensive Projects	Development Studies
Environmental Administration	120(13)	33		4	
Air Pollution	48 (5)	11			7
Water Contamination	41 (5)	9	5		6
Ocean Pollution	15 (2)	5			
Supply/Sewage Water	44 (5)	36	7	3	9
Groundwater Development			3		6
Solid Waste Disposal	21 (3)	9			5
Mining Pollution				3	1
Forest Conservation/Reforestation	109 (9)	13	38	18	7
Biodiversity	26 (4)	21	14	6	2
Water Resources Conservation	11 (1)	7			
Disaster Prevention	91 (7)	12		3	5
Flood Control Measures		6		1	10
Energy Savings	13 (1)				5
Total	539(55)	102	67	38	63

(The number in parenthesis shows the number of courses.)

agency has been involving itself with complex cases that target poverty countermeasures, aid consideration and environment countermeasures and general environment cases that target action capacity improvement for environmental problems.

Environment Related Technology Cooperation and Development Studies (Fiscal 1992) by JICA

East Europe

- **Bulgaria**
  * Plan for Rational Use of Energy
  * Plan for Waste Disposal in Sofia
- **Czechoslovakia**
  * Study on Flue Gas Desulphurization for Melnik Power Station
- **Hungary**
  * Plan for Regional Air Pollution Measures
  * Plan for Rational Use of Energy
  * Plan for Waste Disposal in Budapest
- **Poland**
  * Plan for Waste Disposal in Poznan
- **Rumania**
  * Plan for Foundry Environment and Energy Reduction Measures

Middle East

- **Egypt**
  * Plan for Groundwater Development in Sinai Peninsula
- **Morocco**
  * Plan for Forest Wood Fuel
- **Saudi Arabia**
  * Plan for Seawater Desalinization Technical Cooperation
- **Tunisia**
  * Plan for Pollution Measures in Sfax
  * Plan for City Flood Measures
- **Turkey**
  * Plan for River Flood Forecast and Warning System
  * Marine Products Resources Study
- **Yemen**
  * Plan for Groundwater Development in Sanaa

Africa

- **Kenya**
  * Social Forestry Training Plan (I), (II)
  * Plan for Nakuru Sewage Facility Reconstruction/Expansion Improvement
- **Mali**
  * Plan for Regional Solar-powered Water Pumping
  * Plan for Regional Agricultural Development (Desertification Control)
- **Senegal**
  * Plan for Dakar environs and region sewage and drainage installation improvement

- **Tanzania**
  * Plan (I), (II) for Kilimanjaro Village Forestry
- **Maldives**
  * Plan for Male Island Coastline Protection

Oceania

- **Fiji**
  * Plan for Northern Groundwater Development
  * Papua New Guinea
  * Forest Research Centre
  * Plan for Port Moresby Service Water Improvement
- **Tonga**
  * Plan for Increased Marine Product Cultivation Research Development
- **Cook Islands**
  * Coastline Conservation and Improvement Plan
- **Kiribati**
  * Plan for Rural Solar Power Generation

Asian Region

- **Mongol**
  * Plan for Ulan Bator City Water Supply
- **Nepal**
  * Plan for Forestry Diffusion
  * Flood and Erosion Control Centre
  * Plan for Karnari River Upper Reaches and Mahakari River Basin Water Resources Development
- **Philippines**
  * Plan (II) for Pantabangan Forestry Development
  * Crocodile Cultivation Research Centre
  * Land Research & Development Centre
  * Plan for Manila Metropolitan Groundwater Development
  * Plan for Makirina Riverhead Forest Development
  * Plan for Pinatobo Volcano Damage and Erosion Control
  * Plan for Specific Regional Cities Flood Safeguard
- **Sri Lanka**
  * Plan for Plant Genetics Resources Centre
- **Thailand**
  * Environment Conservation Measures
  * Plan (II) for Reforestation Research Training
  * Plan for Northeast Thailand Reforestation Diversifying
  * Plan for Marine Products Research Development
  * Environment Research Training Centre
  * Plan for Simpson Fluidized Bed Coal-fired Electric Generation Development
  * Plan for Medium-to-small Factory Offensive Odour Prevention Management
  * Plan for Chao Phraya River Lower Basin Sewage Improvement
  * Plan for Bangkok Metropolitan Ground Subsidence Measures
  * Plan for Southern Thailand Peat Land Regional Agriculture Development
  * Plan for Southern Agricultural Land Revival and Conservation

- **Brunei**
  - * Forestry Research Follow-up
  - * Forest Resources Development
- **Bangladesh**
  - * Plan for Supply Water Hygiene Facility Improvement
  - * Plan for Dhaka Metropolitan Flood Safeguard and Rainwater Drainage
- **Myanmar**
  - * Plan for Central Forestry Development Training Centre
- **Cambodia**
  - * Plan for Phnom Penh Service Water Improvement
- **P. R. China**
  - * Water Pollution and Waste Water Recycling Research Centre
  - * Dairen Province Energy Education Centre
  - * Plan for Huantu Plateau Flood-control Tree Planting Technology Training
  - * Amur River Province General Lumber Use Research Centre
  - * Plan for Fukien Province Forestry Technology Development
  - * Japan and China Friendly Environment Conservation Centre
  - * Plan for Liazhou Air Pollution General Measures and Broad Zone Acid fallout Monitoring
  - * Plan for Lake Poyang Water Resources Protection Measures
  - * Dexing Copper Mine Waste Water Measures
- **Indonesia**
  - * Industrial Pollution Prevention Technology Training
  - * Water Mains Environment Hygiene Training Centre
  - * Plan (II) for Tropical Rainforest Research
  - * Plan for South Suhalese Flood Control Tree Planting
  - * Plan for Tree Nursery
  - * South Sumatra Reforestation Plan Aftercare
  - * Erosion Control Technology Centre
  - * Environment Management Centre
  - * Plan for Solar Power Hybrid
  - * Plan for Surabaya Waste Disposal
  - * Plan for Citaric Water Resources and Forest Creation
  - * Plan for Emergency Riparian Water-Utilization
  - * Coastline Resources Management Strengthening Plan
  - * Plan for Denpasar Sewage Improvement
- **S. Korea**
  - * Plan for Industrial Waste Water Disposal and Recycling
- **Laos**
  - * Plan for Metropolitan Waste Disposal
- **Malaysia**
  - * Sadban Reforestation Technology Training Plan Follow-up
  - * Plan for Sarawak Effective Use of Lumber Research
  - * Plan for Metropolitan Air Pollution Measures
  - * Plan for Northern Sadban Reforestation
  - * Plan for Nationwide River Supervision
  - * Solar Power Regional Electrification Plan

Central and South America

- **Bolivia**
  - * Environment Conservation Special Measures
  - * Marine Products Development Research Centre Plan
  - * Plan for La Paz Water Contamination Prevention
- **Brazil**
  - * Mining Pollution Prevention Training Centre
  - * Sao Paulo State forest and Environment Conservation Research
  - * Plan for Amazon Agriculture Research Cooperation
  - * Plan for Guanabara Bay Water Contamination Prevention
- **Chile**
  - * Resources and Environment Research Centre
  - * Plan for Semi-arid Zone Flood Control Tree Planting Greening
  - * Plan for Plant Genetics Resources
  - * Plan for Northern Region Water Resources Development
  - * Plan for Forest Resources Management
- **Honduras**
  - * Plan for Chamerecon River Basin Flood Safeguard
- **Mexico**
  - * Earthquake Disaster Prevention
  - * Plan for Air Pollution Measures and Incinerating Technology Introduction
- **Nicaragua**
  - * Plan for Managua Service Water Improvement
- **Paraguay**
  - * Paraguay Central Forest Creation Plan Follow-up
  - * Southern Paraguay Forestry Development Plan Follow-up
  - * Comprehensive Plan for Asuncion Metropolitan Waste Disposal
- **Peru**
  - * Japan/Peru Earthquake Disaster Prevention Centre
  - * Trinidad and Tobago
  - * Oil Pollution Measures
- **Uruguay**
  - * Plan for Tree Nursery
- **Venezuela**
  - * Plan for Apure River Recovery
- **Argentina**
  - * Thermoelectric Power Station Air Pollution Prevention Measures
  - * Buenos Aires Metropolitan Sewage Plan

Water Related Work

The following work was carried out in relation to water pollution measures in fiscal 1992.

JICA's technological cooperation related to water pollution measures (fiscal 1992)

Group Training Courses

- Environment Technology (Water Conservation) (10 people)
- Industrial Waste Disposal Technology (6 people)
- Environmental Monitoring of Water Quality (10 people)

- Lakes and Reservoirs Water Conservation (11 people)
- Seas and Oceans Conservation (8 people)
- Environment Management Technology for Semi-closed Sea Areas (9 people)
- Indonesia River Cleaning (Special Establishment) (9 people)
- Korea Water Contamination (3 people)

Individual Training

- 12 people

Individual Expert Dispatch

- **Korea :** Water Quality Automatic Measuring Network Building Seminar
- **Korea :** TBTO Pollution Research
- **Korea :** Han River Basin Water Management (Research Cooperation)
- **Tanzania :** Water Pollution Monitoring
- **Venezuela :** Lake Valencia Cleaning Plan

Comprehensive Technology Cooperation

- **China :** Water Pollution and Waste Water Recycling Research Centre

Development Studies

- **China :** Lake Poyang Water Protection Measures Plan
- **China :** Dexing Copper Mine Waste Water Measures
- **Korea :** Industrial Waste Water Disposal and Recycling Plan
- **Trinidad and Tobago :** Oil Pollution Measures
- **Bolivia :** La Paz Water Contamination Measures Plan
- **Brazil :** Guanabara Bay Water Contamination Prevention Plan
- **Tunisia :** Sfax Pollution Measures

Donation of Facilities

- **Bulgaria :** Water Quality Monitoring Facilities
- **Hungary :** Environment Monitoring Materials

Lake and Reservoir Related Work

JICA is only directly involved with a few projects concerned with lake and reservoir environments, and the majority of these are to do with development studies. Nevertheless, there is not a regional bias toward Asia. Lake and reservoir conservation has been established as one of the training and group courses. The following are several examples of lake and reservoir related work.

Example 1 :
" Ypacarai Lake Basin Water Pollution Measures Plan Preliminary Study" (Paraguay) (1986 to 1988)

This was the first study by JICA that had the direct aim of environmental conservation for lakes and reservoirs. In recent years, the water quality of Lake Ypacarai has worsened at an alarming rate due to factory waste water from the livestock industry and agriculture processing industries in the basin area, domestic waste water from hamlets, hotels and second homes, and landslides caused by logging and housing site development. In order to put forward a water contamination measures plan, the following studies were carried out: 1) status study, 2) contamination mechanism study, 3) inquiry and planning for water contamination measures, and 4) inquiry into proposals for actual action.

Example 2 :
"Eutrophication Prevention Measures Project for Paldang Lake" (Korea) (1988 to 1990)

Paldang dam is an artificial lake with a water-storage capacity of 240 million tons, which is located midway along the Han river, a river that flows through Korea's capital, Seoul. Paldang dam is the sole drinking water supply dam for all 10 million Seoul citizens and the rest of the metropolitan area. However, water quality is worsening as the contamination load rate rises dramatically, along with outbreaks of summertime water-bloom and outbreaks of strange smelling and tasting service water. To counter this, the "Korean Water Improvement System Development Project" was begun based on the Japan and Korea Science Technology Agreement concluded in March 1988. With the cooperation of JICA, the Eutrophication Prevention Measures Project for Lake Paldang was put together around a core of Korean national environment researchers, and the project commenced for three years from 1988. The project started with the construction of a temporary lake laboratory and carried out various research to ascertain the actual quality of the water at the dam lake and upper dam, ascertain the generated load capacity and inflow load rate and constructed a water quality predictor model. In addition to this, the project established environmental standards and discharge standards for nitrogen and phosphate and put forward a plan for eutrophication prevention.

Example 3 :
"Lake Valencia Cleaning Plan Study" (Venezuela) (1991)

Lake Valencia is Venezuela's largest freshwater lake. With a water-catchment population exceeding two million people, numerous factories and agriculture and livestock industries, and an inflow of factory and agricultural waste water from 16 rivers, eutrophication has already gone beyond the set limit, and the lake is dying (a low water level is also spurring on this tendency). The Venezuelan Environment Natural Resources Ministry has made the cleaning of Lake Valencia a matter of utmost importance. The Lake Valencia Cleaning head office is grappling with environmental pollution cleaning and a land improvement national scheme as a combined issue. The following are measures currently being promoted: 1) Factory supervision (large to small factories), 2) construction of pollution treatment facilities (use of natural oxidizing ponds, use of water hyacinths, reuse treated water for agricultural purposes, and partial tertiary treatment), 3) founding of basin office (consisting of officials and local people, an organization with economic backup for regulation control and expenditures by officials and local people), 4) land improvement national plan. JICA cooperated in this study. In fiscal 1994, monitoring equipment worth 84 million Japanese Yen is scheduled to be offered.

⊙ Water sampling at eutrophicated Valencia Lake

This kind of flooding has become a problem since the breakup of a lake in eastern Nepal in 1985. This breakup caused flooding for 100 km down stream, several dozen people died and a hydroelectric power station was damaged. For this reason a status study was undertaken as part of JICA study work. The results of the study showed that this type of flooding had occurred 13 times from 1960 onward in the eastern region - namely, a flood had occurred once almost every three years. The glacial lakes are located at high altitude (over 4,000m high); however, the distribution across the whole of Nepal is not yet clear. Nevertheless, the eastern region study shows that there are several one-to-three km long lakes with a maximum depth of about 100 m that could potentially breakup, and the inhabitants are quite worried. The countermeasures are: 1) lake drainage, 2) moraine strengthening, 3) evacuation from flood risk areas. The problem has surfaced because inhabitants have taken to settling in the vicinity of glacial lakes and suitable sites for hydroelectric schemes have been promoted deep in the mountains. This is a special lake and reservoir problem, so that disaster aid can be sent to a developing country.

Example 4 :
"Yasireta Reservoir Wildlife Salvation Cooperation" (Paraguay and Argentina)

Since 1978 the Yasireta hydroelectric project has been in progress on the Parana River that flows along the border between Paraguay and Argentina. Upon completion, there will be a 160,000-hectare (2.4 times the size of Lake Biwa) reservoir, and the prospect of 10,000 hectares of land being flooded. Numerous species of South American native animals, including the marsh deer and maned wolf, inhabit the region to be flooded. In order to rescue these animals, the following have been carried out for the Paraguay Republic: JICA - at the cost of ¥50 million over three years from 1991 - has sent specialists, supplied equipment and covered running costs and accepted trainees from Paraguay. The work involves: 1) status study, 2) selection of species to be rescued, 3) study of species ecology and head count, 4) creation of a rescue plan, 5) selection of replacement preservation and management plan, and 6) habitat studies. JICA aims to transfer wild animal protection management technology as part of the process for realizing the above.

Example 5 :
"Glacial Lake Breakup Study" (Nepal)

In Nepal, located in the centre of the Himalayas, there is concern about flooding from the breakup of glacial lakes.

Example 6 :
"Lake and Reservoir Water Conservation Group Training" (in Japan) (annually from 1990)

A three-month training course is held for lakes, marshland and reservoir water management in developing countries. The course involves training through theory and practice of measuring techniques, prevention techniques, prediction techniques and management techniques. The International Lake Environment Committee Foundation (ILEC) is entrusted with the office work, and ten people from all over the world receive training each year. The course's distinction is that the actual experiences of regional local authorities dealing with lake and reservoir water management, water contamination prevention technology from the industrial world and the amassed technology of researchers is combined to supply the trainees with practical knowledge.

Example 7 :
"Lake Poyang Water Pollution Measures Planning Study" (China)

With recent industrialization, Lake Poyang's industrial related contamination load and domestic related contamination load has increased remarkably, therefore, an 18-month study over 1992 to 1993 was carried out with the aim of finding water protection measures for Lake Poyang. There are two scenarios for the lake's water conservation -

namely, 1) maintain the water quality at the present level into the year 2000, or 2) set COD levels to 3mg/L so that the lake water in the year 2000 can be used as drinking water. The necessary basin and river measures, measures for within the lake and related measures for fulfilling each target have been proposed.

Continuing on from the Lake Poyang example, an advance study has been carried out in fiscal 1993 for the "Lake Tai-hu Basin Management Plan".

Example 8 :
"Freshwater Fish Aquaculture Breeding Project"
(Nepal) (1991 to 1996)

This is a project that targets the improvement of fisheries production using natural water, while paying attention to water resources that can be used for low-cost production and a supply of animal protein. Within this, fish tank breeding technology is being developed in the lake using only natural fodder. In relation to this, the lake's natural fodder and plankton production capability is being evaluated as part of the technological supervision being carried out for "lake study methods". At Lake Phewa and other lakes in the Pokhara region, Nepalese people are researching seasonal changes in water temperature, light conditions in water, nutrient salts, potential of hydrogen (pH) and dissolved oxygen, and the basic production volume measurements, current volume and species components of plant plankton, and also the seasonal change of the current volume of animal plankton.

Furthermore, in the same way as the above examples which are directly concerned with lakes and reservoirs, capacity building projects for water quality monitoring are also helping lake conservation. Environment monitoring, training and management centres have been established under the cooperation of JICA and the Ministry of Environment in countries like Thailand, China and Indonesia. For example, the Thai Environmental Research and Training Center (ERTC) is contributing toward the improvement in water quality data accuracy for Lake Songkhla. The following is the Indonesia Environment Management Centre (EMC) example.

Example 9 :
"Project System Technology Cooperation for Indonesia Environment Management Centre" (EMC) (1992 to 1998)

JICA sent a study team related to this project in May 1991, sent a long-term specialist, as scheduled, after the start of the project, discussed technology cooperation content and carried out an extra study. The project started in January 1993. The main functions of EMC are as follows.

1) Reference Laboratory

A pact was concluded between ministries, agencies and local authorities, a research group network was set up, and a plan that entrusts environment monitoring to these research groups is being promoted. EMC is the core of the regional environment group network and the reference laboratory is the driving force behind environment monitoring progress.

2) Environment Information System

3) Environment Training Course

⊙ Analyical Laboratory at EMC

Overseas Economic Cooperation Fund (OECF)

1-4-1, Otemachi, Chiyoda-ku, Tokyo 100 Japan
Tel:03-3215-1419 (Public Relations)

Contribution to Environmental Matters

In the ODA outline decided upon by the cabinet in June 1992, the first principle is recorded as "Environment and Development Coexistence". OECF takes note of this kind of plan with internal/external trends for Earth environment issues, and works to prevent environment degradation and improve the environment in developing countries. The major environment-related points that OECF is working on are as follows. Environment ODA with the special characteristic of covering medium-advanced countries that exceed the grant criteria of GNP less than US$2,555 per person.

1. Strengthening of Environment Considerations

In order to strengthen environment consideration and to actually execute development projects, OECF considers the environment - based on "OECF Guidelines for Environment Consideration" - and dispatches environment specialists, making the necessary retrospective evaluations and supervision after the completion of projects, and carries out studies related to environmental impact. In particular, the following three items are being considered.

a) Harmony between development and environment through sustainable development

b) Commitment to environment problems based on talks with countries taking out loans

c) Commencement of environment consideration work from the earliest point possible in the loan offering process

2. Expansion of Environment Related Work

OECF also positively supports projects that target environment improvement and conservation, as shown in the chart below.

Examples of Fiscal 1992 OECF financing for Projects Contributing to Environmental Improvement

Country	Project Title	Signing Date	Agreed Sum (million of yen)
Thailand	Environment Protection Promotion Plan	29/ 1/93	3,000
	Service Water Expansion Work for three regional cities	29/ 1/93	4,754
	Bangkok Service Water Improvement Work	29/ 1/93	16,969
Indonesia	Sector Programme Loan (Living Environment Sector/Forestry Sector)	8/10/92	14,572
	Jakarta Sewage Improvement Work (I)	8/10/92	2,121
			12,995
	Pollution Prevention Equipment Installation Aid Work	30/11/92	
	Central Sumatra Reforestation Work	30/11/92	426
	Surabaya Urban Environment Improvement Work 1st Phase	26/ 2/93	11,251
Philippines	Regional and City Water Improvement Work (II)	26/ 5/92	1,094
	Coal-fired Power Station Unit 1 Environment Improvement Work	31/ 3/93	6,112
India	Yamuna River Basin Cities Sewage Improvement Work	21/12/92	17,773
El Salvador	Medium/Small Sized Cities Service Water/Sewage Improvement Work	19/ 3/93	1,210
Mexico	Mexico Metropolitan Forestation Work	20/10/92	10,403
	Monterrey Service Water/Sewage Improvement Work	20/10/92	13,482
Chile	Valparaiso Service Water/Sewage Improvement Work	20/11/92	5,481
Costa Rica	Medium-sized City Service Water Improvement Work	19/ 3/93	1,656

3. Preparation of Environment Related Information

Preparation of environment related information that will become the basis for working on items a) and b) above.

4. Strengthen Cooperating Relations with Other Aid Organizations

Strengthen cooperating relations with other aid organizations in the environment field through joint financing and environment information exchange for environment related work.

5. Completion of Environment Consideration Structure

An environment specialist post was established in September 1988 and environment inquiry committee, made up of external specialists, was established from fiscal 1990 to strengthen work in the area of items 1. through 4.
In October 1993 OECF established the Environment and Social Development Division.

Water Related Work

As shown above, a large proportion of OECF's water environment related projects are service water/sewage improvement projects. In fiscal 1994, 13 projects out of 19 environment related ones were water/sewage projects.

To South Korea, total 63.8 billion Japanese Yen loaning was made during 1980-1988, and 11 sewage treatment plants were constructed in 9 cities. This accounts for more than 40 % of treatment capacity of the country. Trough the process, technology transfer steadily took place.

Example 1 :
"Great Nakuru Service Water Project" (Kenya)

(Agreement signed in March 1987, finance ¥5,017 million, interest rate 3.5%, loan repayment period 30 years [deferment 10 years], generally unrestricted)

Nakuru city is situated right next to Lake Nakuru - a national park famous for its flamingos - and is an important place for local industry and transport. In recent years, there has been a population influx and increase in Nakuru city, and at present the population is 300,000 (50,000 in the '70s and 200,000 in the '80s). Water amounting to 22,400 tons per day from two water purification plants (built in 1913 and 1956) and deep wells made up the water supply for Nakuru. These circumstances led to the establishment of the Great Nakuru District Water Supply Plan to alleviate water shortages. The Japanese government decided to support the water supply plan for the two towns and four villages of the eastern district, that make up the centre of Nakuru, and are in the east and west districts of the plan.

As this is a large project dependent on the construction of a dam for a water source, the whole project was split into two stages. The first stage being the Greater Nakuru eastern district water mains construction project. A scheme to supply water to Nakuru, which involved the completion of a water-collection dam and water supply piping (total length 81 km) on the Torasha River, a tributary of the Marewa River (several dozen kilometers east from Nakuru) situated outside of the catchment area of Nakuru Lake. The general construction costs of ¥5 billion were covered by finance from the Japanese government. The loan is for materials and equipment supply charges, detailed planning and consulting services. Construction took place from November 1987 to October 1988. The water purification plant's capacity is 18,000 tons per day (more than double the previous volume of supply water).

❶ A look out for illegal fishing at Bung Poraped, an artificial wetland lake in Thailand

Example 2 :
"Large-scale Lakes and Reservoirs Fisheries Development Project (Bung Porapet Fisheries Development Plan)" (Thailand)

(Agreement signed in June 1988, finance ¥2.651 billion, loan repayment period 30 years [deferment 10 years], generally unrestricted)

This project concerned three large lakes and reservoirs including Bung Porapet Lake, and Lake Nong Han in Thailand and was completed in fiscal 1992. The project aims are dredging and dike recovery together with construction and expansion of fisheries stations, extension of breeding technology and the safe supplying of seedlings to greatly increase marine resources, improve the income of people in farming and fishing in poor inland regions, improve nutrition, and reduce flood damage in the vicinity of the lakes and reservoirs. The loan finance covers equipment and consulting services. The work commenced in January 1990. Nihon Koei Inc. and Nissui-Con Inc. were involved jointly in the plan study and construction. Konoike, NKK and Nissan carried out work in accordance with the plan study. The work was completed in 1992.

The Lake Bun Porapet is a manmade freshwater lake located in the west of Thailand's central flatlands (Nakhon, Sarawan state), and is home to 97 types of waterfowl. If Thailand becomes a signatory member of the Ramsar Convention, this lake could possibly be the first registered wetland. There are worries about the disposal of water pollution from continually growing regional industries, including sightseeing. Moreover, it is feared that this pollution will have an impact on the lake and wildfowl.

Example 3 :
"Reconquista River Environment Improvement Project" (Argentina)

The Reconquista River, situated in the northern part of Buenos Aires, is Argentina's top environment improvement project which includes plans to construct a sewage treatment plant and drainage pump plant (because of severe household wastewater contamination), reform rivers and improve flood control channels. The overall cost is ¥35.1 billion. The yen loan made available by Japan is ¥8.15 billion (annual interest rate 5%, loan repayment period 25 years, agreement signed in March 1995). Finance, other than yen loans, comes from the US, Interstate Development Bank (IDB) and the Argentinean government's conciliatory finance. This is the third case, following Brazil and Mexico, in which

environmental ODA has been applicable for a medium-advanced country.

Example 4 :
"Lake Laguna North Shore Urgent Flood Safeguard Work" (Philippines)

(Agreement signed in February 1990, finance ¥454 million, interest rates 2.7%)

This project involves construction of embankments along the north shore of Lake Laguna and the river banks of the Napindan River, both situated in the same suburb of Manila. Together with this the project aims to improve the water supply, prevent flood damage, promote development and improve the living conditions in the same suburb. This loan is an engineering service loan and is being used for an effective potential review study and detailed design.

Example 5 :
"South Sumatra Marshland Improvement Project" (Indonesia)

(Agreement signed in October 1992. Finance ¥5,577 million, interest rate 2.6 %)

This project is a coordinated finance with the International Farming Aid Development (IFAD), and aims to improve farmers' living standards and expand agricultural production by improving and repairing the infrastructure of the developed areas that exist in the marshlands of south Sumatra. This finance targets the repair and improvement of drainage systems, transport facilities and provision of a clean water supply, in addition to covering consulting service fees. The construction of a power station and dam and irrigation work is also scheduled in this project. The land area involved is 116,000 ha.

In 1995, the following two projects came to agreement. The former is directly aimed at lake restoration.

● Bhopal Lake Conservation and Management Project (Bhopal, India)

Construction of sewage treatment plant, dredging, removal of water weed etc.

● Water Environment Improvement Project (Hanoi, Vietnam)

Improvement of drainage system in Hanoi City to alleviate flood damage.

Japan Environment Corporation (JEC)

Nittochi Building 4F, 1-4-1 Kasumigaseki, Chiyoda-ku, Tokyo 100 Japan
Tel:+81-3-5251-1015   Fax:+81-3-3592-5056

Global Environment Fund

Among NGOs that received support from the JEC Global Environment Fund in fiscal 1993, the following are involved in freshwater environment conservation.

Fiscal 1993

- **International Lake Environment Committee**
  "Distribution of world lakes and reservoirs data book to developing countries"

- **International Waterfowl and Wetlands Research Bureau Japan**
  "Extension of development education related to preservation of important wetlands in the Asian region"

- **Ramsar Center**
  "Workshops related to Asian biodiversity wetlands"

- **Eco-Institute/Citizens Bank**
  "Acid rain monitoring at Lake Baikal"

- **Japan Water Environment Institute**
  "Water environment conservation knowledge extension aid in Indonesia"

Example :

Database for Transfer of Environmental Information overseas

JEC has engaged in loaning of pollution abatement funds to small- and mid-sized enterprises. To utilize the experience of those firms to environmental conservation of developing countries, a database is being developed by selecting 514 cases (waste water 300, air pollution 151, solid waste 57, odor 28, noise 10, vibration 5) out of 4,000 cases of loaning. Such items as type of pollution, type of enterprises, methods, achievement, and cost are in the datasheets.

Local Governments (Prefectures and Specially Designated Cities)

Contribution to Environmental Matters

Cooperation Through Encouragement and Aid of Environment Related Organizations

In recent years many local authorities are encouraging and supporting UN organizations, International organizations and International NGOs involved in international environment conservation (organizations with environment related bureaus). These organizations take many forms, such as UN organizations, cooperation foundations, or domestic foundations involved in independent projects, and, as stated above, are supported not by central government but by regional local authorities. This type of example is rarely seen in other parts of the world.

Examples of Local Autonomies Cooperating with International Environmental Conservation Organizations

Kushiro City	Kushiro International Wetland Centre	Wetlands
Tokyo Met.	UN University (UNU) (Environment Unit)	Environment & Peace
Kanagawa Prefecture	International Ecology Centre	Ecology
Yokohama City	International Tropical Timber Organization (ITTO)	Tropical Forests
Nagoya City	United Nations Centre for Regional Development (UNCRD)	Regional Development & Environment
Mie Prefecture/ Yokkaichi City	International Center for Environmental Technology Transfer (ICETT)	Technology Transfer
Shiga Prefecture	International Lake Environment Committee (ILEC)	Lakes/Reservoirs
	UNEP International Environmental Technology Centre (IETC)	Water Environment
Kyoto Prefecture	Research Institute of Innovative Technology for the Earth (RITE)	Innovative Technology
Osaka Prefecture/City	UNEP International Environmental Technology Centre (IETC)	Urban Environment
	Global Environment Centre (GEC)	Urban Environment
Hyogo Prefecture	International EMECS Centre	Semi-closed Sea Area
Kitakyushu City	Kitakyusyu International Technol-cooperative Association (KITA)	Technology Transfer
Okinawa Prefecture	International Society for Mangrove Ecosystems (ISME)	Mangrove Forests

Experts Dispatched to JICA

Recently, as part of the international interaction within local authorities, international cooperation (acceptance of trainees and dispatching of specialists through JICA, etc.) occupies a large proportion of both quality and quantity work. However, the majority of dispatched specialists are only for short-term periods of less than several months; long term dispatchments are minimal. Characteristically, many research staff are dispatched from Tokyo and specially designated cities. In the water quality field, Shiga prefecture, surrounding Lake Biwa, makes a large cooperation contribution.

International Conferences

Shiga prefecture, Ibaraki prefecture (scheduled) and Kushiro city have supported the following international conferences as a link toward international cooperation for lakes and reservoirs conservation.

1) The First World Lake Conference (1984, Otsu, Shiga prefecture)
2) The Sixth World Lake Conference (scheduled) (1995,Tsukuba and Tsuchiura , Ibaraki prefecture)
3) Fifth Meeting of Ramsar Convention (Kushiro Meeting) staging support (1992, Kushiro)

Dispatched JICA Environment Experts from Local Autonomies (1984 to November 1992)

	Dispatched Staff	Water Field	Lakes Field
Hokkaido Prefecture	5		
Chiba Prefecture	4	3	
Tokyo Met.	17		
Kanagawa Prefecture	4	1	
Niigata Prefecture	4		
Ishikawa Prefecture	1		
Nagano Prefecture	1		
Toyama Prefecture	1	1	
Aichi Prefecture	2	1	
Shiga Prefecture	5	5	3*
Osaka Prefecture	4		
Hyogo Prefecture	5		
Hiroshima Prefecture	3		
Yamaguchi Prefecture	1		
Fukuoka Prefecture	2		
Kumamoto Prefecture	1		
Okinawa Prefecture	1		
Yokohama City	5		
Nagoya City	5	3	
Kyoto City	2		
Osaka City	7	1	
Kobe City	2	1	
Kitakyushu City	4	1	
Fukuoka City	4	1	

* : Ypacarai Lake Basin Water Pollution Measures Pre-feasibility Study,
Korea Eutrophication Study, Lake Valencia Cleaning Plan

Section 5-1 International cooperation organizations involved in activities and extension work

---

Kushiro International Wetland Center (KIWC)
Kushiro International Exchange Center, 3-3 Saiwai-cho, Kushiro, 085 Japan
Tel:+81-154-31-4503   Fax:+81-154-23-8041

Work Outline

As a follow up to the 5th Meeting of the Conference of the Parties to the Convention on Wetlands of International Importance held in Kushiro in 1993, an international wetlands conservation information center, with Kushiro as the core, was established. The activity contents are as follows.

1) Form and realize international information exchange and cooperation for wise use and management of wetlands, especially in North Asia.
2) Contribute to related international organs and conventions through wetland conservation related meetings, gatherings and training courses, etc.
3) Give appropriate support to the international activities of organizations in Japan.
4) Support the Ramsar Convention, and follow up on the 5th Meeting of the Conference of the Parties to the Convention on Wetlands of International Importance.

Once the center is up and running, the work will involve the following.

1) JICA nature conservation management trainee acceptance
2) JICA wetlands conservation trainee acceptance
3) East Asia, Australian freeway joint study workshop
   AWB/IWRB, Environment Agency, Hokkaido and the IWRB Japan Committee are scheduled to give cooperation and advice.

KIWC's activities include :

● **Conferences**
* 1994 East Asia/Oceania Wetland and Waterfowl Workshop
* 1995 Northeast Asia/Northern Pacific Environment Forum

● **Training**
* 1993/1994 JICA Course for Nature Conservation and Management
* 1994/1995 JICA Course for Wetlands and Migratory Birds Conservation

---

International Center for Environmental Technology Transfer (ICETT)
3690-1 Sakura-machi, Yokkaichi, Mie 510-12 Japan
Tel:+81-593-29-8111 Fax:+81-593-29-8115

Work Outline

ICETT, in cooperation with AOTS and JICA, etc., uses the experience gained from mastering pollution in Yokkaichi for training related to industrial pollution prevention; notably, air pollution prevention. The following work is planned for fiscal 1994.

● Training and Supervision Work
   ICETT is commissioned by JICA and NEDO to run 12 courses for trainees related to air and water industrial pollution prevention technology and energy reduction. Furthermore, two overseas courses for air and water industrial pollution technology and energy reduction are to be held with the assistance of AOTS, Aeon Group and Global Environmental Fund.

● Research and Development Work
   Under an assistance programme of the Ministry of International Trade and Industry, and as a commission from Yokkaichi city, Mie prefecture, ICETT will carry out research and develop work including carbon monoxide reduction technology and development of a sea and ocean pollution prevention centre.

● Provision of Studies and Information
   As a commission from the Ministry of International Trade and Industry and NEDO, ICETT will carry out studies on environment conservation technology needs in developing countries based on the Eco Phoenix plan.

- Interaction and Development Extension Work
    ICETT will produce videos and stage symposiums related to improving the environment.

Water Related Work

ICETT is involved in training related to industrial pollution prevention (domestic and overseas) and also water contamination prevention. As part of fiscal 1993 study work, ICETT, in cooperation with the Indonesian Ministry of Industry, carried out a prearranged, actual-status study of factory waste water. In 1994 Video training materials on water pollution, prevention technologies were developed. A notable characteristic in this work is the large number of participants from industry attending overseas on-site training. Seminars and training activities include :

- September 1991
    Held water contamination prevention technology on-site training course to suit medium-level government officials and industrial technologists in Bangkok, Thailand (6 days, 40 people, AOTS assisted).

- January 1992
    Held same type of course, "Water Contamination Prevention Technology Course", in Jakarta, Indonesia (6 days, 50 people, AOTS assisted).

- November 1992
    Held "Water Contamination Prevention Technology Course", in Sao Paulo, Brazil (5 days, 56 people, AOTS assisted).

- February 1993
    Held "Water Contamination Prevention Technology Course", in Bangkok, Thailand (5 days, 66 people, AOTS assisted).

- October 1993
    Held "Water Contamination Prevention Technology Course", in Gueiyang, China (6 days, 54 people, AOTS assisted).

- November 1993
    Reported on waste water accumulation disposal project at Thai sugar processing plant at the "Asian Environment Forum" in ICETT.

- January 1994
    Held "Environment Conservation Technology and Water Contamination Prevention Technology Course", in Surabaya, Indonesia (7 days, 56 people, AOTS assisted, Automobile Industry Promotion Committee supported).

- January 1994
    Held "Industrial Waste Water and Industrial Waste Disposal Measures Course" for JICA group training (8 weeks, 8 people, domestic).

- March 1994
    Held "Water Contamination Prevention Technology Course", in Nanjin, China (6 days, 50 people, AOTS assisted, Automobile Industry Promotion Committee supported).

International Lake Environment Committee (ILEC)

1091 Oroshimo, Kusatsu, Shiga 525 Japan
Tel:+81-775-68-4567   Fax:+81-775-68-4568

Work Outline

ILEC is involved in work related to sound management of the world's lakes and reservoirs; in particular, serious consideration is given to aid for developing countries. At the International Conference on Lake Environment in Otsu, Japan in 1984, UNEP felt that there was a need for an organization like ILEC - an international NGO established in 1986 through aid from Shiga prefecture, and specializing in environmental issues concerning lakes and reservoirs. ILEC, through the cooperation of UNEP and overseas NGOs, provides information, training and educational materials as aid for environment conservation of natural and artificial lakes in developing countries. The following is a list of main projects. ILEC is expected to be involved in numerous joint projects with the recently established UNEP International Environment Technology Centre (IETC) as well as carrying out its own individual work.

- Promote exchanges of scientific, technological and managerial information and experiences.
- Advise about preparing and executing development and environment conservation projects in countries; especially, developing countries.
- Offer environment guidelines for efficient use of lakes and reservoirs resources.
- Promote scientific research.
- Promote training projects related to technology and management.
- Support the international mobilization of manpower and material resources needed for lakes and reservoirs improvement.
- Cooperate with various international organizations, government organizations, regional organizations, research organizations and non-government organizations.
- Plan and assist international conferences related to lakes and reservoirs and their environments.

Lake and Reservoir Related Work

Several projects have been promoted to bring the above ideas to realization.

1) Staging of World Lakes and Reservoirs Conferences
   Conferences have been held through the combined efforts of ILEC and local cooperating organizations almost once every two years in the likes of the USA, Hungary, China and Italy. A total of about 3,900 people have participated in the previous five conferences.

2) Accumulation of Data on the World's Lakes and Reservoirs
   ILEC and UNEP are executing a status study of the world's lakes and reservoirs as a joint project. Since 1988, a yearly "Databook of World Lake Environments" is being published in English. In editions one through five, limnology items, environment items and socioeconomic items concerning basins for 217 lakes and reservoirs in 72 countries have been compiled.

3) Publication of Databook of World Lake Environments (English)
   This is a joint project with UNEP, in which an office-level booklet series is being produced and distributed in an easy-to-understand format. The booklets give basic knowledge on subjects such as "lake shore management", "toxic substance management", "lakes and reservoirs acidification" and "socioeconomic element of lakes and reservoirs management". Translation into various languages is underway.

4) Staging of Training and Seminars
   The following examples show the different kinds of training and seminars being held in joint cooperation with numerous international organizations and governments.

- A Basin Oriented Water Environment Workshop (jointly held with UNCRD and UNEP)
   Total of 170 senior government officials and researchers from more than 20 countries participate in this workshop that has been held three times (twice in Japan and once in Thailand from 1988 to 1990)

- Lakes and Reservoirs Water Quality Conservation Technology Training (work commissioned by JICA)
   These are three-month courses offering training for lakes and reservoirs water quality measuring and

water quality monitoring methods. In the five years since commencement in 1990, 48 people from 21 countries have participated.

- Lakes, Marshland and Reservoirs Environment Management International Seminar

    The First seminar of 40 people was held in Argentina in 1992. The second seminar was co-held with UNEP at the La Plata River basin in August 1994.

- Practical Seminar for application of Remote Sensing and GIS for Lake and Reservoir Management

    Over 300 participants including 12 from Thailand, were taught in 1993. (Co-held with UNEP.)

- Limnology Training Course

    A two-week course held twice in 1993 at the Balaton Research Centre, Hungary. (Co-held with UNEP.)

5) Participation in Various Conferences

    Experts are sent to numerous conferences, such as the Zambezi River Expert Meeting, Save Lake Chad Conference, and the Aral Sea Rehabilitation Conference.

6) Other Work

    ILEC issues publications and newsletters, stages domestic conferences and seminars, and does development work for events.

7) Lakes and Reservoirs Environmental Education Pilot Work

    ILEC is carrying out comparative research at 42 schools in six countries (Japan, Denmark, Brazil, Argentina, Thailand and Ghana) to develop teaching materials and a curriculum for lakes and reservoirs environment education in compulsory education courses.

⊙ 4th World Lake Conference in China

Kitakyushu International Technol-cooperative Association (KITA)

Kitakyushu International Exchange Center, 1-1-1 Hirano, Yawata-Higashi-ku, Kitakyushu, 805 Japan
Tel:+81-93-662-7770   Fax:+81-93-662-7782

Work Outline

The city of Kitakyushu is using its accumulated industrial technology and pollution control and environment improvement technology to make a useful contribution to technology transfer to developing countries through training.

Kitakyushu supports all facets of KITA's work. Since 1986, Kitakyushu has been promoting international environment cooperation by drawing on its specialty as an industrial city. In 1992, with the cooperation of Kitakyushu International Technol-cooperative Association (foundation), Kitakyushu founded the KITA Environment Cooperation Centre as a new organization to genuinely realize environment international cooperation. The overseas dispatching of specialists began with technical supervision of work in Dairen, China, and, up to now, 26 people involved in administration work and research work have been dispatched to 11 countries. Five Kitakyushu city office staff, one advisory staff and one staff from industry comprise the seven staff on loan to the KITA Environment Cooperation Centre. Furthermore, a system has been set up for emergency workers and researchers, such as environment participants, environment advisors and environment researchers.

Kitakyushu has staged seven international symposiums and conferences concerned with the environment since 1989. These events have acted as the platform for discussion on the environment cooperation requirements of developing countries faced directly with environment problems; in addition, the events made clear the possibility of technology transfer to developing countries. This technology comprises pollution prevention and environment conservation technology accumulated by the Kitakyushu administration and the industrial world. The staging of international symposiums incur various costs and require long-term use of human resources but offer a chance to accumulate the latest environment information together with the improvement of international status in the staging area and environment awareness for the citizens through the move toward internationalization. At times, the events create the opportunity to open up new policies and dramatically expand new work. In appraisal of pollution abatement efforts, Kitakyushu city received the "Global 500 Award" from UNEP in 1990.

Water Related Work

Since 1986, Kitakyushu has held five courses for international group training in the environment field. Up to present, 205 trainees from 41 countries have been trained. Amongst these, the following courses are directly related to water quality. Staff from the city administration and research centre, industrial technologists and university researchers etc., have been involved as instructors for this international group training.

- Industrial Waste Water Disposal Practical Training Course
  From 1988, 41 people, 14 countries

- Household Waste Water Measures Course
  From 1990, 32 people, 16 countries (current figures up to January 1994)

In addition to group training courses at the Center, KITA is also active in researches.

- 1992 Appropriate environmental measure in developing countries (Indonesia) Commissioned from JICA
- 1993 Promotion of Environmental Technology Transfer (Indonesia)
- 1994 Industrialization of East Asia and Environmental Problems (South Korea, China)
- 1994-5 Research on environmental conservation at rural cities in developing countries (Indonesia)

International Society for Mangrove Ecosystems (ISME)

C/O Ryukyu University, 1 Senbaru Nishihara-cho, Okinawa 903-01 Japan
Tel:+81-98-895-6601 Fax:+81-98-895-6602

Work Outline

ISME was established in 1990 to take over the project related to mangrove ecosystem conservation and sustainable use that UNESCO and UNEP had been running for eight years.

ISME is registered as a roster NGO with the UN Economic and Social Affairs Council. Work includes the staging of workshops and symposiums for status studies and conservation measures for mangroves in the Asian Pacific region and studies of mangrove ecosystems in South America and Africa.

Overseas Environment Cooperation Center (OECC)

5-16-2-201 Hiro-o, Shibuya-ku, Tokyo 150 Japan
Tel:+81-3-3351-2272 Fax:+81-3-3473-4481

Work Outline

OECC has been carrying out the following work since 1991 to privately promote international cooperation in the environment field as part of Japan's international cooperation work.

1. **Environment Studies for Overseas Cooperation**
   (commissioned by the Environment Agency)

   a) **Classification by Nationality Environment Base Study**
   (1990 to 1993: Brazil, Malaysia, Kenya, Vietnam, Venezuela, Egypt)

   b) **Classification by Nationality Environmental Conservation Plan Support**
   (1991 to 1994: Poland, Hungary, Thailand, Philippines, Chile)

   c) **Technology Transfer Promotion Study**
   (1992 to 1993: Indonesia)

   d) **Global Warming Classification by Nationality Support Study**
   (1991 to 1993: Indonesia, West Samoa, Fiji)

2. **Research Related to Overseas Environmental Conservation**

   - Environment Consideration Guideline Research (commissioned by the Environment Agency in 1991)
   - Nature Conservation Debt Swap Guideline Research (commissioned by the Environment Agency in 1991 and 1993)

   - Developing Country Environment Conservation Technology Transfer Research (1992 to 1993)
   - Desertification Prevention Measures Research (1992 to 1994)
   - Tropical Forest Environment Problem Research (1992 to 1994)

3. **Developing Human Resources for International Cooperation**

   a) **Training for Staff of Developing Countries**
   - Environmental Research Training Center Support (commissioned by JICA)

     Thailand (ERTC, 1991 onward), Indonesia (EMC, 1992 onward), China (China and Japan Friendly Environment Conservation Centre, 1993 onward)
   - Developing Countries Staff Environment Assessment Technology Employment Training (commissioned by JICA from 1991 onward)

   b) **Domestic Experts Training**
   - Consideration of Environment Expert Cultivation Long-term Plan (commissioned by the Environment Agency from 1992 to 1993)
   - Orientation Seminar for Overseas Environment Cooperation (1992 onward)
   - Overseas Environmental Cooperation Administrative Work (1993 onward)

4. **International Conferences and Lectures Related to Environmental Problems**

   a) **Staging Support for Environmental Problems International Conference**
   - Staging Support for Japan and Korea Environment

Cooperation Conference (commissioned by the Environment Agency in 1990 and 1991)

- Staging Support for Environment Cooperation Conference surrounding the Japan Sea (commissioned by the Environment Agency in 1992 and 1993)
- Staging Support for Global Warming Asia Pacific Region Seminar (1990 onward)
- Staging Support for East Asia Acid Rain Monitoring Network Experts Meetings (commissioned by the Environment Agency from 1993 onward)

b) Staging of Lecture Meetings and Symposiums
- Staging of International Environmental Cooperation Symposiums
  - * "Environmental Problems and Japan's Contribution in Asian Region" (co-staged in 1994)

- Staging of Nature Conservation Debt Swap Lecture Meetings and Explanation Meetings
  - * "Nature Conservation Debt swap Status and Japan's Implementation" (co-staged in 1991)
  - * "Swap Implementation by World NGOs" (co-staged with WWF US, CI, TNC in 1992)
  - * "South America Nature Conservation Debt Swap Example (examples: Ecuador, Bolivia)" (1993)

5. Accumulating and Offering Information Related to Overseas Environmental Conservation
- Environment Information Accumulation, Classification and Offering for Developing Countries (commissioned by the Environment Agency from 1991 onward)

- Domestic Environmental Problems Information Accumulation and Provision (from 1993 onward)
- Overseas Nature Conservation Debt Swap Example Study and Information Offering (Philippines, Ecuador, Bolivia, Costa Rica 1990 to 1994)

6. Support of Overseas Environmental Conservation Activities

a) Support for environmental Conservation Conferences in the world
b) Support of Overseas NGO Activities (support of nature conservation video education material production by Haribon Foundation, Philippines in 1993)
c) Employment of Overseas Environment Experts (total of 25 people from 9 countries 1990 to 1994)

Water Related Work

Within the above study work, OECC also makes statements about water quality problems in foundation studies classified by nationality.

Lakes and Reservoirs Related Work

OECC supports the following conferences as a link to supporting world environmental conservation conferences.
1) Staging Support for World Lakes and Reservoirs Conference (1991: Lake Xi, Hangzhou, China; 1993: Lake Maggiore, Italy)
2) Staging Support of Ramsar Convention Kushiro Conference (1992: Kushiro, Japan)

The Organization for Industrial, Spiritual and Cultural Advancement - International (OISKA)

3-6-12 Izumi, Suginami, Tokyo 168 Japan
Tel:+81-3-3322-5161   Fax:+81-3-3324-7111

Work Outline

OISKA was established in 1961 as an international organization promoting "education and development". In 1969, it became a co-managed foundation of the Ministry of Foreign Affairs, Ministry of Agriculture, Forestry and Fisheries, Ministry of International Trade and Industry and the Ministry of Labor. OISKA has training centres in countries in the Asian Pacific region, and it is engaged in technical supervision (based around the development of agricultural materials) and in development studies, reforestation, and manpower development of key personnel (in agriculture, industry, marine products and forestry). Also, OISKA is taking in technology trainees and promoting development education in Japan.

Contribution to Environmental Matters

Within the entire work of OISKA, reforestation has become a major concern in recent years and the forest destruction issue is being tackled as the most important issue among global environment problems. Aid is being sent to schools in such environmental destruction zones as money for sapling trees and fertilizer. OISKA is promoting a "Children's Forest" project where local children plant trees by hand (300 Asian schools have received aid as participants up to 1994), sending reforesting volunteers, supporting reforestation projects, and carrying out various education activities. A total of more than 2,600 reforestation volunteers have been sent to various Asian regions, and 5 million trees have been planted in approximately 1,000 hectares. OISKA is not directly involved with lakes and reservoirs projects; nevertheless, a contribution to basin conservation is being made through reforestation.

Water Re-use Promotion Center, Japan

107 Sengoku-yama Annex, 5-3-20 Toranomon, Minato-ku, Tokyo 105 Japan
Tel:+81-3-3583-5431   Fax:+81-3-3583-9436

The Center was established in 1973. In collaboration with the Ministry of International Trade and Industry, the Center is promoting recycling of industrial discharge, less water consuming industrial technologies and purification of sea water. As a part of MITI's "Water Hope 21 Plan" (International Cooperation in Water Environmental Conservation), the Center developing appropriate industrial water treatment systems for Southeast Asian countries. Technical cooperation through JICA is also active.

Global Industrial and Social Progress Research Institute (GISPRI)

7th fl., Mori Building No. 33, 3-8-21 Toranomon, Minato-ku, Tokyo 105, Japan
Tel:+81-3-5563-8800   Fax:+81-3-5563-8810

Primary Activities

GISPRI was established in 1988. It is affiliated with MITI, and conducting research in such areas as resources conservation and environmental issues, the international order, and relationships between industry and the economy on the one hand and culture and society on the other.

In fulfilling its purpose, GISPRI engages in the following activities

(1) Research and Study

Research in resources conservation and environmental issues, the international order, and relationships between industry and the economy on the one hand and culture and society on the other

(2) Policy Proposals

Holding of meeting of the Global Industrial and Social Progress Policy Forum to draw up general policy proposals on global problems that need to be addressed, and submission of these proposals to entities both in Japan and abroad

(3) Joint Research

Exchange of research data and personnel and conducting of joint research with institutes in Japan and abroad

(4) Other Activities

Such information activities as symposia, seminars, and personal-computer communications forums, as well as publication of GISPRI Newsletter.

Research Institute of Innovative Technology for the Earth (RITE)

9-2 Kizugawa-dai, Kizu, Souraku-gun, Kyoto 619-02 Japan
Tel:+81-7747-5-2300   Fax:+81-7747-5-2314

Water Related Work

RITE is not directly involved in aid for developing countries; however, RITE has carried out a three-year study on the source of large-area outbreaks of acid rain in the northwest sea region of Kyushu, Japan, and discovered that some of the substances that cause outbreaks of acid rain on mainland China extend to airspace over Kyushu.

Infrastructure Development Institute - Japan (IDI)

New-Koji-machi Building, 5-3-23 Koji-machi, Chiyoda-ku, Tokyo 102, Japan
Tel:+81-3-3263-4821   Fax:+81-3-3230-4030

IDI is affiliated with the Ministry of Construction and promoting following international cooperation in the field of civil engineering:

(1) Feasibility and pre-feasibility studio on the construction projects in developing countries
(2) Investigations commissioned from JICA etc.
   Map drawing in developing countries. Management of training courses for river engineers.
(3) Investigations commissioned from the Ministry of Construction and affiliated organizations.
   Water resources survey, GIS for global environments. Basic investigation of international cooperation needs in civil engineering. Guidelines for urban waste water treatment technologies appropriate for developing countries. Investigation on EIA procedures overseas.
(4) Acceptance and support of trainees
   Acceptance of about 50 trainees from developing

countries. Support to member companies in their acceptance of trainees (approx. 50 annually).

Support for International Construction Cooperation by NGOs

In 1992 the Ministry of Construction inaugurated a subsidy system for Japanese NGOs to dispatch experts to developing countries. IDI is commissioned for the subsidy. Out of 10 cases of support in 1994, six cases were water related.

- Well digging at Mindanao Island in the Philippines.
- Construction of a septic tank and waste water treatment at an orphanage in Thailand.
- Guidance to resident students in Cambodia on the ground water quality monitoring techniques.
- Installation of treatment facility at a shared laundry place in Guatemala.
- Small-scale waste water treatment facility to prevent lake pollution in Hanoi, Vietnam.

Global Infrastructure Fund Research Foundation Japan (GIF)

107 Sengokuyama Annex, 5-3-20 Toranomon, Minato-ku, Tokyo 105, Japan
Tel:+81-3-3432-4451   Fax:+81-3-3432-4541

Work Outline

GIF is a foundation established in September 1990 through the cooperation of the construction industry with the idea of promoting - with international cooperation - the development and preparation of a global infrastructure. The foundation aims to show clearly what current uses of land and water resources are and what future potential they have.

Lakes and Reservoirs Related Work

The foundation has a global environmental improvement

committee that is tackling projects such as the Aral Sea Region Environment Improvement Project and the Himalayan Water Resources Development Project. The first step of the work was to carry out a satellite land usage survey and at the same time commence computer analysis of water resources utilization. The Aral Sea basin problem is being approached with an international cooperation format cored around Japan, the USA and the former Soviet Union; however, no real work has been undertaken, yet. In September 1992, the Aral Sea Problem International Symposium was co-staged with the United Nations University.

World Wide Fund for Nature Japan (WWF Japan)

Nihon-seimei Akabanebashi Building, 3-1-14 Shiba, Minato-ku, Tokyo 105 Japan
Tel:+81-3-3769-1711 Fax:+81-3-3769-1717

Work Outline

The World Wide Fund for Nature Japan (WWF Japan) is the Japanese section of WWF, which was formed in 1971. Most activities are centered around issues in Japan, but international cooperation, such as fiscal 1992 financing of WWF/International for necessary nature conservation based on the concept of "potentially sustainable development" and "economic and environmental unification" in developing countries. Also being carried out are nature conservation debt swap agreement and cooperation work in the Malaysian environmental education project.

Water Related Work

WWF/Japan, as a commemoration of its 20th anniversary, organized from November 1990 a campaign, "The Conservation of Biodiversity", covering three major areas: conservation the Southwest Islands, tropical forests and wetlands. From within this, the wetlands campaign was implemented - mainly targeting domestic extension and education - from August 1992, which was before the Kushiro meeting of the Ramsar Convention. The '93 Wetland Conference, a wetland photo contest and a campaign advertising series on a newspaper were organized. Among these, WWF/Japan's support and participation in the "Asia Wetlands Symposium" helped promote participation from developing Asian countries.

International Waterfowl & Wetlands Research Bureau, Japan Committee (IWRBJ)

4th fl., KB-Miyashita Building,,1-22-10 Shibuya, Shinjuku, Tokyo 150 Japan
Tel:+81-3-3407-0240 Fax:+81-3-3407-0243

Work Outline

Originally, the protection section of the Wild Bird Society of Japan was in charge of the committee's office, however, the full-time office manager at IWRBJ has now taken charge. IWRBJ gathers material and produces videos related to lead poisoning of waterfowl, cooperates with the Ramsar Convention and assists the Kushiro Wetlands Center. The following overseas wetlands protection activities were carried out as aid work using global environment funds of fiscal 1993.

Example :

Extension Activities Related to Important Wetland Protection in the Asian Region

A Model Wetland was selected from the wetlands in the Asian region for extension and education projects, and work related to this is being carried out - such as, production of a development extension pamphlet, holding of workshops, implementation of an education programme for local people and development of educational materials. This is a three-year project.

- Published Japanese translation of "Wetland Benefit", a pamphlet issued by AWB in 1993.
- Produced work report: "Wetland Protection Status in Asian Region" (B5, 10 items).
- Cooperated in staging of Ramsar Southeast Asian Region Workshop co-staged by the Indonesian government and AWB from March 29 to April 1, 1994.

Wild Bird Society of Japan

International Center of Wild Bird Society of Japan, 2fl. Woody-Nanpeidai Building,
15-8 Nanpeidai, Shibuya-ku, Tokyo 150 Japan
Tel:+81-3-3463-8861   Fax:+81-3-3463-8844

Water Related Work

The organization is creating an information network targeting Asian Migratory waterfowl protection to gather data from groups in other countries about wildfowl threatened with extinction. Personal computers are scheduled to be offered to Asian groups to establish the information network. The current status of wetlands used by migrant birds is being checked as a link to studies. Also, international joint surveys on radio-telemetric tracking of migratory waterfowl is in progress.

Ramsar Center Japan

2-10-3 Minami-Kugahara, Ohta-ku, Tokyo Japan
Tel:+81-3-3758-7926   Fax:+81-3-3758-7926

Work Outline

The center was established to extend instruction related to the Ramsar Convention and wetland conservation. The center functions as a wetland related information center with the purpose of producing an Asian and Japanese wetland database, expanding domestic Ramsar registered wetlands and staging workshops and symposiums.

Lakes and Reservoirs Related Work

The following are international cooperation activities.

Example 1 :
"Asian Wetland Symposium"

This symposium was co-held with the Environment Agency, International Lake Environment Committee Foundation and local authorities in Otsu city and Kushiro city from October 15th to 20th, 1992, in the offices of the Ramsar Center. The theme was "Towards the Wise Use of Wetlands". Around 300 people participated in the symposium, including 60 overseas participants from 24 countries, and it was the first real meeting related to wetland to be held in Japan.

Example 2 :
"Workshop on Biodiversity in Asian Wetlands"
(Indonesia and thailand)

This workshop was mainly staged by the Ramsar Center Japan between the 24th and 26th of February 1994 at the Environment Management Center (EMC) (established through the cooperation of JICA in 1993) in the suburbs of Jakarta, Indonesia. The aim of the workshop was to find methods for extending education about biodiversity in wetlands, and 24 Asian NGO researchers participated. The work was supported by the Global Environment Fund for fiscal 1993. The results of the workshop have led to the planned publication of a booklet giving instructions about biodiversity in the wetlands of developing countries. The second workshop was held at Mahidol University in Thailand in September 1994.

↻ Regional Workshop held by RCJ at EMC in Indonesia
(1994)

Eco-Institute / Citizens Bank

1fl. Yamasa-Mita Building, 1-12-22 Mita, Meguro-ku, Tokyo, Japan
Tel:+81-3-3793-1641   Fax:+81-3-3711-8550

Work Outline

This office advises - from the citizens' point of view - administrations and citizens about social systems incorporating environment conservation. In addition, the office also makes model examples. In 1986, a citizen-based company was founded as the mother group undertaking work to solve issues, such as the North-South Problem, welfare, peace and environmental problems through personal computer communications. In 1989, the company formed an affiliation with the Eitai Trust Union, founded the Citizens Bank and started financing a waste cooking oil recycle soap factory and a handmade bread shop using domestic wheat. The office also became earnestly involved with environmental issues through the paper manufacturing "Kenaf" project.

Water Related Work

The institute is calling on citizens nationwide to participate in acid rain and drinking water monitoring, opening an environment monitoring school and setting up the same kind of network and information exchange overseas.

Lakes and Reservoirs Related Work

The office provided pH meters and water quality measuring equipment for Lake Baikal and the people of Hungary, sent

specialists to supervise the technology front, and is engaging in a joint study.

Example :
"Lake Baikal Acid Rain Monitoring" (with support from fiscal 1993 Global Environment Fund)

In the Lake Baikal region, contaminated water inflow due to a thermal power station, and pulp plant and forest damage due to acid rain are beginning to appear. For this reason, some automatic rain gathering equipment and pH measuring meters and water quality monitoring kits for rivers and lakes were taken to the headquarters of "Baikal Watch" in California, USA. Institute members joined the young members of "Baikal Watch" to show local university students how to use the measuring equipment; furthermore, the equipment was taken into nearby mountains and actual water monitoring and tests were carried out. Japan and the USA have supplied Russia with this equipment and the monitoring know-how, and Russia is intermittently observing the lake. The acquired data is being jointly analyzed in an effort to find positive improvement measures. A broad range of the public are participating in current status checks on Lake Baikal in an effort to create a monitoring network for the total area of this vast lake - some 600 km long and with around 300 inflowing rivers.

Lake Kasumigaura Information Center

657-45-202 Tsukata, Ami, Ami-cho, Inashiki-gun, Ibaragi 300-03 Japan
Tel:+81-298-88-3118   Fax:+81-298-87-9227

Work Outline

An active grass-root NGO composed of 600 citizens mainly targeted at conservation of Kasumigaura. Its activity include: publication of monthly and annual reports, lake observation meets, environmental seminars and publication of recommendation papers.

International activities are mainly to promote exchange with overseas NGOs and researchers in Asian countries.

There are many other local grass-roots NGOs around Lake Kasumigaura and the Center is collaborating with them.

Konan Consumer Union/Lake Biwa and Lake Baikal Linking Group

1803-2 Kagami, Ryuo-cyo, Gamo, Shiga 520-25 Japan

Lakes and Reservoirs Related Work

The work, based around the Konan Consumer Union in Shiga prefecture, involves a Baikal fund and related interaction for environmental conservation of Lake Baikal. In the summer of 1992, 44 Japanese people, including 16 students, participated in a week-long camp at Lake Baikal. Technical cooperation for soap manufacturing from waste food oil is being currently investigated at the recycle soap association in Japan.

Keiyo Culture and Education Centre

3-11 Tatsumidai-higashi, Ichihara, Chiba Japan
Tel:+81-436-74-2151   Fax:+81-436-74-2152

Work Outline

The centre is involved in a human interaction project and Asian interaction tours (youth interaction, studies by specialists and issue interaction), overseas aid, studies and support work in order to contribute to the raising of international understanding and peace.

Lakes and Reservoirs Related Work

In 1991, two members from the Philippine, Lake Laguna environment NGO "Solidarity for People's Power" (SPP) were invited to Japan to exchange opinions with citizens' groups. Exchange on the current state of lakes and reservoirs conservation in Japan was made.

Friends of the Earth Japan (FOEJ)

4-8-15 Nakameguro Meguro-ku, Tokyo 153 Japan
Tel:+81-3-3760-3644   Fax:+81-3-3760-6959

Work Outline

Destruction of the environment in the third world is being brought about by finance from industries, bilateral aid and multilateral aid. FOEJ's aim is to stem this tide and change development methods to "sustainable" ones by holding symposiums, pressuring governments and industries and publishing material (e.g. newsletter entitled "Development Assistance Watch".

Water Related Work

FOEJ held a symposium for local people from the Narmada development site in India and held successive international symposiums in the run up to the Ramsar meeting.

In the area of wetland protection work, while maintaining a network with domestic and overseas environment protection groups, FOEJ is making information available through a booklet covering views and issues on wetlands (lakes and reservoirs included) protection that also includes the current state of development aid and wetland destruction.

Japan Society on Water Environment (JSWE)

12 Honshio-machi, Shinjyuku-ku, Tokyo Japan
Tel:+81-3-3351-2272

Water Related Work

This institute carries out scientific studies and research and the extension of knowledge in relation to water contamination as well as cooperating with other countries. International committees made up of member researchers are affiliated. The following international cooperation is being carried out by each sectional meeting, such as the UNEP sectional meeting and JICA sectional meeting.

Example 1 :

"Environment Technology (Water Conservation) Training Course" (group training commissioned by JICA)

This course - run by the Water Environment Institute - was established in 1974 and has a long history in amongst JICA group training. Annually about 10 participants (227 people up to date) are accepted for this course. The training course is made up of the following.

1) Trainees report on the water conservation status for their respective countries as a country study
2) Lectures related to water conservation
3) Curriculum centered around study by inspection

Lectures cover a broad spectrum of water conservation and each field is overseen by researchers or administrative officials. The main history, knowledge and technology points of Japanese water conservation are passed onto the trainees. The course curriculum is as follows.

Curriculum for Water Quality Conservation Course

	No. of Lectures	No. of Inspection Sites
Environmental Administration	6	5
International Cooperation	2	-
Public Hygiene and Supply Water	2	1
Monitoring	3	2
Water Contamination Mechanism		
Eutrophication, etc.	4	1
Groundwater	2	-
Non-point Loadings	2	1
Waste Water Disposal		
Waste Water Disposal System	1	-
Household Waste Water	1	1
Industrial Waste Water	3	7
Re-use	2	1
Waste Management	1	4
Environmental Planning	1	-
Country Case Study		

Example 2 :

"Production of Manual for the Development of Human Resources for River Water Management" (joint project with UNEP)

From April 1991 to May 1995, the Japan Water Environment Institute - in cooperation with UNEP/Water Unit - carried out a project (costing approximately US$ 350,000) to develop human resources for river water management in the Asian region. Malaysia, Thailand and the Philippines were chosen as the developing countries covered by the study and Japan, Korea and Singapore were chosen as the advanced countries. The status of water contamination prevention measures, related organizations and human resources development status were examined through study reports and workshops held by consultants. The results were produced as a report together with the production of a human resources manual for river water management for the relevant authorities based on the examination results.

Example 3 :

"Knowledge Extension Support for Water Environment Conservation in Indonesia"

The institute held a seminar in Jakarta, Indonesia, on 4 October 1993, with the aim of extending Japan's accumulated water environment technology and knowledge to developing countries. Participating instructors comprised four Japanese and five Indonesians, who introduced environment regulations, monitoring methods and environment study techniques for rivers, etc. The 200 participants included Indonesian technologists and NGO workers. This seminar received staging finance of ¥4 million from the fiscal 1993 global environment fund, and it acted as the pre-meeting for the IAWQ Asian region conference being held at around the same time.

In 1994, a similar seminar was held in the Philippines. (global environment funding aid work in fiscal 1993 and 1994)

Japanese Association for Baikal International Research Programme (JABIRP)

National Institute of Environmental Studies, 16-2 Onogawa, Tsukuba, Ibaragi, 305 Japan
Tel:+81-298-51-6111 Fax:+81-298-51-4732

Work Outline

JABIRP is a council of researchers in Japan that cooperates with the "Baikal International Center for Ecological Research" (BICER), an internationally co-run research facility located in the vicinity of Lake Baikal. The council does not just promote its own research themes but also combines to strengthen and financially help the support structure for Russian research. There are 130 members, and 43 people participated in studies in fiscal 1993.

Lakes and Reservoirs Related Work

The following are the three fundamental aims of JABIRP's research.

- Archaeological environment analysis and reproduction (established Baikal Drilling Project and drilled 1km)
- Genealogy and evolution analysis and evolution and genealogy tree production
- Current ecology analysis and species proliferation conservation

The following are being checked as methods for strengthening a Russian research support system.

- Strengthening of BICER's funds and base along with research support (appropriate increase in funding with government support)
- Increased funding for work load, provision of facilities (for example, general testing chemicals, study boat repair costs, researchers' accommodation, vehicles, communication equipment and computers)
- Covering of study costs, provision of materials, consumer goods, testing chemicals, etc., and collection of documents and materials
- Strengthening and supporting of living conditions for researchers
- Acquisition and provision of research aid funds
- Strengthening of long-term research conditions and international co-working system
- Supporting of BICER participation by Asian and Oceania region researchers and organizing of international co-working and an international database

National Institute for Environment Studies (NIES)

16-2 Onogawa, Tsukuba, Ibaragi 305 Japan
Tel:+81-298-56-6111 Fax:+81-298-58-2645

NIES is an integral part of the Environment Agency, Japan.

International Cooperation

NIES recently started a feasibility study on the environmental technologies applicable to developing countries. Technology for Environmental monitoring, environmental impact assessment, environmental rehabilitation and pollution abatement will be evaluated. At the same time socio-economic background survey will be made in order to select joint-research topics of NIES in the future.

Water Related Research

Water Related Joint Research with developing countries include:

- Comparative study of eutrophicated lakes in Japan and China (1992, jointly with Chinese Research Academy of Environmental Sciences).
- Development of environmental management technologies for Han River basin (1990-1992, Korean National Institute of Environmental Studies).

Environment Information Centre

The Environment Information Centre of the National Institute for Environmental Studies (NIES) was established

in 1990 to gather, organize and make available by computer domestic and international material related to environmental conservation.

- INFOTERRA Domestic Focal Point

    The institute functions as the domestic focal point for INFOTERRA (International Referral System for Sources of Environmental Information), a global scale environment information network set up by UNEP. The institute maintains a database of information sources in Japan in order to be able to respond to domestic and overseas requests about where information can be acquired.

- Cooperation as a node GRID/Tsukuba

    The institute cooperates from its own budget to support GRID, a UNEP information resources database that uses remote sensing.

- Global Wetland Vegetation Map

    Tests have been started at the institute's environment research centre to try and make available global wetland vegetation maps in a remote sensing map form.

- "Environment Information Guidebook"

    This guidebook was produced by the institute's environment research centre. Environment information itself is not included in the book; what is included is an index information database - "where and what kind of information exists and the necessary measures for getting that information" - related to national-level environment information held by government organs, non-profit foundations and private organizations. As titles of material not open to the public are also published in the index, the material can be used to identify where and what kind of study is being carried out, even if the material cannot be seen itself. There is only a small amount of overseas information, and indexing is only possible in Japanese. The guide is accompanied by a floppy disk with DOS programme and file, and it is copyright free.

Public Works Research Institute
1 Asahi, Tsukuba City, Ibaraki 305 Japan
TEL:+81-298-64-2211 Fax:+81-298-64-7183

The Institute is an integral part of the Ministry of Construction.

Water Related Cooperation

Since 1987 jointly with the Korean government, the Institute is developing the improvement system for urban river waters.

The Institute of Public Health

4-6-1 Shirogane-dai, Minato-ku, Tokyo 108 Japan
Tel:+81-3-3441-7111

Water Related Work

The institute cooperates in gathering water quality data in Japan as part of the UNEP/WHO water quality monitoring network: GEMS/WATER. A large amount of international research cored around service water quality is being carried out.

Example : Joint Research with Korea

In 1989, a Japan and Korea joint research group was set up to carry out international scientific research for the Ministry of Education. The group's objectives are experimenting to find water improvement methods for the Nak-Dong-Gang water system together with testing for the appropriate harmony between human activity and the water catchment ecosystem. This joint research has continued intermittently up to this day. Actual research involves: 1) development of a water treatment system based on analyzed results of a study on basin contamination load development, discharge and fate of pollutants and the development of a water management system that generally evaluates industrial working methods, 2) water utility problems research on safety evaluation of water service, appropriate water management from a water service point of view, and staging of symposiums based on these research results for people in universities, research organs and private companies.

The following research cooperation is being carried out joimtly with Korea.

1) Provision of Information Related to Service Water Resources Contamination

Existing Japanese research results related to environment status and impact assessment together with abatement technology for disinfectant byproducts (such as trihalomethane), surface active agents and mutant spontaneous generation - as a status evaluation indicator of service water contamination - were made available to Korea.

2) Execution of Fact-finding Survey for Service Water Resources, Water Purification Process and Supply Tap Water

Japan carried out a fact-finding survey of service water pollution indicator items.

3) Measuring Method Technology Transfer and Data Analysis

Measuring methods were transferred to Korea for the intermittent study of pollution indicator items at Nak-Dong-Gang. The acquired data was jointly analyzed.

Lake Biwa Research Institute (LBRI)

Address:1-10 Uchide-hama, Otsu, 520 Japan
Tel:+81-775-26-4800   Fax:+81-775-26-4803

Lakes and Reservoirs Related Work

Besides cooperating internationally in the following lakes and reservoirs research, LBRI (since the establishment of the International Lake Environment Committee Foundation [ILEC] in 1986) has been cooperating in the editing of ILEC's Survey of the State of World Lakes, and international training programmes run by ILEC.

Example 1 :
Japan and China Lake Biwa and Lake Tai Joint Research

Joint research has been carried out since 1985, mostly in the hydro-meteorology and sedimentation study fields for comparative research of Lake Tai-hu and Lake Biwa from a limnological viewpoint. The research groups were mainly made up of LBRI and Shiga University for Japan and Nanjing Institute of Geography and Limnology, Academia Sinica of China.

Research results were announced at a symposium held in Nanjing in September 1987.

Example 2 : Lake Erhai Joint Research

A joint study with UNCRD was carried out for regional development and environment management of the Dali and Lake Erhai districts in Yunnan province, China from 1991 to 1992.

Example 3 :
Lake Biwa International Joint Monitoring (BITEX-93)

Several dozen researchers including those from developing countries gathered from eight countries (the main nucleus being LBRI and West Australia University) to carry out international joint monitoring of substances in Lake Biwa during August and September of 1993.

○ Sediment sampling at Lake Biwa

Center for Ecological Research, Kyoto University

4-1-23 Shimo-sakamoto, Otsu, Shiga 520-01 Japan
Tel:+81-775-78-0580 Fax:+81-775-79-8457

Lake and Reservoir Related Work

Kyoto University has been continuing research since 1979 mainly on an ecological study of fish types in Lake Tanganyika through scientific research grants from the Ministry of Education, international joint research grants from the Academic Promotion Society and support from the JICA research cooperation programme. More than 40 researchers from Japan have participated in this study up to now. In particular, joint research with CRSN/Uvira (Zaire National Natural Science Research Centre, Uvira Research Centre) at the northwest tip of Lake Tanganyika has spanned a long period. JICA - who have put a lot of effort into marine product related research - have cooperated with the Uvira Research Centre. This research centre has biology, ecology and limnology departments, and of the 12 researchers and research technologists, eight are involved in fish-type related research. In recent years, joint research has started with the Marine Product Agency of Zambia. This type of activity is very beneficial in the development of local researchers.

International Geoshpere- Biosphere Programme (IGBP)

Work Outline

This is the Japanese office of IGBP, a programme promoted by UNESCO and involving the cooperation of scientists worldwide. The programme also includes assessment and research for the global-scale aquasphere environment.

Water Related Work

IGBP does not have actual lakes and reservoirs projects but handles projects for inland and ocean interaction in coastal regions.

Japan Research Association Kazakhstan (JRAK)

c/o Prof. Ishida, Faculty of Agriculture, Kyoto Univ., Kita-shirakawa-oiwake-cyo, Sakyo-ku, Kyoto, Japan
Tel:+81-75-753-6133 Fax:+81-75-753-6133

Lakes and Reservoirs Related Work

JRAK in cooperation with the Kazakhstan Science Academy and the Agricultural Science Academy is promoting from 1990 a study of "the influence exerted by large-scale irrigation agriculture on the ecological environment and social economy in central Asia" in order to understand the seriousness of the environmental problems faced by the Lake Balkhash basin, Aral Sea. This study is supported by the Toyota Foundation and Ministry of Education International Science Research Fund. JRAK is not only interacting with Kazakhstan on scientific level but is also trying to develop relationships across a broad spectrum.

Organizations that have financially supported lakes and reservoir conservation activities

The following are non-governmental organs that have supported international cooperation activities related to domestic NGO lakes and reservoirs conservation.

In addition to these, governmental subsidy to NGO activities include :
- NGO support programme of the Ministry of Foreign Affairs.
- Volunteer Saving Account of the Ministry of Posts and Telecommunications.
- Global Environmental Fund backed by Environment Agency
- NGO International Construction Cooperation of the Ministry of Construction.

The Japan Trust for Global Environment
1-9-7 Azabudai, Minato-ku, Tokyo 106 Japan
Tel:+81-3-5561-9735 Fax:+81-3-5561-9737

As part of fiscal 1992 and 1993 activities, support was given to the Japan BICER Representative for a Lake Baikal ecosystem study.

The Trust also supported convening of Eurasian Lake Forum and production of lake data CD-ROM by ILEC in 1995.

The Toyota Foundation
37th fl., Shinjyuku-Mitsui Building, 2-1-1 Nishi-Shinjyuku, Shinjyuku-ku, Tokyo 163-04 Japan
Tel:+81-3-3344-1701 Fax:+81-3-3342-6911

Support is being given to Japanese researchers participating in international research and the research work of overseas researchers - mostly from Southeast Asia. Recent examples of research support include Kazakhstan research of the environmental problems in the Aral Sea and the surrounding region and Chinese research into water quality improvement in rivers, lakes and reservoirs by aquaculture.

Nihon Seimei Foundation
3-1-7 Imahashi, Cyuo-ku, Osaka 541 Japan
Tel:+81-6-204-4011 Fax:+81-6-204-0120

The foundation was established in 1989, and it supports Japanese researchers participating in environment related research. Examples of support related to overseas lakes and reservoirs include the Japan and China joint comparative research of Lake Tai and Lake Biwa and the pollution accumulation and ecology toxicity in the Great Lakes.

Aeon Group Environment Foundation
1-5-1 Nakase, Mihama-ku, Chiba 261 Japan
Tel:+81-43-212-6022 Fax:+81-43-212-6815

Support was given in 1993 to the International Lake Environment Committee related to the development of a transmission method for lakes and reservoirs environment information.

The Foundation for Earth Environment

1109 Shuwa-Kioicho TBR Building, 5-7 Chiyoda-ku, Tokyo 102 Japan
Tel:+81-3-3234-0111 Fax:+81-3-3237-8610

Support was given to people from developing countries attending the Third World Lakes and Reservoirs Meeting.

The Nippon Foundation

Senpaku-Sinko Building, 1-15-16 Toranomon, Minato-ku, Tokyo 105 Japan
Tel:+81-3-3502-2371 Fax:+81-3-3502-0041

Support was given to the International Lake Environment Committee for the publishing of a world lakes and reservoirs data book in fiscal 1989 and 1990, and for a handbook of international cooperations in lake conservation in 1995.

Chapter 2

◆

Trends in Freshwater Wetland Conservation Funding in Southeast Asia

(Jonathan Davies & Nasaruddin Rahman)

This report has been produced for ILEC as a contribution to their report on world aid projects relevant to the conservation of freshwater wetlands.

The report has some limitations in that it is bound to be a somewhat incomplete listing of freshwater wetland related projects funded by aid agencies in SE Asia. This is due to two main factors. The first is that many aid agencies, especially bilaterals, do not seen to have easily available listings of all projects they are funding. Despite contacting the major funding agencies for such listings, very few were able to provide such a listing. AWB has had this problem in the past when trying to obtain details of EIA guidelines of bilateral agencies. Secondly, large programmes concerned with the conservation and management of natural resources will often include a sub-component on wetland conservation, but obtaining details on such sub-projects has proved to be very difficult. This may lead to some under-representation of projects funded by certain bilaterals. For example, although we could find no major projects being funded by USAID specifically for freshwater wetlands, USAID funds some large programmes concerned with the management of natural resources which include components on freshwater wetlands.

Moreover, it must be borne in mind that many programmes and projects, whilst not directed primarily towards wetlands, may benefit wetlands directly; for example, any projects aimed at prevention of soil erosion in upland areas are bound to benefit any wetlands downstream.

This listing, then, should be seen as a preliminary attempt to assess what sorts of projects aid agencies are funding. In order to supplement the listing of projects funded in SE Asia, we have included two additional sections. The first, "Status of wetland activities in the countries of SE Asia" gives some idea of the broad range of wetland-related activities in countries in SE Asia, including those activities not primarily focussed upon wetlands, but which would include measures relevant to their conservation; for example, the production of National Conservation Strategies. This would go some way to filling in the gaps in the listing and would also include activities which may be funded by the national governments themselves. The second section, "Work by NGOs in SE Asia related to wetland projects" puts the listing of projects in the context of the strategy of the organisations as a whole and includes organisations which at times fund wetland projects, but for which no details on specific projects are available at present.

↑ Tasek Bera, a wetland in Malaysia (see color page)

Summary Of Trends

First, it should be remembered that the number of projects which an aid agency has on this list may be merely a reflection of the amount of information available from that agency rather than a reflection of the true situation. Nevertheless, some trends can be discerned.

Firstly, there seems to be relatively little funding directed to conservation and management of marsh ecosystems as compared to lakes and reservoirs. While the benefits of conservation and wise use of lakes and reservoirs is fairly obvious, it seems that funding agencies still do not yet appreciate the many benefits that marsh ecosystems provide to society. Indeed, freshwater marshes may be some of the most threatened types of wetlands in SE Asia because the benefits they provide to society are not yet fully appreciated. This observation links in with a review of EIA guidelines of the major donors AWB is undertaking which has found that the guidelines did not sufficiently emphasise the full range of benefits of wetlands which has led to a number of development projects which have degraded or destroyed important wetlands together with their benefits.

Many are also funding long-term programmes on wetland assessment and management; e.g. the ODA of UK, rather than funding short term projects. The Australian aid agencies particularly are funding a wide range of projects on wetlands, including many with regional dimensions such as the East Asia-Australasian migratory bird flyway.

The most comprehensive information available is from the Mekong Secretariat, which has expanded the number of projects under their environment programme to include specific components on assessment and monitoring of wetlands. Such data is urgently needed so that the environmental effects of large scale developments such as dams can be properly assessed. The Mekong Secretariat is also implementing a wide range of projects, mostly funded by Scandinavian aid agencies, on catchment management in order to safeguard the actual and potential benefits of natural wetlands within the basin. With regard to this, there seem to be very few projects which explicitly fund wetland conservation and management projects in relation to the management of the catchment. One project, funded by UNEP and to be implemented by AWB is attempting this at the moment, but it seems that more emphasis in freshwater conservation projects should be given to management of the catchment in which the wetland occurs.

⬆ A wetland lake in Indonesia (by Wim Giesen)

Section 2

Preliminary listing of projegts funded in Southeast Asia for freshwater wetlands from 1990 by funding agency and donor country

SWEDEN

- Management of acid sulphate soils, Vietnam (Mekong delta)
- Inventory and management of the wetlands in the lower Mekong Basin
- Water quality monitoring network in the lower Mekong Basin, Phase II (with UNEP)
- Integration of environmental components into projects (Mekong Basin)
- Control of soil erosion, sedimentation and flash flood hazards (Mekong Basin)
- Environmental training fund (Mekong Basin)

DENMARK

- Assessment and management of freshwater capture fisheries of Cambodia, Phase I
- Pasig River rehabilitation project, Philippines
- Fisheries in Mekong reservoirs

AUSTRALIA

- Water resources training, Cambodia (part funding)
- Forestry-based development on the Long Xuyen Quadrangle, Mekong delta, Vietnam
- Naujan Lake community-based resources management programme, Philippines
- Water resources training programme (Mekong Basin)
- Developer ı s guide, regional   (AIDAB)
- Towards sustainable harvesting of waterbirds on the East Asian Flyway, regional (AIDAB)
- Coordination of flyway research and site protection in the East Asia Flyway, regional (AIDAB)
- Preparation of an action plan for migratory waders in the East Asian-Australasian Flyway, regional (ANCA)

CANADA

- Development of awareness book on mangroves, Malaysia (CIDA)

UK

- Conservation and management of wetlands in Cambodia (Darwin Initiative)
- UK-Indonesia tropical forest management project, sub-project 5 ; conservation.developing a model to combine community-based exploitation and conservation in Danau Sentarum Wildlife Reserve, West Kalimantan, Indonesia (ODA)

- Wetland training, survey and evaluation, regional (ODA/WWF-UK)
- Wetland planning and management, regional (ODA/WWF-UK)

JAPAN

- Philippines-Japan Crocodile Farming project (JICA)
- Lake water quality management training courses, regional (JICA)

FRANCE

- Development plan for Tonle Sap, Cambodia

NETHERLANDS

- Community fisheries management in rural reservoirs, Thailand
- Improving wetland management and conservation in Indonesia: Part One, Sumatra

SWITZERLAND

- Fishermen's communities in the Nam Ngum basin, Phase II, Laos
- Mekong watershed assessment and management

IUCN

- Large waterbird survey, Cambodia
- Assistance to the government in the management of Xuan Thuy reserve in the Red River delta, Vietnam
- Assistance to the government of Laos to develop a detailed inventory and to formulate a National Wetland Action Plan

WWF-International

- Philippines wetland conservation programme
- Olango Island community wetland programme, Philippines

WWF-UK

- wetland training, survey and evaluation, regional (with ODA)
- wetland planning and management, regional (with ODA)

WWF-US

- Debt-for-nature-swap programme for the Philippines

WWF-Malaysia

- Coastal aquaculture plan for Selangor, Malaysia
- Action Plan for the North Selangor Peat Swamp Forest, Malaysia
- Socio-economic values of wetland plants, Phases I and II, Malaysia
- Survey of freshwater fishes in peninsula Malaysia

WWF-HK

- Translation of the Vietnamese Wetland Directory
- Study tour by Red River Delta staff to Mai Po reserve, Hong Kong

MACARTHUR FOUNDATION

- Conservation of wetland biodiversity (regional) This project includes some components as described below:
- Waterbird survey, Mekong delta
- production of education materials, Vietnam
- leaflets on wetlands of Vietnam

RAMSAR

- Inventory and listing of Ramsar sites, Cambodia

UNDP

- Master plan for the integrated development of the Mekong delta, Vietnam
- Preparatory organisational and legal studies for water resources management in the Mekong Basin (with EC and ADB)

UNESCO

- Listing of Tonle Sap as a World Heritage Site, Cambodia

UNEP

- Water quality monitoring network in the lower Mekong Basin, Phase II (with Sweden)
- Study tour for the Myanmar Forest Department Staff
- Development of guidelines for environmentally sound management of Asian wetlands in relation to their role in watershed management (regional)

WORLD BANK

- Development of an Integrated Protected Area System (IPAS) for the Philippines

EC

- Preparatory organisational and legal studies for water resources management in the Mekong Basin (with UNDP and ADB)

ADB

- Preparatory organisational and legal studies for water resources management in the Mekong Basin (with EC and UNDP)

Preliminary listing of projects related to the consideration and management of freshwater wetlands in Southeast Asia by recipient country

CAMBODIA

A) IMPLEMENTING AGENCY- THE MEKONG SECRETARIAT

- **Mekong GIS ; Cambodian component**
    * OBJECTIVES :

    To enhance the capability of the agencies in Cambodia to use remote sensing techniques for mapping and monitoring the physical environment as part of the Mekong GIS programme.
    * TIME FRAME : 24 months
    * FUNDING : being sought.

- **Inventory and management of the Cambodian wetlands**
    * OBJECTIVES :

    To design and implement a Cambodian Wetlands Conservation Programme.
    * TIME FRAME : 48 months
    * FUNDING : being sought.

- **Development plan for Tonle Sap and Chakdomuk**
    * OBJECTIVES :

    The ultimate objective is to develop the Tonle Sap's resources in a sustainable and environmentally sound way. The immediate objectives are to identify and examine the morphological changes , the present use of the natural resources and the development possibilities; and to propose specific actions for preserving the environment and to select priority projects for short and long term development of the area and to select and implement priority projects.
    * TIME FRAME : 20 months, for future.
    * FUNDING : secured from France ; other funds being sought.

- **Assessment and management of the freshwater capture fisheries of Cambodia, Phase I**
    * OBJECTIVES :

    To strengthen and develop research, monitoring, regulatory and management capability of the fisheries sector in order to ensure the sustainable utilisation, conservation and management of the freshwater capture fisheries resource in Cambodia.

    N.B. One of the outputs of this project is the establishment of a Cambodia Inland Fisheries and Wetlands Ecology Institute to conduct station-based and in-field applied research and investigation in the long term.

    * TIME FRAME : 36 months, for the future
    * Funds Being secured from Denmark

- **Water resources training programme : Cambodian component**
    * OBJECTIVES :

    To improve, through postgraduate education and training, the capability of Cambodian personnel to undertake water resources development planning and projects.
    * TIME FRAME : 42 months, for the future
    * FUNDING : partially secured from Australia

B) OTHERS

- **Large waterbird surveys in Cambodia**
    * OBJECTIVES :

    To undertake field and desk surveys in Cambodia to identify important sites for large waterbirds (herons, egrets, ibises, cranes) and to make recommendations for the protection of the waterbirds and their habitats.
    * TIME FRAME : 13 weeks from April 1994
    * FUNDING : secured from IUCN ; implementing agency AWB

- **Technical assistance to conduct an inventory and develop a profile of a wetland site in Cambodia for Ramsar listing and other assistance to enable Cambodia to become a signatory to the Ramsar Convention**
    * OBJECTIVES :

    To develop a preliminary inventory and profile of candidate wetland sites; to provide assistance to Cambodia for site listing and accession to the Ramsar Convention; and to assist the Ministry of Environment in determining the role and activities of the newly created Wetland and Coastal Management Office.
    * TIME FRAME : 3 months from April 1994
    * FUNDING : secured from the Wetland Conservation Fund of the Ramsar Bureau; implementing agency AWB and GoC

- **Preparations for listing of Tonle Sap as a World Heritage Site**
    * OBJECTIVES :

    To prepare background materials proposing the inscription of Tonle Sap on the World Heritage List.
    * TIME FRAME : 3 months starting April 1994 (to be confirmed)

* FUNDING : secured from UNESCO ; implementing agency UNESCO

- **Aiding Cambodia in the conservation and management of wetlands and their biodiversity**
  * OBJECTIVES :

    To assist the Cambodian government to conserve and wisely manage their wetlands through training, institutional strengthening, compiling inventories of wetlands and their resources and aiding in on-site management.
  * TIME FRAME : 3 years starting September 1994
  * FUNDING : secured from the Darwin Initiative, UK ; implementing agency AWB.

VIETNAM

- **Management of acid sulphate soils** (Mekong Delta)
  * OBJECTIVES :

    To formulate environmentally sound reclamation strategies for acid sulphate soils and anticipate the reaction of acid sulphate soils to various development and management measures through an adequate understanding of the processes set in motion by these measures.
  * TIME FRAME : 45 months from October 1989 to June 1993
  * FUNDING : from Sweden; implementing agency Mekong Secretariat

- **Master plan for the integrated development of the Mekong Delta**
  * OBJECTIVES :

    To develop a master plan for the integrated development of the Mekong Delta and to formulate scenarios for the implementation of projects in the short to medium term (before upstream storage works are constructed), and for long-term perspective based on the future increase in low flow.
  * TIME FRAME : 36 months from November 1990 to October 1993
  * FUNDS : secured from UNDP ; implementing agency Mekong Secretariat

- **Forestry-based development on the Long Xuyen Quadrangle, Mekong Delta**
  * OBJECTIVES :

    To establish which multiple resource use models based on artificial forests together constitute an effective base for sustainable development on the inundated soils of the quadrangle; to determine the likely environmental and social consequences; and to establish the economic and marketing prospects for such development.
  * TIME FRAME : 48 months from November 1991 to October 1995
  * FUNDING : secured from Australia; implementing agency Mekong Secretariat

- **Fish culture in ponds and lakes of the Tay Nguyen region**
  * OBJECTIVES :

    To improve fish seed and table fish production in lakes and ponds in the Tay Nguyen region, Vietnam.
  * TIME FRAME : 24 months; future project
  * FUNDING : being soght; implementing agency Mekong Secretariat

- **Assistance to the government in the management of Xuan Thuy reserve in the Red River delta**
  * OBJECTIVES :

    To encourage wise use of resources in the delta and to develop demonstration models of such wise use for application in other areas.
  * TIME FRAME : Ongoing
  * FUNDING : from IUCN ; implementing agency IUCN Wetlands Programme

LAOS

- **Fishermen's communities in the Nam Ngum basin reservoir, Phase II**
  * OBJECTIVES :

    Improvement of the socio-economic status of the fishermen at Nam Ngum in order to secure their effective participation in fishery management in the reservoir.
  * TIME FRAME : 24 months, from August 1991 to July 1993
  * FUNDING : scured from Switzerland ; implementing agency Mekong Secretariat

- **Small scale aquaculture development in Laos**
  * OBJECTIVES :

    To identify the constraints to small-scale aquaculture development and make an assessment of the potential resources available for increasing productivity; to devise simple aquaculture strategies, methodologies and appropriate extension materials for the transfer of the strategies to a larger number of small scale farmers; to formulate a national aquaculture research strategy oriented towards the small scale farmer and to devise a suitable methodology for on-farm research and extension appropriate for Laos.

* TIME FRAME : 42 months, future project
* FUNDS : being sought ; implementing agency Mekong Secretariat

- **Assistance to the government of Laos to develop a detailed wetland inventory and to formulate a National Wetland Action Plan**
  * OBJECTIVES :

    To gather information on the wetlands in Laos to input into a National Wetland Action Plan.
  * TIME FRAME : Preliminary inventory completed 1993; on-going
  * FUNDING : from IUCN ; implementing agency IUCN Wetlands Programme

- **Fish ecology and fisheries of the Mekong in the southern Lao PDR**
  * OBJECTIVES :

    To undertake preliminary observations on fish migrations, the status of the wetland habitats and fishing methods in this area of southern Laos (the Khone Falls) which is thought to be biologically very important.
  * TIME FRAME : June-July 1993
  * FUNDING : from AWB and Canada Fund

THAILAND

- **Community fisheries management in rural reservoirs**
  * OBJECTIVES :

    To formulate appropriate fish stocking programmes for the sustainable development of fisheries resources in rural reservoirs in north-eastern Thailand and the other countries in the lower Mekong basin.
  * TIME FRAME : 27 months, future project
  * FUNDING : being secured from the Netherland ; implementing agency Mekong Secretariat

- **Chaiyaphum brackishwater aquaculture centre for salt-affected lands in the Korat Plateau**
  * OBJECTIVES :

    To develop environmentally sound and economically viable strategies for the utilisation of salt-affected areas in the Korat Plateau through the development of brackishwater fish culture.
  * TIME FRAME : 36 months, future project
  * FUNDING : being sought ; implementing agency Mekong Secretariat

PHILIPPINES

- **Pasig River rehabilitation project**
  * OBJECTIVES :

    Improvement of water quality in the Pasig River system and the enhancement of fishery/aquaculture potential in Laguna de Bay.
  * TIME FRAME : 1991 to 1993, ongoing
  * FUNDING : from DANIDA

- **Development of an Integrated Protected Area System (IPAS) for the Philippines, Phases I and II**
  * OBJECTIVES :

    To identify remaining areas of high biodiversity in the Philippines in terrestrial, marine and wetland areas; to investigate their feasibility for management (Phase I) and to initiate protective and management measures on ten priority wetlands (Phase II).
  * TIME FRAME : Phase I completed February 1992; Phase II to begin in 1994.
  * FUNDING : secured from the World Bank for Phase I, Phase II funding from Japan and World Bank.

- **Debt for Nature Swap Programme**
  * OBJECTIVES :

    To write off part of the foreign debt and use that part written off for conservation measures in the country. It is administered by the Philippine Program of WWF-US. Part of the money has been used to set up the Foundation for the Philippine Environment (FPE) which funds small projects. Some wetland-related projects have been undertaken such as rehabilitation of one of the San Pablo lakes by removing over growth of water hyacinth.
  * TIME FRAME : Ongoing
  * FUNDING : writing off of part of foreign debt

- **RP-JAPAN Crocodile Farming project**
  * OBJECTIVES :

    The propagation and conservation of the saltwater crocodile Crocodylus porosus and the critically endangered Philippine freshwater crocodile Crocodylus mindorensis. The farm is based in Palawan and has met with success in its efforts to propagate crocodiles. Several freshwater sites are now being looked at which can serve as crocodile sanctuaries and for re-introductions.
  * TIME FRAME : Started in 1988; ongoing
  * FUNDING : by JICA.

- **Naujan Lake : towards a community based resources management program**
  - * OBJECTIVES :

    To review the status and utilisation of the resources of Lake Naujan and to develop, in conjunction with the fishermen's communities, sustainable methods of resource use.
  - * TIME FRAME : Started in 1993 : ongoing
  - * FUNDING : partly by AIDAB; implemented by Tambuyog Development Center, a Philippine non-stock, non-profit NGO.

- **Philippines wetland conservation programme**
  - * OBJECTIVES :

    To inventory the wetlands of the Philippines and to identify priority sites for conservation action.
  - * TIME FRAME : 1987 TO 1992
  - * FUNDING : from WWF-International ; implemented by AWB-Philippines

- **Olango Island community wetland programme**
  - * OBJECTIVES :

    To work with the local communities on Olango Island to conserve areas important for migratory shorebirds.
  - * TIME FRAME : 1989 TO 1992
  - * FUNDING : from WWF-International; implemented by AWB-Philippines.

INDONESIA

- **UK-Indonesia tropical forest management project. Sub-project 5 : conservation: developing a model to combine community-based exploitation and conservation in Danau Sentarum Wildlife Reserve, West Kalimantan.**
  - * OBJECTIVES :

    To inventory the flora and fauna of the area and those natural resources upon which the local people depend and draw up a management plan to ensure that utilisation of the resources is compatible with biodiversity conservation; and to assess the feasibility of applying such models to other areas.
  - * TIME FRAME : Started in 1992, running for 4 years
  - * FUNDING : from Overseas Development Administration (ODA) of the UK; implementing agencies : AWB-Indonesia and PHPA.

- **Improving wetland management and conservation in Indonesia; Part One, Sumatra**
  - * OBJECTIVES :

    To improve the quality and availability of data on wetlands in Sumatra; to build greater awareness of the value of wetlands and their role in supporting sustainable development; and to assist the Department of Forest protection and Nature Conservation (PHPA) in promoting the conservation of wetlands and to design and implement management plans for wetland conservation areas.
  - * TIME FRAME : January 1990 to December 1991
  - * FUNDING : secured from DGIS (Netherlands) ; implementing agencies, PHPA and AWB-Indonesia

REGIONAL (SE ASIA)

- **Wetland survey and evaluation**
  - * OBJECTIVES :

    To develop training programmes to promote professional development and institutional strengthening in the field of wetland assessment and management, through mobilising the resources of key institutions in Asia.
  - * TIME FRAME : January 1992 to March 1997
  - * FUNDING : from ODA of the UK and WWF-UK through their joint funding scheme, implemented by AWB

- **Wetland planning and management**
  - * OBJECTIVES :

    To minimise the loss of Asian wetlands through the establishment of a network of viable wetland reserves through and the management of Asian wetlands on a biologically sustainable basis.
  - * TIME FRAME : January 1992 to March 1997
  - * FUNDING : from ODA of the UK and WWF-UK through their joint funding scheme; implemented by AWB

- **Lake water quality management training courses**
  - * OBJECTIVES :

    To train appropriate government personnel from developing countries in management of water quality in lakes.
  - * TIME FRAME : Courses offered in 1992-1994
  - * FUNDING : from JICA, implemented by ILEC

- **Developer's guide**
  - * OBJECTIVES :

    The production and distribution of a guide to development design and management in tropical coastal and urban areas.
  - * TIME FRAME : 1991, completed
  - * FUNDING : from AIDAB, implemented by AWB

- **Towards sustainable harvesting of waterbirds on the East Asian Flyway**
  - * OBJECTIVES :

    To determine the extent of hunting and to devise approaches for moving towards sustainable hunting of waterbirds at selected sites in the East Asian Flyway.
  - * TIME FRAME : July 1990 to June 1994
  - * FUNDING : from AIDAB, implemented by AWB and collaborating agencies in Thailand, Indonesia and China.

- **Coordination of flyway research and site protection in the East Asia Flyway**
  - * OBJECTIVES :

    To promote the protection of key sites for shorebirds on the flyway; to identify future research needs to ensure that the most significant sites will be identified; to coordinate migratory waterbird research in the flyway; and to promote the protection and appropriate management of significant sites.
  - * TIME FRAME : May 1991 to May 1993
  - * FUNDING : from AIDAB, implemented by AWB.

- **Preparation of an action plan for migratory waders in the East Asian-Australasian Flyway**
  - * OBJECTIVES :

    To formulate an action plan for the conservation of migratory waders in the East Asian-Australasian Flyway ; to organise a workshop to bring together key wader specialists/researchers/government representatives from countries in the flyway to prepare the action plan; and to recommend specific activities for subsequent funding to improve conservation of migratory waders and their wetland habitats.
  - * TIME FRAME : 15 months starting June 1994
  - * FUNDING : secured from Australian Nature Conservation Agency (ANCA) ; implemented by AWB

- **Development of guidelines for environmentally sound management of Asian wetlands in relation to their role in watershed management**
  - * OBJECTIVES :

    To promote the wise use of wetlands in the context of wise watershed management; to emphasise the role of wetlands in the hydroligical functioning of watersheds and to persuade Asian governments to act upon the guidelines by the production of case studies wth quantitative data.
  - * TIME FRAME : 15 months starting March 1994
  - * FUNDING : from UNEP ; implementing agency AWB

MEKONG BASIN-WIDE PROJECTS (Implementing agency the Mekong Secretariat)

- **Preparatory organizational and legal studies**
  - * OBJECTIVES :

    To study criteria for and legal implications of the equitable allocation, use, conservation and development of the water resources of the lower Mekong Basin; to investigate possible organisational and legal frameworks and to provide training to Mekong Secretariat staff and government staff in legal and institutional aspects of water resources management.
  - * TIME FRAME : 36 months from Decemeber 1990 to November 1993
  - * FUNDING : secured from EC, UNDP, ADB

- **Inventory and management of the wetlands in the lower Mekong basin.**
  - * OBJECTIVES :

    To establish a database to formulate management plans for sustainable productive use of basin wetlands while conserving their natural ecological and socioeconomic functions.
  - * TIME FRAME : 36 months from January 1990 to June 1993
  - * FUNDING : from Sweden 651,000

- **Water quality monitoring network in the lower Mekong basin, Phase II**
  - * OBJECTIVES :

    To develop a comprehensive water quality conservation policy and establish systems for early recognition of water quality problems arising from current and future development activities; to develop predictive tools and ameliorative strategies for special, highly complex water-related environmental problems of natural and anthropogenic origin.
  - * TIME FRAME : 60 months from October 1988 to September 1993
  - * FUNDING : secured from SIDA and UNEP

- **Integration of environmental components into projects**
  - * OBJECTIVES :

    To strengthen the capability of EIA of projects; to gather basic/project specific environmental data and to support training in EIA.
  - * TIME FRAME : 40 months from March 1990 to June 1993
  - * FUNDING : secured from Sweden

- **Control of soil erosion, sedimentation and flash flood hazards**
  * OBJECTIVES :

    To elaborate appropriate preventative/ameliorative strategies for the protection of water and land resources from environmental degradation caused by flood erosion and flash floods;to identify areas affected or likely to be affected by erosion and sedimentation problems ; to elucidate processes and chain reactions responsible for the problems; and to formulate pilot management programmes to test/demonstrate suitable strategies.
  * TIME FRAME : 48 months from January 1990 to June 1993
  * FUNDING : secured from Sweden

- **Mekong watershed assessment and management**
  * OBJECTIVES :

    To elaborate a watershed classification system for the lower basin; to make a cartographic assessment of the watershed; to analyse the causes of watershed degradation and the processes involved; to establish apriority list of areas which are in urgent need of corrective intervention, as well as areas with a high risk of degradation; and to elaborate a comprehensive programme of activities for the rehabilitation of the watershed, including formulation of 4-6 priority projects.
  * TIME FRAME : 24 months from June 1990 to May 1992 (extension requested up to 1994)
  * FUNDING : secured from Switzerland

- **Creation of national parks along the Mekong River**
  (Basin-wide, but firstly for Laos and Thailand)
  * OBJECTIVES :

    To assess the feasibility of the creation of a transboundary park along the Mekong River (Pa Tam and Phou Xiang Thong National Parks); pending the outcome of the above, to formulate management plans for the parks; and to promote cooperation between Laos and Thailand through coordination of activities in the fields of national parks and conservation.
  * TIME FRAME : 24 months, future project
  * FUNDING : being sought

- **Fisheries in Mekong reservoirs**
  * OBJECTIVES :

    To formulate planning strategies for the development of different ecotypes of Mekong reservoirs on the basis of a basin-wide survey; and to establish pilot demonstration projects on fisheries management in reservoirs selected on the basis of these ecotypes.
  * TIME FRAME : 36 months; for the future
  * FUNDING : being secured from Denmark

- **Management of regional fisheries resources**
  * OBJECTIVES :

    To identify fish stocks in the lower Mekong basin threatened with decline or extinction through overfishing, destructive fishing practices or habitat deterioration, with emphasis on fish stocks which cross national boundaries and which require cooperation for effective management.
  * TIME FRAME : 24 months, for the future
  * FUNDING : being sought

- **Investigation of commercially important fish species in the lower Mekong basin**
  * OBJECTIVES :

    To collate existing information on the economic status of fish stocks in the mainstream, large tributaries ad delta branches; to generate new information through research on *Pangasius* and *Pangasianodon* (giant catfish) stocks inhabiting these ecosystems and to formulate a management plan for these important fish stocks (other species may be included if necessary); to train fisheries personnel from riparian fisheries institutions in research methodologies and management of Mekong basin fish stocks; and to upgrade the facilities for research and management of Mekong fish stocks available in riparian fisheries institutions.
  * TIME FRAME : 30 months
  * FUNDING : being sought

- **Assessment of impacts of water management on fishery resources**
  * OBJECTIVES :

    To anticipate negative impacts of water resource development activities such as flood control, drainage of wetlands and irrigation on fishery resources; and to develop appropriate preventive/corrective measures to maintain productivity and socio-economic benefits of basin fisheries.
  * TIME FRAME : 36 months, for the future
  * FUNDING : being sought

- **Environmental training fund**
  * OBJECTIVES :

    To assist staff working on environmental matters at the Mekong Secretariat and riparian institutions to attend meetings/workshops to acquire the needed exposure to new environmental concepts and techniques; and to provide opportunities for professionals to share experiences with international organisations/research institutes.

* TIME FRAME : 31 months, from December 1989 to June 1993
* FUNDING : secured from Sweden

● **Water resources training programme**
 * OBJECTIVES :

   To improve, through postgraduate education and training, the capability of riparian personnel; to undertake water resources development and planning projects.
 * TIME FRAME : The project will be implemented over a 6 year period (1990-1996) and is a continuation of the previous Mekong-Australian Fellowship Programme.
 * FUNDING : partially secured from Australia

● **Training programme for water pollution control**
 * OBJECTIVES :

   To strengthen the required technical capability of the human resources of the riparian countries for supporting basin-wide cooperation in water pollution control and for implementing national water pollution control programmes through provision of training and education. The immediate objectives are to formulate training and education programmes in the field of the environment, with particular emphasis on water pollution control, taking into account the prioritised needs of the riparian countries; and to implement, in cooperation with the national and international agencies concerned, formulated above.
 * TIME FRAME : 48 months, for the future
 * FUNDING : being sought

Indonesia

In 1991, Indonesia was the first country in S.E. Asia to become a full party to the Ramsar Convention. The government has designated Berbak National Park in Jambi province, Sumatra as a wetland of international importance under the Convention. Management of the site for conservation and wise use is on-going.

To date, there is no overall wetland policy in Indonesia. This may be due to the difficulty in coordination between no less than six ministries which are directly involved in planning, management and utilization of wetlands and their resources in Indonesia. They are the Ministry of Forestry; Ministry of Agriculture; Ministry of Public Works; Ministry of Transmigration and Forest Clearing; Ministry of Environment and Ministry of Home Affairs.

Some of programmes pertaining to wetland planning and management in Indonesia include :

1) The publication of a preliminary directory of wetlands of Indonesia in 1987 through a joint programme of PHPA and AWB. Subsequently, an Indonesian Wetland Database was set up through a grant from the Netherlands.

2) Biodiversity Action Plan for Indonesia (1993) - produced by : Ministry of National Development Planning/National Development Planning Agency.

3) National Strategy for Mangrove Forest Management in Indonesia (1993) - produced by State Ministry for the Environment; Ministry of Forestry; Indonesian Institute for Sciences; Ministry of Home Affairs; and Mangrove Foundation.

4) Indonesian Forestry Action Programme (1991)- produced by Ministry of Forestry.

Since 1987, the Ministry of Forestry, through its agency the Directorate General of Forest Protection and Nature Conservation (PHPA) has been cooperating with Asian Wetland Bureau (AWB) in wetland programmes. These programmes have been very successful in several aspects of wetland management, land use planning and policy development. These programmes have placed wetlands on the agenda for policy makers and managers in relevant government agencies. It also has set the trend for developing profiles of important wetland areas at the provincial level as a basis for integrating wetland conservation and wise use into land use planning frameworks.

Philippines

In recognition of the importance of wetlands to the livelihood of Filipinos, the Philippine government has initiated several programmes for wetland conservation and management. Various government agencies are involved in this programme but the Department of Environment and Natural Resources (DENR), through the Protected Areas and Wildlife Bureau (PAWB) acts as the lead implementing agency.

● **Initiatives include**

1) In 1987, the Wetland Conservation Programme was initiated to determine the conservation status of Philippine wetlands and their importance as wintering and breeding sites of migratory birds in Eastern Asia. This programme has been very successful in supporting the establishment of Olango Island as a Wildlife Sanctuary and the publication of a directory of important wetland sites in the Philippines.

2) In 1989 the National Bird banding Scheme was established, the aim of which is to identify ecologically important wetland habitats for the protection of migratory birds.

3) A project to identify important areas to include in the Integrated Protected Areas System (IPAS) for the Philippines included a wetland component in which the most important freshwater wetland, Agusan Marsh in Mindanao, was designated as a reserve together with Siargao Island, which contains the largest remaining area of mangroves in the Philippines.

4) A National Workshop on the Conservation and Sustainable Use of Wetlands was held in September/October 1992. A draft National Wetland Action Plan was produced for consideration at the workshop and an ad-hoc National Wetland Committee was set up to finalise the action plan.

Thailand

There is at present no overall national policy on wetlands in Thailand. A variety of policies has been formulated by different agencies which contain elements which relate to wetland conservation. However, there is little coordination between these agencies to encourage integrated conservation and management. In response to this, several government agencies including Royal Forestry Department; Office of Environmental Policy and Planning; Land Development Department; Department of Fisheries; and Royal Irrigation Department together with local universities have agreed to establish a committee on wetland conservation, one of the first activities of which is to produce a national wetland action plan.

Malaysia

In Malaysia, there is no overall national policy or strategy for wetland conservation, but there is a variety of legislation at the state level pertaining to wetlands. Jurisdictional matters relating to wetlands are unclear due to the number of agencies which have responsibility for different aspects of management.

A National Forest Policy which covers management of mangroves in Peninsular Malaysia, and as such is relevant to wetlands, is aimed at ensuring the conservation, management and wise utilization and development of valuable forest resources.

In 1985 the Malaysian Wetland Working Group was established under the aegis of the Department of Wildlife and National Parks.
The group has strongly recommended that a National Policy of Malaysian Wetlands be prepared in view of the values and roles of wetlands in national development. This recommendation, however, was not translated into action.

The recent wetland workshop held at the State of Pahang recommended that a State Committee on Wetlands be established towards production of a State Action Programme for Wetlands.

In 1987, Malaysian official attended the conferences of the Contracting Parties to the Ramsar Convention at Regina. Following this, significant progress has been made and now the Malaysian Government is considering to joining the Convention.

Important priorities for Malaysia are seen as the holding of a national wetland workshop, the production of an action plan and accession to the Ramsar Convention. The development of management plans for internationally important sites, particularly in terms of developing zoning of activities within these areas, is of the utmost importance.

Cambodia

Cambodia is just now emerging from decades of war so there is only a rudimentary institutional framework and little expertise in wetland conservation.

Recently, several efforts towards wetland conservation have been shown by Cambodia Government. Several projects concerning inventory and management of wetlands have been initiated in conjunction with AWB: identification of internationally important sites and assistance for accession to the Ramsar Convention funded by the Wetland Conservation Fund of Ramsar, a survey of important wetland areas for large waterbirds funded by IUCN and the possible declaration of the Great Lake as a World Heritage Site by UNESCO. Furthermore, AWB is also working with the Ministry of Environment in planning a National Wetland Workshop. This workshop will be targetted at producing a National Action Plan for wetlands in Cambodia. The government is also reintegrating into the activities of the Mekong Secretariat; mapping of wetlands using remote sensing has been carried out and water quality monitoring stations are to be set up under the MS Environment Programme.

Laos

As with Cambodia, until recently, Laos has been subjected to civil strife and has remained fairly isolated from the rest of the world. As such information on the protection and conservation of natural resources has been very limited such that there has policy or programme on natural resource management in the country. However, in 1990, under the National Office for Nature Conservation and Watershed Management in the Department of Forestry, the Wetland Management Programme/Wetland Unit was established.

The objectives of the Programme are :

1) To inventory and classify the wetlands of the country.
2) To collect, analyse and compile wetland data
3) to propose guidelines for preserving natural wetlands and their biological resources.

The World Conservation Union (IUCN) Wetlands Programme acts as advisor to the government on wetland issues and provided technical assistance for a preliminary inventory of wetlands in Laos.

SUMMARY

Whilst most SE Asian countries are constrained in their attempts at wetland conservation and management due to an inadequate institutional framework, lack of trained personnel and funding, it is encouraging to note that almost all countries of the Asian region recognise wetlands as very important types of ecosystems which must receive priority for protection. In most countries where a National Conservation Strategy has been produced, special mention has been made of the need to conserve and wisely manage wetlands. Several countries have taken the initiative to prepare national wetland directories, to hold national workshops on wetland conservation to develop a national wetland action plan, to establish National Wetland Committees and to develop a national wetland policies.

Work by NGOs in Southeast Asia related to wetland projects

One of the most promising channels for achieving wetland conservation in Asia is the NGO sector. These bodies have the potential to influence the users of wetlands in a way that governments agencies cannot do.

Listed in this section are selected organizations, both atthe international and national level, which are actively involved in wetland conservation programmes in Asia, or have components of wider activities which feature wise use of wetlands. Brief details of on-going and past projects are given.

Section 5-1 International organizations

Asian Wetland Bureau (AWB)

AWB is actively engaged in promoting the protection and sustainable utilisation of wetlands and their resources in the Asia-pacific region. AWB works in a catalytic fashion in collaboration with national organisations, essentially helping to strengthen local institutions and to develop local expertise.

The Bureau's work covers five main themes; maintaining an overview of the wetland conservation situation in the region; assisting in development of regional and national wetland action plans; disseminating information materials; providing support to local organisations to manage wetlands on a sustainable basis; and providing linkages with international organisations, conventions and expertise.

Numerous projects have been conducted by AWB including surveys of more than 10,000 km of coastline and nearly 150 coastal and inland wetland sites. The Bureau has prepared national wetland directories in collaboration with relevant government agencies in Malaysia, Indonesia, Philippines, Thailand, India and China and has provided substantial input to the Asian Wetland Directory. The Bureau has conducted extensive surveys to locate potential conservation areas in the region and has worked on reserve management in Sumatra, Malaysia, Philippines and China. AWB has conducted and organised more than 40 training courses on wetland subject and produced training manual in various Asian languages. AWB also published over one hundred reports and books. The newsletter (Asian Wetland News) is the main vehicle for the Bureau. Produced twice a year, it features articles and notes on the conservation and management of Asian wetlands.

IUCN Wetlands Programme

The World Conservation Union (IUCN) Wetland Programme coordinates activities of the Union concerned with the management of wetland ecosystems. The core of the programme is a series of field projects which develop the methodologies for wetland management, in particular in developing countries. IUCN established a Wetland Programme office in Bangkok in 1991 to strengthen support to wetland conservation activities of IUCN's members and partners in South and South East Asia.

The IUCN approach has been to provide assistance for national workshops to identify priorities for action. A series of workshops was held in Vietnam in May 1992, Bangladesh in November, 1992 and Nepal in March 1993. The work in Vietnam links with IUCN's interest in the wetlands of the Mekong delta and IUCN is working closely with the Mekong Secretariat on wetland issues.

In Laos, IUCN acts as adviser to the government and in Cambodia it will provide support through its new office.

On a more general level, other IUCN programmes are assisting governments in developing National Conservation Strategies, which have great relevance to wetland conservation in that the NCS is accepted by the governments and defines how to achieve effective conservation of wetlands. In both Nepal and Bangladesh, for example, support for wetland conservation is closely linked to the IUCN National Conservation Strategy process.

World Wide Fund for Nature (WWF)

WWF is an international non governmental organization established in 1961 with headquarters in Switzerland. It operates with a network of national organizations and associates located in 28 countries across five continents. WWF has been working to preserve the diversity of life on earth and to prevent the extinction of species. WWF 's ultimate goal is to stop and eventually reverse the accelerating degradation of the planet's natural environment and to help build a future in which humans live in harmony with nature. A full fledged

Asia and Pacific program came into effect in 1985, operating largely through WWF national organizations in the region.

PADEK

Partnership for Development in Kampuchea (PADEK) is a non-religious international consortium of 5 donor organisations - NOVIB (Netherlands), FOS (Belgium), and Oxfam of Belgium, America and HK.

It is mainly involved in agriculture in Cambodia but has a small-scale aquaculture project which may help in taking some fishing pressure off wild stocks.

Conservation International (CI)

CI is a U.S. based non-stock, non-profit organisation formed in 1987 to work with local conservation groups and government agencies to preserve biodiversity and promote sustainable development. In Asia, CI works in Indonesia and the Philippines. In Indonesia, CI has projects in the Mentawai Islands where it is conducting research and working with local communities on the management of a biosphere reserve. In the Philippines, it has an on-going project on the Tubbataha Reef, one of the best and most diverse reefs in the Philippines.

Earth Island Institute (EII)

EII works in both Thailand and southern Laos, mainly on supporting community-based fisheries and protecting the Irrawaddy dolphin.

Section 5-2 National organizations

MALAYSIA

● WWF Malaysia

WWF Malaysia has produced a national and state conservation strategies for Malaysia and has collaborated and funded AWB on a number of wetland conservation projects such as the development of guidelines for coastal aquaculture in Selangor state, an action plan for the North Selangor Peat Swamp Forest, and a freshwater fish survey of the Pahang River basin.

● Malayan Nature Society

The Malayan Nature Society (MNS) founded in 1940, is a non government organization dedicated to the study, conservation and enjoyment of the Malaysian natural heritage and the surrounding region. The Society has a number of branches within Malaysia, each of which organizes its own programme. The Society also manages the Kuala Selangor Nature Park. This 600 acres park consists of different wetland habitats such as mudflats, lakes and mangroves.

Numerous nature oriented indoor and outdoor activities are being carried by the Society at this park. These includes bird watching, photography, studies of reptiles and plants. The centre also hosts field courses for children and adults. In addition the Society publishes a number of books on the natural history of the region including wetlands.

THAILAND

● Wildlife Fund Thailand (WFT)

WFT was founded in 1983 and is an associate organisation of the World Wide Fund for Nature. It is working on the buffer zone of Khao Yai National Park and has a number of environmental awareness programmes.

● Project for Ecological Recovery (PER)

PER is a national organisation founded in 1986. It acts as a coordinator and facilitator for environmental projects in Thailand. One of its main projects concerning wetlands is lobbying against large dams and their consequences on the Mekong River.

● Yadfon (Raindrop Association)

Yadfon was formed in 1985 to promote sustainable development in fishing communities along the west coast of peninsular Thailand. It has a mangrove reforestation project in Pattani Bay with the local villagers.

VIETNAM

● World Wide Fund for Nature International - Vietnam Programme

WWF conducts studies to develop management plans for Vietnam's national parks and works on habitat protection for endangered species. Activities in Laos are coordinated from the WWF Vietnam office.

● Centre for Natural Resources Management and Environmental Studies (CRES)

CRES was founded as a research centre of the University of Hanoi. In the wetland field, it is active in mangrove and Melaleuca management.

PHILIPPINES

● Conservation International (CI)

As mentioned above, CI has a country programme which includes the protection and management of Tubbataha Reef.

● Haribon Foundation (HF)

The HF is the premier conservation NGO in the Philippines and has worked in a number of wetland issues. In 1986, it launched a programme for the wise use of Laguna de Bay. At present, they are supporting a marine mammal project of Silliman University, a private university in the central Philippines. They have been active in coastal community - based resource management activities since 1988 and in the design and management of marine sanctuaries.

● World Wildlife Fund - U.S. Philippines programme

A WWF-US country office was established in June 1991. It has acted as Chief Technical Advisor on the Integrated Protected Area System (IPAS) for the Philippines in which AWB covered the wetland component. WWF-US has also negotiated a Debt-for-Nature Swap for the Philippines and has set up the Foundation for the Philippine Environment (FPE) to oversee the disbursement of this money. Several of these projects are wetland-related; e.g. for the rehabilitation of lakes for fisheries which are infested with water hyacinth.

● Tambuyog Development Center (TDC)

TDC works with local communities to encourage sustainable community-based resource use in coastal and inland wetlands. They are presently working on Lake Naujan in Mindoro and on the coast of NE Mindoro. They have also aided subsistence fishermen on Lake Taal and Laguna de Bay.

Community Extension for Research and Development (CERD)

CERD works with poor fishermen's communities in both freshwater and coastal wetlands. They have carried out many projects on Laguna de Bay.

Kinaiyahan Foundation Inc. (KFI)

KFI is a non-stock, non-profit NGO dedicated to preservation of ecosystems upon which poor communities depend. They have had an extensive programme on lake Lanao to lobby the government regarding large scale developments for the lake which may affect the fishermen communities adversely.

⬆ Lake Songkhla, a lagoon lake in Thailand

♦

Lake Environmental Conservation and International Cooperation in Developing Countries

(This text is based on *Survey of the State of World Lakes*, Vols. 1-5, ILEC/UNEP, 1988-93, and *The pollution of Lakes and Reservoirs,* UNEP, 1994, and other sources.)

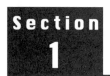

Section 1 Types of lakes and reservoirs targeted by international cooperation

Seen from an environment and development viewpoint, the world's lakes and reservoirs can be generally portrayed in a totally separated form from their limonological classifications as follows. (The environment conservation measures concerned with each type of lake and reservoir and the international cooperation approach for those measures are completely different.)

Quasi-untouched Lakes that Appear to Have No Problems

In many cases, these lakes are in remote locations with minimal economic activity in the basin areas. However, these lakes are part of the global water circulation, and, as such, cannot be ignored. For example, the lakes of the Pantanal, as a retarding basin, are thought to be useful in controlling floods in the lower reaches. There are also indications that methane emissions from wetland, lakes and reservoirs in the tundra zone are possibly influencing the climate. These lakes are valuable in many ways including their scientific research value.

Acid rain damage is occurring in small lakes of northeast Canada even though the region is remote. Despite the remoteness of these lakes, they cannot be protected from pollution traveling in the atmosphere. A feature of these lakes is the lack of information about them as they have hardly had any individual studies carried out on them. As they form part of the world's water circulation, international cooperation is necessary to put together a global monitoring system.

Examples :
- Pantanal lakes of Brazil
- Northern lakes of Canada
- Lakes and wetlands of tundra zone of Siberia, Russia
- Arid zone salt lakes of Central Asia, Australia, etc.
- Plateau region lake groups of Tibet, China

♦ Untouched Tianchi, a caldera lake bordering China and North Korea

Traditionally Used Lakes that Have No Pressing Environmental Problems but Maybe Targeted for Development Discussions

For example, Lake Tanganyika - one of the world's oldest lakes with numerous types of precious fish - is only used by the local inhabitants for small-scale fishing and local water transportation, but in recent years a fishing industry promotion plan is being advocated foremost by FAO. Furthermore, there is a crude oil drilling plan, which is causing anxiety over environment pollution and has led to a biodiversity project commencing under GEF finance. In Lake Turkana there is a gradual increase in the use of motor boats in addition to traditional fishing methods. Although no major problems have occurred, a drop in the water level can be seen. In Lake Wulianshuhai, traditional fishing and harvesting of reeds takes place. The current international cooperation for these lakes mostly takes the form of development projects for fishing industry promotion. From now on, sufficient environmental consideration should be given by development corporations. There is a need for development cooperation organizations to ensconce themselves in an environment conservation effort. Moreover, new uses for lakes and reservoirs - such as tourism - should be considered.

Examples :
- Lake Tanganyika, Zaire, Burundi, Zambia)
- Lake Turkana (Kenya/Ethiopia)
- Lake Wulianshuhai (China)

⬆ Lake Turkana having potential of fishery development

Lakes with Sedimentation, Dropping Water Levels, Eutrophication and Introduced Species Problems but with No Easy Way of Implementing Countermeasures

In general, these are lakes that are both vast and have international borders. For example, the Nile perch, that was introduced to Lake Victoria in the 1950s, came extremely close to bringing about the extinction of a particular species of fish. Also, an invasion of water hyacinth caused considerable problems. An unsuitable drainage plan in the basin of the Aral Sea is causing the lake to shrink, which in turn has caused health problems and economic losses. Moreover, large amounts of chemical fertilizers and pesticides infiltrating the lake have spurred on the worsening quality of drinking water. In Lake Chad the water level is dropping due to climatic changes. And in the Caspian Sea the water level is rising due to meteorological changes. In Lakes Tonle Sap and Dongting sedimentation has reached a critical level.

The main reason that relief of these problems is difficult is that these lakes are very large and so minor countermeasures do not yield results. These lakes are often by nature international lakes with, in a lot of the cases, the lake basins straddling numerous international borders. These countries are economically weak, which causes international clashes of interest over water. For this reason, multinational reconciliation and support through international organizations is essential because effective action would be difficult to achieve with just bilateral cooperation. However, UN organizations, such as UNEP, only get involved in projects to the extent of diagnosing the current situation and are not actively involved in trying to implement recommendations they make.

Examples :
- Lake Victoria (Kenya, Uganda, Tanzania)
- Caspian Sea (Russia, Iran)
- Aral Sea (Kazakhstan, Uzbekistan, Azerbaijan, Turkmenistan)
- Lake Tonle Sap (Cambodia)
- Lake Dongting (China)

◔ Fishermen's village on the heavily used Tonle Sap (the Great Lake in Cambodia)

Lakes that are Important as Water Sources and Fishing Grounds but Have Reached Critical Levels in Eutrophication and Toxic Substance Pollution

There are many lakes with critical levels of eutrophication in the densely populated areas of Southeast Asia and South Asia as well as a few in Africa. In particular, these types of lake are numerous in China (Lake Dong, Lake Chao, Lake Tai, Lake Dianchi and Lake Hongze). Fish hauls are beginning to decline in Lakes Dianchi and Laguna due to hypernutrition. Moreover, heavy metal pollution has reached a dangerous level in Dianchi due to factory waste water from a metal refinery. In fact, it has come to the point where the lake-bred fish will have to be banned from the dining table. Lake Valencia South America is in the same situation - a feature here is the large livestock load in the basin.

These lakes are in need of urgent action and there are strong requests for such action from the countries in question. On the whole each basin is inside the border of just one country, which means bilateral aid can be applied in many cases. For this reason, there are numerous examples of bilateral technological cooperation, including specialists sent to Lake Valencia by JICA. Nevertheless, the salvation of polluted lakes is economically and technologically extremely difficult. There are many examples of numerous aid organizations carrying out diagnosis studies while not actually implementing any relief measures, as in the case of Lake Valencia. Combined cooperation in the area of development planning and environment action is necessary, as seen in the case of supply water and sewage maintenance in Lake Nakuru.

Examples :
- Lake Laguna (Philippines)
- Lake Ypacarai (Paraguay)
- Lake Valencia (Venezuela)
- Lake Nakuru (Kenya)
- Lake Dianchi (China)

⊙ Lake Nakuru famous for flamingo receives untreated sewage of Nakuru City

Artificial Lakes

Problems appear far more easily in artificial lakes than in natural lakes. Just as such lakes are constructed to meet the need for electricity generation, drinking water and water sources for agriculture and industry, the likes of water contamination and drinking water deterioration due to eutrophication, impaired water supply due to escalating growth of water hyacinths, impaired facility equipment due to a lack of oxygen (anoxia) cause direct economic damage. Eutrophication occurs easily as dams are quickly constructed, which does not allow the ecology to stabilize. Furthermore, this environment deterioration occurs rapidly after a dam is completed. Notably, tropical dam lakes easily succumb to eutrophication, even though there is no manmade pollution sources up stream, because large quantities of organic substances in the inflowing water from up stream and submerged trees in the lakes cause eutrophication to occur easily. Natural eutrophication is occurring in several of the enormous dam lakes in the Amazon and Aswan High Dam Reservoir areas and manmade eutrophication is occurring in the dam lakes of Sao Paulo State, Brazil. Artificial lakes are often located in developing countries, where, more often than not, only the minimum amount of monitoring is carried out and examples of environmental aid for dam lakes are few and far between.

Examples :
- Aswan High Dam Reservoir
- Several enormous dam lakes on the Amazon
- Dam lakes in San Paulo State, Brazil

⊙ Tukurui Dam in Brazil suffering from annoxic water

Asia and Oceania

In this region - notably Asia - all forms of deterioration in lake environment can be seen, such as numerous lakes suffering from eutrophication, toxic waste pollution, silt accumulation due to catchment area soil erosion, and dropping water levels and reduced lake size due to excess use of water. There is no shortage of examples; in particular, China has many lakes in these categories, and lakes with critical problems can also be seen in the Philippines, Thailand, Cambodia and Indonesia. The status of international cooperation for Southeast Asia is covered in Chapter Two.

The state of eutrophication in Lake Laguna in the Philippines is such that it is having a major impact on fish farming. For this reason, numerous UN organizations and bilateral aid organizations have carried out diagnosis studies (see chart below), but hardly any concrete aid work has been done other than the cleaning of outflowing rivers, as restoring this polluted lake is extremely difficult - both economically and technically. Furthermore, only a limited number of projects are being carried out in other lakes and reservoirs in the Philippines.

Cooperation is advancing via JICA for water quality protection of Lakes Poyang and Tai in China; however, the number of cooperation projects seems to be small when the critical state of eutrophication and sedimentation in China is considered. Lake Songkhla in Thailand and Lake Tonle Sap in Cambodia are getting attention from various organizations; however, no clearcut environment projects have been put together so far.

In the case of Central Asia, UNEP is diagnosing the current status of the Aral Sea, which is shrinking due to excess use of water for irrigation. Also, the World Bank is planning a basin project that incorporates environmental considerations. Moreover, organizations in Europe, starting with NATO, are showing interest in the Aral Sea, and numerous study groups are visiting the lake. Small-scale study groups from Japan are also visiting the lake. These include UNEP specialists sent through the cooperation of ILEC, intermittent studies by the Japan Research Association Kazakhstan (JRAK) and a display of interest by the Global Infrastructure Fund Research Foundation Japan (GIF). However, despite numerous organizations showing interest, no clearcut action has been commenced. In the case of Lake Baikal (also found in the Republic of Kazakhstan), where the same low water-level problems as the Aral Sea exist, overseas aid organizations cannot be seen, apart from a slender amount of research cooperation.

Lake Laguna Studies Carried Out with the Cooperation of Domestic and International Organizations

Year	International Organizations	Collabolate Organs	Study Content
1970	UNDP	LLDA	Feasibility study on water quality, public sanitation, irrigation agriculture, flood control & hydraulics
1974	ADB	LLDA	Feasibility study on lake management & waste water infrastructure development
1974	USAID	LLDA	Deveropment report on the basin irrigation agriculture
1978	WHO/UNDP/ADB	LLDA	Comprehensive water quality & public sanitation planning report
1978	ADB	LLDA	Feasibility study on lake water & waste water infrastructure development
1980	UNDP	LLDA	Pre-feasibility study report on Sewage Pilot Project
1984	ADB	LLDA	Environment evaluation of the lake
1985	ADB		Post-project evaluation on lake development project
1985	ADB		Terminal report on lake development
1986	UNEP-ROPE	Haribon Found	Institution & fishery
1987-90	UNCRD/ILEC/UNEP	Philippine Univ.	Institution, lake management, fishery
1987	SEAFDEC		Monitoring and evaluation
1988	WHO		Evaluation report on water quality
1990	WHO		Simulation report on water quality
1991	SIDA		Workshop
1992	WHO		Basin water quality management report

Europe

As many countries in Europe are advanced, examples of aid for lake and reservoir environment conservation measures are few. Moreover, the appropriate international cooperation is taking place for lake and catchment area measures in international lakes, wetlands and rivers, as can be seen in the examples of Lake Boden, Lake Leman and the Rhine River. Nevertheless, in the case of former socialist countries in eastern Europe, a critical level of freshwater pollution can be seen in the likes of the Danube River and the Black Sea. Organizations, such as the Regional Environment Centre for Central and Eastern Europe (REC), specialize in the environment problems of these regions, however, the latest study was unable to grasp the current status of international cooperation.

Africa

African lakes and reservoirs are in a similar state to Asian ones with all forms of environmental deterioration visible other than acid rain. There is no shortage of examples - for instance: eutrophication due to the contamination load from catchment areas; pollution due to agricultural chemicals; low water levels and shrinkage due to excess water use; and sedimentation and ecology disturbance due to various types of immigration. The

major managerial problem in lakes and reservoirs in this region is the lack of intermittent and long-term study and research data, so the current situation is not known. Notably, water quality data and load data from catchment areas are meagre. In the case of research cooperation, examples, such as Lake Tangyanika (Japan, Zaire and Zambia) and Lake Turkana (Norway and Kenya), can be seen; however, these are not associated with environmental problems.

The borders of African states were set during the colonial era with little regard to natural topography. For this reason, many lakes and basins are "international" as they are spread across a tangle of national borders. Therefore, coordinating between the numerous countries involved is essential for lake related work. Inevitably, the ratio of multilateral aid carried out through UN organizations increases. Countries are coordinating efforts for management of international lakes, wetlands and basins, such as UNEP's work on the Zambezi River (including Lake Kariba), the River Nile (including Lake Victoria) and the Lake Chad basin; however, there is a clash of interests among the coordinating countries (for example, the River Nile) and insufficient capacity and finance in local action organizations (such as SADC for the Zambezi River and LCBC for Lake Chad). Therefore, there have been no real results as efforts have stopped at the current status diagnosis and basic agreement level.

Examples of Water Related Projects at Lake Victoria in Recent Years

- Remote sensing system for early warnings in eastern and southern Africa (FAO/Japan)
- **1990 to 91**
  Monitoring, forecasting and simulating for Nile basin
- **to 1993**
  Consolidation of agricultural weather forecast bureaus for global information, early warnings and locust control (FAO/Belgium)
- **to 1993**
  Hydraulic status evaluation for Africa south of the Sahara desert (FAO/WB)
- **from 1988**
  Production aid for Ugandan national wetland plan (IUCN/NORAD/DGIS)
- **from 1992**
  Diagnosis study for Nile basin (UNEP)
- **from 1993**
  Water hyacinth control for east Africa (GEF/UNEP/WB/FAO)
- **from 1993**
  Government policy and system for water resources management in Lake Victoria region (FAO/Italy)

- **from 1993**
  Support for efficiency improvement in Lake Victoria Fishing Commission (FAO)
- **from 1993**
  Support for TECCONILE [Nile Basin Technology Cooperation Conference] (CIDA)
- **1994 to 99**
  Information system work for water quality monitoring and planning in Lake Victoria region (FAO/Japan)
- **Intermittent**
  Support for Ugandan water resources management (DANIDA)
- **Intermittent**
  Study project for Lake Victoria fishing industry (EU)
- **Intermittent**
  Office-type water resources management and information system for Nile basin (FAO)
- **Intermittent**
  Land cover for east Africa using remote sensing (FAO/Italy)
- **Planning stage**
  Environment management for Lake Victoria (GEF/UNEP/FAO)

Several international cooperation projects are progressing parallel to each other. The following series of projects for Lake Victoria and the Nile basin (see FAO for details) are examples of essential but typical coordinating. Numerous organizations (FAO, UNEP, GEF, WB and EU, etc.) are involved in multilateral aid for the African region. Finance from countries like the USA, Italy and Japan goes via the trust funds of these organizations to be used. The likes of Canada, Holland, Norway and, recently, NGOs like IUCN have been cooperating in multilateral aid. As many organizations are involved, numerous areas of these projects overlap. For example, the Nile Basin Technology Cooperation Conference (CIDA) and the Nile River Basin Diagnostic Study (UNEP) both receive cooperation from Nile basin countries.

Also, water monitoring is an important aspect of almost all projects, such as water resources development, water hyacinth countermeasures, fishing promotion and wetland conservation. The project for Lake Victoria and the project for the Nile basin overlap, because they inevitably have the same aim. And though inter-project cooperation has a lot of significance, it does not always seem to be sufficiently implemented.

North America

There are no international aid projects for this region as the USA and Canada are both advanced countries. The environmental problems in the great lakes are of marked importance in this region. The USA and Canada have formed a joint committee to manage these lakes. This is one of the successful examples of international lake management by advanced countries.

Central and South America

There are many lakes and reservoirs spread across South America. All examples of lake environment deterioration, other than acidification, can be seen in this region. Adding to the problems are numerous local giant dams. In the case of lakes and reservoirs in this region - just the same as Africa - there is a lack of intermittent and long-term study and research data and the current situation is not known. Notably, water quality data and load data from catchment areas are meagre. Eutrophication is critical in Lake Guaiba (Brazil), Tukurui Reservoir and Parana High Dam (Brazil) and Lake Valencia (Venezuela). Study cooperation for some of these lakes is being carried out by JICA. Environment management plans have been started at Lake Managua by SIDA and at Lake Titicaca by UNEP, but the activities of other organs are not adequately clear.

⊙ Kariba town people fishing on Lake Kariba (Zimbabwe/Zambia)

A view of current international cooperation for important lake and reservoir environment problems

This study's report for fiscal 1992 groups global lake and reservoir environment problems into several patterns and outlines their outbreak causes and current situations. The following are summaries of each type of problem noting the type of international cooperation, particularly in the cases of lakes and reservoirs in developing countries.

Catchment Soil Erosion Caused by Rapid Sedimentation

In the case of catchment areas in developing countries, soil erosion is occurring at a savage pace as a result of deforestation, farming and ranching abuses in catchment areas. This soil erosion leads to soil and sand flowing into and rapidly clogging lakes and reservoirs. A typical example of this is the rapid speed at which Lake Dongting is becoming shallow due to indiscriminate development in the mountain region in the upper reaches of the Yang-zhe River. Moreover, as nutrient salts are included in the washed-down top soil, soil erosion is also attributable to eutrophication of lakes and dam lakes. This can be seen at Aswan High Dam.

A real concentration of lake and reservoir conservation aid work cannot be seen in response to this problem, as extremely large-scale and comprehensive conservation measures for complete basin areas - such as revision of afforestation and cultivation methods - are necessary. Nevertheless, there are numerous cases of desertification prevention and promotion of sustainable farming. Many organizations see the importance of these fields and are developing work accordingly. A typical example is the use of a special grass (Vetiver grass), recommended by the World Bank, for soil erosion prevention work. Japanese NGOs - OISCA - are also taking afforestation support work seriously. But once soil and sand have settled in lakes, there seems to be no aid work for rescue purposes.

Dropping Water Levels Due to Excessive Water Use and Natural Water Level Changes

In the cases of Lake Chad's reduced water level and the Caspian Sea's increased water level (both of which are thought to be linked to water-level changes accompanying climatic changes), UNEP is initiating coordination between relevant countries, but clearcut action has not developed. In the case of Lake Chad, IUCN is promoting sustainable farming and fishing as a traditional management method base for the Logone River, an inflowing river that is a source of flooding; however, this work is not directly related to the reduced water level problem of the lake.

⬆ Erosion at Lake Victoria basin

In the case of reduced water levels due to water used for hydroelectricity, examples can be found at Lake Toba in Indonesia, Lake Sevan in Armenia and Lake Balkhash in Kazakhstan, but there seem to be no examples of counter action. In future, this problem should be considered as part of the environment consideration that takes place in the financial reviews of development finance organizations.

Lake Water Acidification Due to Acid Rain

· The distribution areas of acid rain are restricted to two advanced-regions: North Europe and the northeast area of North America. And as the damaged lakes are limited to medium-to-small lakes, international cooperation for countermeasures cannot be seen. However, East Asian countries - including Japan - are cooperating in acid rain monitoring as future acid rain damage is expected due to China's economic development.

Pollution Due to Toxic Substances

In the case of this problem, information - starting with the existence/nonexistence of damage in developing countries - itself is insufficient. On this point, GEMS/WATER is setting up a global monitoring system for water quality through the help of WHO and UNEP. A success example is the cooperation by Countries in the Rhine River region to set up a system for regional monitoring and contamination reduction. Furthermore, strengthening of developing countries' monitoring capacities is being realized through the likes of

JICA working on project technology cooperation in technology training for groups and establishing global monitoring and training centers. International cooperation does not directly target lake and reservoir conservation; however, pollution countermeasures, such as factory waste water, is considered in this field.

Manmade Eutrophication

The relative importance of pollution sources differs depending on the region. Starting with Japan, the need for action against scattered sources (especially, agricultural waste water) in advanced countries has increased relatively. The base for eutrophication countermeasures in developing countries is basin measures such as waste water regulations and appropriate land use. Non-point source pollution, such as livestock, are also important, but measures for grouped sources (factory zones and cities) are so extremely overdue that they should be given relatively serious consideration.

Examples of water quality recovery in advanced countries (Lake Boden and Lake Maggiore) through the expansion and modernization of sewage disposal facilities can be seen. These are the base of contamination source countermeasures in cities. Sewage disposal facilities have also been introduced to regions in developing countries. Usually bilateral aid - such as OECF aid - is suitable in these cases. In nearly all of these cases, the target point has not been eutrophication prevention, and yet, in the case of Nakuru city in Kenya, sewage improvements seem to have helped in the prevention of eutrophication in

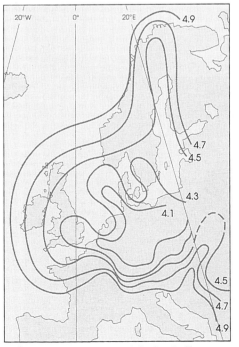 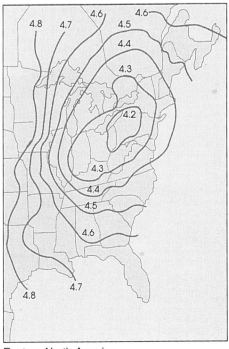

⊙ Acidity levels in precipitation in Europe and Eastern North America

lakes and reservoirs. Because a tropical forest was flooded for the Tukurui Dam, temporary but rapid eutrophication occurred. This problem should be examined as an environment consideration when dams are constructed from now on.

Furthermore, fish farming in lakes in Southeast Asia and China (notably, Lake Laguna in the Philippines) is thriving, which, in many cases, is causing acute eutrophication beyond environmentally acceptable levels. Many of the aid organizations heavily promote fishing (FINNIDA at Lake Tonle Sap, FAO at Lake Victoria, etc.). This type of aid must be managed appropriately from now on.

Transformation and Collapse of Lake Ecology

Endemic species are wiped out and ecology system structures are transformed dramatically due to foreign species overwhelming native species and multiplying in vast quantities. Cases of economic damage are numerous. Representative cases of quick-multiplying fish intentionally introduced to lakes are: the Nile perch introduced to lakes of inland Africa (for example, Lake Victoria), roach introduced to Lake Poyang and black bass introduced to Lake Biwa and Lake Ashino. Moreover, examples of unintentional intrusion of foreign species have been reported as follows: damage to char (troutlike fish) in the Great Lakes due to the intrusion of lamprey eels, damage to waterway facilities in Korea and China due to a kind of freshwater mussel and damage in Europe and the Great Lakes of North America due to the zebra mussel. The overgrowth of aquatic plants, such as water hyacinths and egeria densa is universal in lakes and reservoirs in tropical regions. These problems are basically due to foreign species. Eutrophication coupled with the extreme multiplication of species is causing shipping and supply water hazards.

A GEF project for action against water hyacinths has begun at lakes and reservoirs in East Africa including Lake Victoria. This is a large-scale project in this field. There is also an example of small-scale international cooperation at lakes and reservoirs in San Pablo in the Philippines where nature conservation debt swapping was used to combat water hyacinths. Whereas an interest is readily shown in the extreme multiplying of foreign species, there is a lack of interest and countermeasures for the endemic species driven to extinction by these foreign species. However, the GEF Biodiversity Projects at Lakes Victoria and Tanganyika are scheduled to tackle this problem.

These types of damage are fundamentally difficult to solve, and in many cases treatment of the problems has stopped at the manual removal of aquatic plants in dam lakes. This is why, other than the GEF projects, very little international cooperation is taking place for the problems. When future development plans, such as freshwater fishing promotion, are to be carried out, environment consideration, that takes into account these problems, should be made and preventive measures searched for.

⊕ Algal bloom with foul odour at Teganuma Lake in Japan

142

In the case of the above international cooperation for lake and reservoir environment conservation action, many organizations have involved themselves in projects aimed at improving monitoring capabilities and environment management capabilities; however, hardly any real action is taken as the exorbitant costs involved in action work are well known. In the case of basin action, there has been a large swing towards considering the environment when undertaking development projects. This can be thought of as being useful for the prevention of lake and reservoir contamination; however, there seems to be hardly any basin action that targets lake and reservoir conservation itself in developing countries.

⬆ Abnormal growth of exotic water weed (*Elodea nuttallii*, North American origin) in Lake Biwa, Japan

Lakes, wetlands and reservoirs are valuable in many ways as water sources, flood control, fishing, tourist and biodiversity locations. However, these values are not sufficiently recognized. International cooperation projects for the conservation of lakes, wetlands and reservoirs are limited; in particular, there is hardly any action being taken to directly improve water quality in lakes. In many cases, lakes and reservoirs are just being used for even bigger development schemes.

In the case of lake and reservoir related aid, all organizations - irrespective of the fact that they are UN organizations, bilateral aid organizations or NGOs - are inclined to favour working on lakes and reservoirs with specifically prominent issues, such as the Aral Sea, Lake Victoria and Lake Laguna. Moreover, coordination between projects being run in these places is not always sufficient. And, examples of international cooperation for the eutrophication and sedimentation problems faced by lakes and reservoirs in China are relatively few in comparison to the acuteness of the problem.

UN Organizations Programmes

A look at UN organizations involved in regions targeted for aid for water-environment related work, shows the tendency for African projects that need multilateral coordination because of the large number of international water systems. An example of this is FAO's distinct effort in Africa.

In the case of each UN organization's work portfolio, there is not much of a difference even though organization names suggest otherwise; in fact, nearly all the projects are carried out jointly with other UN organizations. Almost all the other UN organizations - such as WHO, the World Bank, UNICEF, HABITAT and FAO - are involved, in some way or form, in the areas of water supply and sanitation. Regional pollution prevention work or basin conservation action - including financing from development banks - are rarely carried out as costs are immense. All the organizations work to strengthen practical methods like training for environment awareness and system strengthening.

The reshuffling of international organization was among agenda of the Halifax Summit held in June 1995 in Canada. As there seems not a little overlapping among activities of such bodies as UNDP, UNEP and CSD, reorganization of them according activity fields, for example Deveropment, Environment and Humanitarian Assistance, was taken up.

The UN organizations' approach to freshwater in the 1980s was cored around the idea of "Safe Drinking Water Supply and Sanitation", which is shown in the Mar del Plata Action Plan. Starting with UNEP, WHO, WB, HABITAT, FAO, nearly all of the UN organizations became involved in "water" in the urban environment through the likes of service water and environment sanitation projects. Foe example, UNEP's programme for freshwater over the past ten years has been largely based around water quarity monitoring through GEMS/ WATER, a joint programme between UNEP and WHO, and management of international water systems that straddle the borders of two countries or more through the work of the EMINWA programme started in 1985. Both of these programmes target the promotion of sustainable water supplies and sustainable utilization (including the protection of drinking water supplies and inland water ecology systems).

In the case of environment issues in developing countries, the work of UN organizations is centered around improving combating capabilities for environment problems by strengthening systems and developing human resources - as talented people, knowledge and research are just as essential as funding and technological support for pollution prevention, environment conservation and education. On the other hand, the costs for pollution action (such as water contamination prevention) and basin conservation action (such as sewage measures and reforestation) are so immense that hardly any work is being carried out other than finance work by various development banks. Furthermore, there are only a few UN projects spanning five or more years (outside of normal financing conditions); in other words, long-term stable support is minimal.

As the UN organizations head toward the 21st century, the main water issue concerning them is the same as other environment fields - the realization of sustainable development (this was an UNCED issue). For this reason, chapter 18 of Agenda 21 (Freshwater Resources and Supply Protection Issues) is a clearly defined programme that proposes: a) general management of water resources, b) water resources evaluation, c) water resources, water quality and hydrosphere ecology system protection. However, this agenda does not have a priority order for action and lists very diversified "desired actions"; so, the UN organizations common target will be still "safe drinking water supply". As their effort toward concrete action for "sustainable deveropment", up to now, the UN organizations have been limited to "taking environmental considerations into development planning".

The following are the main action plans and statements concerning water extending across the 1980s from the 1972 Stockholm Human Environment Conference.

● **Mar del Plata Action Plan**

A UN conference on water and the environment was held at Mar del Plata in Argentina from the 14th to 25th of March 1977. The outcome of this conference was the adoption of 12 related resolutions (starting with the Mar del Plata Action Plan) as government policy guidelines that countries and international organizations should use in relation with future water issues.

The use of polluted water in developing countries is the cause of 80% of all illness and 33% or more of deaths. Therefore, the "Safe Water Supply and Environment Sanitation" item was emphasized at this conference from the viewpoint that safe water is extremely important for environment protection, sanitation improvements and poverty alleviation as well as being important for many traditional and cultural activities. The actual efforts of UN organizations during the 1980s was based on this knowledge.

● **International Decade for Water Supply and Sanitation**

The most notable result of the "Mar del Plata Action Plan" (adopted in 1977) was the inauguration of "The International Decade for Water Supply and Sanitation" (IDWSS) in 1981. A commonly agreed point is that all people have the access rights to drinking water of an amount and quality equal to their basic requirements regardless of status in development, society or economy. The aim of IDWSS was to offer safe drinking water and sanitation facilities by 1990 to cities and rural communities that did not reach the required level.

● **The New Delhi Statement**

This statement was made at the world conference for safe water and sanitation in the '90s held in New Delhi, India from the 10th to the 14th of September 1990. The statement emphasized the sentiment of "some for all rather than more for some" as a base for sustainable practices and recognized the need to create an access to sufficient amounts of safe water and appropriate sanitation for all people. The following are four guiding principles as plan goals.

1) Protect the environment and safeguard health through the integrated management of water resources and liquid and solid wastes.
2) Promote institutional reforms for an integrated approach including revisions in procedure, attitude and behaviour, and encourage sufficient participation from women at all levels in the system.
3) Manage community services backed with measures to strengthen local institutions for implementing and sustaining water sanitation programmes.
4) Achieve sound financial practices through better management of existing assets, and widespread use of appropriate technologies.

● **The Dublin Statement**

The International Conference on Water and Environment is the most comprehensive freshwater resource meeting to be held by the UN since the 1977 Mar del Plata Conference. This international conference was held in Dublin, Ireland in 1992.

The following were the main aims of the conference.

1) Evaluate the current status of freshwater resources related to future water demands and produce concrete priority issues for the 1990s.
2) Develop an approach that covers all coordinated sectors through the strengthening of cooperation in related work.
3) Construct a sustainable strategy and action plan for the environment in the 1990s.
4) The above issues, strategies and actions should be the base of each country's work, involvement from governments should be sought, and an understanding of environment and development issues in the revision of water resources management should be deepened.

The following six main fields were debated at the conference :a) Mutual Water Resources Development and Management, b) International, National and Regional Action and Cooperation Mechanism, c) Water Resources Evaluation and The Impact on Water Resources Due to Climatic Changes, d) Conservation of Water Resources, Water Quality and Water Ecology Systems, e) Water and Sustainable Urban Development and Drinking Water Supply and Sanitation (Urban Related),and f) Sustainable Food Production and Water Supply and Sanitation (Rural Development Related).

The Conference achieved the adoption of the "Dublin Statement", and the conclusions of that statement are reflected in the UN Conference on Environment and Development (UNCED).

- **Agenda 21**

Agenda 21 was adopted at the UN Conference on Environment and Development (UNCED) held in Rio de Janeiro, Brazil in July 1992. Agenda 21 is a concrete action plan geared for the 21st century. It depicts programmes for clearcut issues such as atmosphere conservation, ecology system protection and freshwater resources, and stipulates what kind of technology transfer, international structure and international law ought to be provided.

1) Social and economic factors
2) Conservation and management resources for development
3) Strengthening of roles in principal groups
4) Implementation measures

Chapter 18 raises conservation issues in quality and supply of freshwater resources. The following programme was proposed for these issues: a) mutual water resources management, b) water resources evaluation, c) water resources, water quality and hydrosphere ecology system conservation.

The UN Committee for Sustainable Development (UNCSD) was established as a follow-up organ for UNCED to realize the goals of Agenda 21. The immediate work over the next several years is scheduled to be inquiries into medium-term action plans, national and international projects, technology transfer/technology cooperation and finance. From previous experience it was agreed that each country would have to decide its own individual specific targets to realize the action plan. Agenda 21 requests that proposals be made as individual country action plans to enable each country to follow up its own plan. For example, Japan accepted this request and announced a national action plan in December 1993.

Official Development Assistance (ODA) Trends for Major Donor Countries

The 21 leading countries that are signatories of the OECD Development Assistance Committee (DAC) provided $57 billion of ODA for developing countries and multilateral organizations in 1991. Among this ODA, 80% was bilateral aid. Furthermore, OECD non-signatory countries (central and eastern European countries, the former Soviet Union and Arab countries) as well as a small number of developing countries also received US$4 billion in the same year. However, this was well below the figure of US$8.6 billion for the previous year.

In the past ten years, the aid amounts of DAC signatory countries has increased at a rate of 2.4 percent per year, so an increase of US$11 billion can be seen between the years 1980 to 1981 through to 1990 to 1991. This increased amount is mainly due to increased aid by Japan, France and Italy, with Finland, Portugal, Norway and Switzerland also making increased contributions. During the same period, only the United Kingdom, Belgium and New Zealand reduced the absolute amount of aid; while, during the same period, there was a slight reduction in aid by Holland, Australia, Germany and the USA in comparison to their GNPs. The countries giving the most aid for 1990 to 1991 were the USA and Japan followed by France and Germany.

For 20 years or more, the aid amount for DAC countries has continued at a proportion slightly below 0.35 percent of GNP. This low level is half of the internationally agreed target of 0.7 percent. This proportion varies considerable depending on the country. The ODA/GNP ratio for the USA is 0.20 percent and 0.32 percent for the UK. In contrast to this, the target ODA/GNP ratio of 0.7 percent is exceeded by Scandinavian countries and Holland. France, a country trying to increase ODA, has the respectable ratio of 0.61 percent.

More than half of the aid from DAC countries is for low-income countries. The EU, Scandinavian countries and Canada concentrate their aid on Africa south of the Sahara desert. USA aid is mostly for the Middle East (Israel and Egypt), Africa south of the Sahara desert and Central America. Japanese aid is mostly made available to Asian countries; however, recently, aid is beginning to be increased for Africa south of the Sahara desert.

UNCED also has an agreement stating that bilateral aid strengthening is necessary to promote sustainable development. Nevertheless, with the end of the cold war, the stagnation of domestic and global economies, and the need for emergency aid for poverty stricken countries, many of the countries giving aid are beginning to reconsider the scale and content of their aid. For example, in the area of how aid ought to be handled, the US Agency for International Development (USAID) in the USA seems to be refining a new overseas development system which calls for: "the overcoming of natural and human-induced disasters and the promotion of sustainable development overseas" as a feasible target for limited action in the event of reduced aid. At the same time, it is also strengthening its organization in a bid to become more efficient.

A view of the last couple of years shows that aid from advanced countries - excluding a few countries like Japan - to developing countries is decreasing rapidly. The DAC aid amount of US$6.4 billion in 1992 was an increase of 0.5 percent over the previous year. In actual fact, the USA's aid expenditure for fiscal 1993 and 1994 decreased by US$1.3 billion. Also France - a country that increased aid during the 1980s - has tended to make slight reductions in the aid budget starting from 1991. French aid for 1993 is 40 percent of its 1991 aid figure. The main cause behind this negative approach to aid expenditure is the global recession which is making fiscal administration in advanced countries difficult. And governments are also losing domestic support due to aid fatigue.

Countries, other than Japan, that are showing an inclination toward increased aid include Denmark, Ireland and New Zealand. However, the aid these three countries provide only occupies 2.6% of the aid figure for DAC countries. On this point, Japan is providing aid of approximately US$11.2 billion (1992), which is nearly 20 percent of the aid provided by DAC countries. On top of this, the Japanese government is expected to take a key role in making up the reductions of other countries as increased aid is planned for the five-year period up to 1997.

Water Related Projects

The bilateral aid projects of West European states are the same as the UN projects - namely, they are centered around improving combating capabilities for environment problems by strengthening systems and developing human resources. The costs for pollution action and basin conservation action are so immense that hardly any work is being carried out. A feature of cooperation is the application of homegrown knowledge, such as Holland's thorough support cored around wetland conservation.

In the case of water and environment related aid work, targeted regions tend to be defined as follows: West European countries spread aid across Africa, Central America and Asia; North European countries concentrate their aid in southern Africa (SIDA is also extensively cooperating in Asia and Central America); the USA - as part of government strategy - concentrates its aid on Egypt and Israel; and Australia targets Southeast Asia. The targeted fields are diverse but direct water quality improvement work is minimal. As well as bilateral aid through the organizations of concerned countries, there are many cases of multilateral aid through UN organizations. Depending on the region, project importance among aid organizations can be seen and coordination is insufficient.

Aid organizations of various countries - in the same way as UN organizations do - concentrate on capacity building such as developing human resources to help improve action capacity for environment problems. Whilst pollution prevention work and basin conservation is hardly ever touched as costs are enormous.

A feature of Holland's cooperation is its thorough water environment aid work, mostly in the field of wetland conservation. Even though this work is on a small scale, Holland makes good use of its specialist knowledge in the field.

Japanese International Cooperation Related to Water and the Environment

● **Official Development Assistance (ODA)**

The Ministry of Foreign Affairs, the Ministry of Finance, the Ministry of International Trade and Industry and the Economic Planning Agency are the main participants in Japanese Government development aid (ODA). This participation comes in the following three forms: 1) bilateral donations (gratuitous financial cooperation and technological cooperation), 2) bilateral loans (onerous financial cooperation), 3) investment and contributions to international organizations. Bilateral aid is mostly carried out via the Japan International Cooperation Agency (JICA), the Overseas Economic Cooperation Fund (OECF) and the Export-Import Bank of Japan (EXIM).

At present, OECF is the second largest development funding organization in the world after the World Bank. Many of the projects deal with infrastructure preparation and large-scale development of natural resources. Japanese consulting companies, construction companies and other industries (equipment manufacturers, etc.) are widely utilized for these projects. JICA oversees many areas of bilateral donations that are centered around technological cooperation. JICA also executes plan studies (environment impact assessment excluded) for OECF projects. EXIM provides credit and project loans along with the extension of other cooperation; it does not provide ODA for technology.

Japan also renders service as an important financier of multilateral banks. Japan is the biggest financial contributor to the Asian Development Bank (AsDB), it is the second biggest financial contributor to the World Bank (WB), the International Monetary Fund (IMF), the Inter-state Development Bank (IDB) and the African Development Bank (AfDB), and it is even a major financial contributor to the

Europe Recovery Development Bank (ERDB). Furthermore, there are many examples of Japan supplementing the funds of multilateral banks under the format of bilateral conciliatory funding.

● Environmental Cooperation

At the UN Conference for Environment and Development (UNCED) held in Rio de Janeiro, Brazil in June 1992, Japan made clear its intention to broadly expand and strengthen environmental ODA with aid of ¥900 billion to ¥1 trillion over five years and concluded a "government development aid outline" (30/6/92) by cabinet decision to enable effectively efficient use of aid. Consideration of the environment has become a major item, which is reflected by four principles that emerged from the above decision:

1) Environment and development coexistence
2) Avoiding the use of military services
3) Sufficient caution concerning the tendency to heavily invest in the military from the viewpoint that funds should be distributed toward reasonable priority resources for economic and social development
4) Sufficient consideration about the development of democracy and basic human rights

A view of the regions covered by Japanese ODA shows that the ODA range has extended from the conventional concentration in Asia to truly poor regions in southern Africa. Even though aid organizations in West Europe show a bias toward certain regions, their aid work comparatively covers the globe. Likewise, in water environment cooperation, OECF and JICA activities are expanding into various regions, such as Africa and South America.

Japanese environment ODA financed project examples (see OECF for details) show that current action is centered around human settlement improvements and pollution prevention through improvements to supply water and sewage. Another large part of Japanese general aid goes toward irrigation and flood control. These, in a broader sense, can be thought of as environment ODA. However, only a limited number of lake and reservoir environment conservation projects are being tackled (there are a few examples for Lake Nakura, but primarily work is centered around supply water improvements).

JICA's environment technical cooperation covers nearly all environmentally related fields (these fields are more extensive than OECF finance examples), such as pollution countermeasures, supply water and sewerage, waste-material disposal, forest conservation, natural environment conservation, disaster prevention, improvement of action capacity for environment problems, energy reductions and conservation of natural resources. A view of the technical cooperation content shows that a major proportion involves development studies, specialist dispatching and training. However, unlike the Canadian International Development Agency (CIDA) and the Swedish International Development Agency (SIDA), that positively support the staging of conferences and publish NGO booklets, JICA does not seem to aid low-budget projects that potentially reach many people or projects that require extremely detailed aid. In an effort to combat this problem, the Ministry of Foreign Affairs has established and consolidated a small-scale gratuitous aid system and the Environment Agency is opening the way to support NGOs in developing countries through the global environment funds of the Japan Environment Corporation (JEC). However, in the case of small-scale gratuitous aid, negotiations with local embassies are necessary for each individual item. In the case of the global environment fund, there is still room for improvement in utilization promotion of NGOs in developing countries, as they are still not that well known.

Moreover, in the case of multilateral aid for countries in one region, the majority of aid is distributed via UN organizations and regional development banks. There are very few examples of direct aid to regional inter-governmental

Japan's Official Development Assistance to Developing Countries (including Eastern Europe)

		(1990)	(1994)
Bilateral ODA	Grant	3,019.4	5,302.0
	Gratuitous Funding	1,680.1	2,402.8
	Technology Cooperation	1,339.3	2,899.2
	Governmental loan	3,920.2	4,257.3
	Total	6,939.6	9,559.3
Contribution to Multi-lateral Organizations		2,282.3	3,787.2
(Unit :1 million US$)		(1$ = 144.8 Yen)	(1$ = 102.23 Yen)

organizations, like CIDA's aid for the Nile Basin Technology Cooperation Committee and aid from North Europe for SADC.

● Water Related Cooperation

Conventionally, Japan's water related international cooperation is centered around technology and funding cooperation for service water and sewage improvements and disaster prevention, however, in recent years, technology cooperation for pollution action is being consolidated. Notably, there are few other countries that concentrate on aiding pollution action from a technology aspect. There are only a few countries that deal with a relatively broad environment field including pollution action, residential environment, basin conservation, disaster prevention, natural resources conservation and the improvement of combating capabilities for environment problems. In the case of support related to combating capabilities for environment problems, technical cooperation is being consolidated in recent years through training programmes for the strengthening of monitoring capabilities and support for construction of environment centres in various countries. However, within these environment combating capabilities, results in the area of government policy - such as capability strengthening in government policy - are limited.

Ordinarily, Japan's foreign aid is based on a request system from the viewpoint that the sovereignty of the recipient countries should be respected. However, the 1992 ODA outline demands consideration of human rights and the environment by recipient countries. From now on, an environment consideration condition will be also applied to aid that is unrelated to environment fields. As enormous amounts of money are needed for lake and reservoir environment action, projects that target such action are difficult to mount; therefore, from now on, sufficient lake and reservoir consideration through environment impact assessments in development work will be needed to achieve realistic lake and reservoir conservation aid.

● Need for Collaborating NGOs

Euro-American aid organizations, in many cases, have powerful cooperating organization domestically located for international cooperation (for example, CITEC's cooperation for SIDA). Also, each country's aid organizations do not just give aid to the governments of targeted countries but also makes positive practical use of international NGOs (for example, IUCN) and local NGOs (for example, AWB). This has given rise to numerous cases of low-budget aid - like staging support for meetings and production of extension development materials - that brings people into easy reach of the ideas being promoted. Nevertheless, aid organizations need large staffs (as seen at USAID) to strengthen this kind of aid. In addition, efforts are also being made to locally decentralize authorities for distribution of aid budgets in order to carry out aid more precisely.

In the case of Japan's international environment cooperation, excluding cooperative financing with various types of development banks, there are not many examples of Japan cooperating with UN organizations or other bilateral aid organizations. Furthermore, there are not many non-profit cooperation organizations in Japan that can offer organized cooperation. As Japanese aid is usually cored around hard consolidation work, consulting companies have come to fulfill the role of cooperation organizations. However, at present Japan does not have any suitable cooperation organizations, domestic or overseas, that aim to improve environment combating capabilities (like system consolidation and strengthening of training and monitoring) in targeted countries. In the case of accepting trainees, various types of cooperation organizations are being cultivated through the aid of regional self-governing bodies, but government organs and research organs only cooperate in the dispatching of environment specialists dependent on the conditions of each case - there seems to be no organized cooperation system.

In the case of Japanese aid flowing through NGOs, the Ministry of Foreign Affairs' small-scale gratuitous aid and the Japan Environment Corporation's global environment fund are continually being strengthened, but the scale is still small, and there have hardly been any results in the field of water environment. In the case of Japanese domestic environment NGOs, international cooperation is stuck at an extremely small scale because NGOs do not have economic power as budgets and human resources are limited. Moreover, environment ODA cooperation organizations have not yet reached the level where they can be sufficiently depended upon.

● Fading boundaries between domestic and international projects

In the case of transboundary environmental projects, as exemplified by a joint monitoring of acid rain, not only recipient countries but also the donor country can be benefited directly from the cooperation project. Another notable and very recent change in our working circumstances is the surprisingly quick popularization of Internet. Databases and forums on the Internet, as far as they are accessible anonymously, will benefit everyone in developed and developing countries even if they were originally developed for domestic use. This has a large potential to change the modalities of international cooperation projects aiming at provision of information which is documentable on a paper.

Sadao Kojima
Director, Central Research Institute
Nissuicon Inc.

1. Lake Environment Problems Facing Developing Countries

The following should be noted as lake environment problems facing developing countries:

a) Proliferation of water hyacinths

Since water hyacinths wither during the winter, this problem is not serious in Japan; however, they proliferate at tremendous rates in tropical lakes. When the entire surface of a lake is covered by water hyacinths, navigation becomes impossible; yachts are even prevented from returning to harbor. In addition, since the surface cover prevents light from entering, photosynthesis by plankton does not take place, causing the lake to become anoxic, and tap water to become malodorous. Many countries, including Zimbabwe (e.g. Lake Maclaine close by Harare), Brazil, and Costa Rica, suffer from this problem.

Although the removal of water hyacinths is practiced as a countermeasure everywhere, their tremendous proliferation rates easily surpass any human efforts. Collection of water hyacinths incurs a high transportation cost, as their water content is not less than 95%, and transportation is unavailable in many places. Furthermore, livestock are reluctant to eat them. In many cases, scarcity of farms in the vicinity often prevents collected water hyacinths from being utilized as compost, and transporting collected water hyacinths to remote farms poses the problem of transportation costs. In addition, the fermentation efficiency of water hyacinths is low. Burying collected water hyacinths in pits similarly incurs excavation costs. Once we attempted to feed grass-eating fish on water hyacinths; they eat water plants growing on the lake bottom but they do not pull off and eat leaves of floating water hyacinths; they eat only the roots. This is what the author observed at Lakes Kizaki and Matsubara. It may be, however, possible to raise grass-eating fish in a fish preserve and feed them on water hyacinths. It may also be possible to use the fibers of water hyacinth leaves as a raw material for paper, but this may incur problems regarding marketing routes. It should be possible, as a basic remedy, to simply turn floating water hyacinths upside-down and prevent light from striking their leaves, without taking them out of the lake where they thrive. Might it not also be possible to suppress the proliferation of water hyacinths simply by bunching plant communities of water hyacinths together with nets and thereby reducing the light receiving area? No solution may be assessed as genuine unless it includes a recommendation for the utilization of collected hyacinths.

b) Eutrophication of Dam Impoundments

Dam impoundments in the tropics easily become eutrophicated, which causes deep water to become anoxic. This phenomenon not only exerts great influence on the ecological system, but also the hydrogen sulfide generated through this process may damage turbines used for the dam. A typical case example is provided by the Tukurui Dam impoundment in Brazil, where the Itaipu reservoir, the world's largest dam, is becoming anoxic. The cause for this is a constant inflow of nutrition load from upstream. In tropical rivers, fragments of plants, not decomposed on the jungle forest floor, are carried off in huge amounts with muddy water; it is, therefore, impossible to remove nitrogen and phosphorus. It is important to note that those fragments are not a form of pollution produced by human activity upstream. Eutrophication of Lake Sagling Dam in Indonesia may be attributed partly to the influx of waste water from the city of Bandung; it should be noted, however, that even dams upstream of Bandung exhibit considerably high values of N.P. and green water surfaces.

When removal of phosphorus and nitrogen is not feasible, shutting off the light necessary for breeding of plankton can be considered as a countermeasure against eutrophication. Breeding of plankton should be suppressed by sending phytoplankton in the surface layer to the bottom, where light does not reach. This purpose should be served by circulating water through aeration by column pipes. This method has been put into practice at as many as fifty facilities in Japan with remarkable results; Lake Sagami provides an example of success using column pipes. Lake Kamafusa is another such success story. Electric power for pumping is far less expensive than activated charcoal for water treatment. A lake in Brasilia is among projects planned by the author. Circulating water requires energy for aeration, which can be met by allocating a few percent of the total power generation where power is available. This method, however, cannot be applied to lakes with shallow bottoms, because shallow lakes permit light to reach the bottom layer.

c) Eutrophication by Evaporative Concentration

Soil erosion causes not only earth and sand sedimentation but also eutrophication. With dry zones upstream, water evaporation from the soil concentrates nutritive contents during the dry season; the concentrated nutrients are carried off during flooding in rainy season to cause eutrophication. This could also be classified as eutrophication without pollution through human intervention. A typical case is provided by the Aswan High Dam, with a parallel example being Lake Mead on the Colorado, deep green water flows through the Grand Canyon. In Ethiopia, where soil over the entire country is said to decrease at a rate of 1 mm/year, even natural lakes are deep green in color. In order to prevent soil erosion, Ethiopian peasants place stones in their fields or plant different crops on the same land to prevent crops from being totally lost due to soil erosion or weather fluctuation. In the long run, however, afforestation would be the only way to prevent soil erosion. Should not it be possible to respray and recirculate eutrophicated water over savannas to allow it to permeate into the soil?

As a countermeasure against lake eutrophication, dredging is attempted, often without sufficient preliminary investigation; the effect is temporary and lasts for half a year at best. Elution does not affect deep portions of the bottom mud, because it takes place only on the surface of the bottom mud. To implement thorough improvement of the quality of lake water even in the Temperate Zone, a positive result will not be obtained without going as far as resorting to diverting influent out of the lake, as is practiced at Lake Mendota.

2. Consulting Activities in Developing Countries

In the case of developing countries, consulting activities that take into account the situation of respective countries are indispensable; there are many instances in which those things that a consultant takes for granted in his or her own country may not apply. For example, in many developing countries, there are plentiful supplies of land and manpower; materials such as cement, gravel, and sand are available everywhere. In such countries, labor-intensive facilities will be more welcome to the local people than unmanned water purification facilities. The process by which basic policies are determined plays a very important role in selecting a design.

In designing a facility to be built in a developing country, reference data are often unavailable, and designing work must proceed on the basis of estimation from qualitative conditions and circumstances. Let us consider one example; in Ethiopia, a water purification facility from France was found incapable of supplying the designed quantity of water. This was due to lack of foresight that the construction of a dam would result in eutrophication, causing plankton to increase, thereby halving the sedimentation rate of SS. In another case in Indonesia, two water purification plants were built at the same time. One of them, relying on the action of gravity, except for pumping operation carried out at the start of the purification process, worked for ten years without trouble; the other one, using machinery to carry out every process, often suffered from breakdowns. Designs such as that adopted in the latter case should not be adopted except in countries where established troubleshooting skills, technologies and parts supply systems are available.

What is important in the consulting business is "on-site thinking." An idea arrived at before departure from Japan can rarely be applied as is; one must think out aspects that one has never previously experienced before putting it into practice there. Ideas usually develop after one has stayed at the site as long as one month, applying repeated trial and error. Rarely is the cause of a problem clarified immediately after one's arrival at the site; frequently ideas are hit on in the course of discussion with one's partners. In addition, the site should be observed at different times (for example, both dry and rainy seasons). If the site had not been thoroughly investigated, in the case of the lake eutrophication in Ethiopia cited above, blame would have been assigned to pollution by human activity. In addition, a consulting team should be composed of members from different specializations, such as civil engineering, biology, and mathematics; people from the same field tend to think in a stereotyped manner.

It is of great importance in consulting activities to pay attention to details. A number of reports list several solutions, making the reader suspect that their authors lack confidence. Upstream pig-raising accounted for 60% of environmental load on Lake ? in Taiwan, our consulting firm limited itself to three solutions, as follows: 1) removal of the pigs from upstream to areas outside the river basin; 2) installation of column pipes in the lake; 3) water treatment using activated charcoal. Our consulting firm proposed each together with its respective cost estimate. In this case, the least expensive solution 1) was adopted and successfully implemented.

The most crucial factor in consulting activities regarding developing countries is cost effectiveness. It is the responsibility of the engineers of the country concerned to find cost-effective materials, such as bamboo substitutes for honeycombs for septic tanks; the principle may be international, but the technology should be local. For instance, in developing countries where installing sewage facilities is difficult, an alternative approach is to have household waste water permeate into soil through perforated pipes, if a spacious garden is available. Night soil treatment technology may be regarded as a technology developed in Japan, where sewage systems are yet to be developed and, in this sense, may be useful to developing countries.

One problem with engineers in developing countries is that they sometimes lack the capability to respond to a new situation. Let us consider one example. Egypt has long accumulated long-term water quality monitoring data and is older than Japan in terms of the history of its water supply; therefore, it is capable of addressing the problem of muddiness in water. However, it lacks the capability to analyze and respond to a new situation, represented by the proliferation of algae in the Aswan High Dam. We have seen a case of an Ethiopian water purification plant where lack of viscosity measuring units for chemicals lead to wrong treatment operation. Although using pipettes can be simply substituted for a viscosity measuring unit in this case, nobody carried out this measurement. It may be also a problem with local engineers that they are reluctant to do things on their own initiative, saying that they cannot do anything because of "lack of money and materials." Leaders in the developing countries, though university graduates, have never been to the site and know nothing about it; therefore, they cannot pick up the site staff's mistakes. As an example, the author would like to cite

a case in which the site engineers dug holes in sand as a countermeasure against slow filter clogging.

The balance between environmental preservation and convenience of life, as determined by environmental impact assessment, is also important. For Lake Toba in Indonesia, a plan is under consideration to increase the flow rate of River Asahan, the effluent river, by providing a tributary from another water source and thereby to increase the power generating capability of the river by 100,000 kW. Although concerns are expressed fearing possible changes in the ecological system, there is no doubt about the inhabitants' need for electricity. At best the actual concern is change in the color of lake water due to humic acid, the quantity of which is within the allowable drinking limits. Officials, both from central and local governments, should give more consideration to inhabitants. In addition, environmental impact assessment for the tropics requires appropriate technological development; for example, the quality of treated waste water is a standard of European origin, based on the water of the Thames, where changes in water quantity are small; on the contrary, Japan's rivers, which experience great changes in water quantity, lose their diluting capability during the dry season, failing to meet the standard.

(Translated from original manuscript in Japanese. ILEC Secretariat is responsible for translation.)

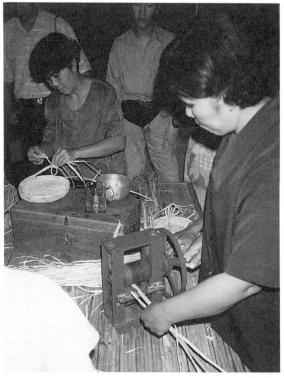

A trial at a rural community of Thailand to utilize ↻ water hyacinth as material for baskets

Masahiro Ohta
JICA Chief Advisor,
Indonesian Environmental Management Center (EMC)

For over more than twenty years, numerous international organizations (including, first of all, the United Nations in addition to other donor organizations) have steadily endeavored to promote the transfer of technology to developing countries. In this connection, a great number of projects have been pursued calling for countless meetings, the dispatch of consultants, and the expenditure of enormous sums of money. Technology transfers have been regarded as the key to the economic development of recipient countries. Despite this tremendous effort, the lives of citizens in many developing countries have become increasingly difficult and a great number of reports have been issued that focus on how conditions continue to worsen.

A recent World Bank report was intended to contribute to the progress of developing countries and regions by analyzing the reasons for the success of rapidly growing Asian nations. This report cites numerous reasons for this success, and provides a detailed analysis thereof. However, the primary reason for the growth of these Asian nations owes to a rapid increase in the level of direct investment by other advanced countries. Direct investment has served as the basis for the establishment of joint ventures through which needed capital can flow from the advanced countries to the recipient countries. Further, the advanced countries conducting these investments have brought in to the recipient countries the manufacturing equipment, technology, and technicians that are necessary to carry out production. As a result, high quality products are made that can compete on international markets, enabling the recipient companies to secure shares of these markets. The economic progress of these nations has been supported by the increase in exports resulting from these investments.

Viewed from the standpoint of recipient nations, the introduction of technology from advanced nations, together with the establishment of production facilities, has increased opportunities for employment. Moreover, through the OJT the quality of the labor force has improved. Finally, increases both in domestic production and amount of the total exports have set these economies on a favorable course of development.

One fact to focus upon is that anti-pollution equipment is regularly installed in newly-established production facilities, so that only an exceedingly small number of these factories have been found to discharge high levels of pollutants. On the other hand, most of the pollution in developing countries owes to aging factories established in an era prior to the creation of environmental protection agencies. It is also a fact that most Japanese companies which have entered developing countries are recognized as superior companies by technicians from the environmental management bureaus of each nation concerned.

In the course of these events, not all forms of investment have succeeded. Some recipient countries have claimed that technology transfers are insufficient, and investments in some companies have failed owing to differences of opinion with the management of the recipient companies. Other problems include the frequent occurrence of labor strife and walk-outs in connection with demands for higher wages. Nevertheless, in spite of these instances, examples of success that contribute to the economic progress of recipient countries are in fact far more numerous.

The production technology which has been transferred to rapidly-growing Asian nations has not been the "appropriate technology" typically promoted by international bodies. Rather, this technology has been similar to the high-grade, leading-edge technology of advanced countries. The use of this technology enables recipient companies to maintain high levels of productivity and product quality which are necessary to compete in product markets. Accordingly, these companies has had to make great efforts in connection with the OJT, and thereby has contributed to the improvement of the labor force. In addition, it should not be overlooked that the transfer of production technology has been accompanied by the transfer of environmental protection technology.

Following is a discussion of ideas for the methods to transfer technology:

1) First, instead of conducting technology transfers through international organizations and donors, it is much more effective for private companies in developing countries to pay money for the transfer of technology. The theory that it is possible for high-grade and leading-edge technology to be transferred from advanced countries to developing

153

countries is wrong. Moreover, it is natural that technology received by developing countries without compensation is less effectively used than technology for which compensation is paid. This especially holds true in the case of business technology utilized by private companies.

2) Technology exists in a myriad of forms, including technology needed by governments. Some developing countries desire the transfer of technology for use by the government. It is necessary in these cases to conduct an investigation regarding how the recipient government can utilize the transferred technology and to make clear the type of technology to be received. Recipient countries have typically lacked the mechanisms to utilize transferred technology. Accordingly, there are many examples of technology that has been transferred with much effort only to be unutilized or left dormant.

3) There are many examples of transferred technology which is unutilized. The reason in many cases is that administrative policies for the promotion of science and technology and the administrative organs in charge of carrying out these policies do not function well. Often, government decision-makers and other senior officials who possess high levels of education from the United States and likewise thoroughly consider what needs to be done. However, in reality the policies are not carried out on account that the government as a whole does not function well owing to the low-level of ability among mid-level employees.

4) One of the problems is the ethical views of government employees in developing countries. On account of the organizational structure, the future of low and mid-level government employees is in the hands of their bosses. In general, these employees have a weak sense of duty with regard to the pursuit of work aimed at improving the lives of citizens. Instead, these employees usually are concerned most of all with carrying out work to support their immediate bosses. Their work is to perform the duties ordered by their bosses. If they try to do something to contribute to the citizens, they fear being instructed by their bosses not to perform unnecessary work. Moreover, the bosses is not usually inclined to cooperate with and to support other administrative organs, or to lend assistance to private businesses. There is a strong tendency for these bosses to try and achieve everything on their own accord.

5) It is necessary to reform organs to carry out administratively-developed policies, to discuss mechanisms to effectively

utilize transferred technology to the full extent possible, and to develop a system for the functioning of these mechanisms. In the past, the failure of these mechanisms and systems to function has been the primary reason for the waste of transferred technology.

6) The JICA has emphasized technology transfers aimed at mid-level government employees and technicians in the recipient countries. However, despite having conducted these transfers, almost no appraisals have been conducted regarding how the transferred technologies were utilized in the recipient countries. There are many examples of transferred technologies that are unutilized. Furthermore, in the course of transferring technology, there are cases whereby no parallel effort is made simultaneously to provide the support and to develop the mechanisms needed to utilize the transferred technology.

The lack of effort to provide support is especially common among experts who actually perform the technology transfers. The function of these experts is only to transfer the technology, whereas whether the technology is utilized is decided by the governments of the recipient countries. There seems to be a trend of thought that utilization of transferred technology is not a matter to be weighed by JICA experts. Unfortunately, in many cases the idea of supporting the work of recipient countries to develop the mechanisms to utilize transferred technology is viewed as interfering in the internal affairs of such nations. As a result, there is no effort made to provide the neededsupport.

7) The fact should be realized that the mere transfer of technology is insufficient to improve the deteriorated conditions in recipient countries. A great amount of public and private investment is required in order to solve problems regarding the atmosphere, water quality, and the discharge of harmful pollutants. Regarding the money needed for maintenance of the environment, it is surely necessary in each developing nation to hold discussions to determine how much public and private investment are possible.

The financial strength of each developing nation is a key factor in regard to any discussions on the possible levels of investment. Nations in which the per capita income is U.S. $700 cannot be expected to contribute much investment, whereas in the event per capita income exceeds U.S. $2500, a significant amount of public investment becomes possible. Further, if per capita income exceeds U.S. $4000, experience shows that a large amount of private investment is possible. However, provided that a national budget is two or three trillion yen, the construction of a sewer system for the entire capital which costs three hundred billion yen is impossible.

The financial strength of each country determines the extent possible of organizational expansion, personnel increases, research facilities for environmental monitoring, research personnel, analytical equipment, expenses for the management of operations, and operating costs.

In summary of the above, suggestions are as follows:

It is necessary to clarify which technology transfers should be carried out by governmental organizations and which should be conducted through private channels. Environmental monitoring techniques are necessary for inspections made pursuant to the environmental laws. As long as government agencies in many developing countries fail to possess the technology needed accurately to monitor factory emissions, the environmental laws and regulations are just words on paper. In addition to the central government level, it also is important to increase the environmental administrative abilities of local government bodies, and to donate the technology to local bodies which actually conduct inspections.

Many environmental problems need to be solved by further infrastructure development, including the expansion of water systems, sewers, waste disposal facilities, and transportation networks. In these cases, the mere transfer of technology is not by itself sufficient to resolve these problems. It is important to remember these facts as such.

It is necessary to support the creation of mechanisms in each developing nation for the utilization of transferred technology. In regard to maintenance of the environment, a system is needed to conduct environmental monitoring, to inspect factory waste water and gas emissions, and to enforce environmental standards which are not in form only. Normally, this process is called "institutional development." The World Bank has made numerous attempts in this regard, but has had difficulty in succeeding in its support work in the field of environmental protection.

As an example, CIDA from Canada carried out technology transfers and dispatched over ten experts each year for a period of almost fifteen years to Indonesia. This work aimed at establishing environmental laws, environmental standards, and environmental administrative systems, but visible results could not readily be achieved. Indeed, this can be understood as the type of project in which positive results are difficult to achieve. At present, the World Bank is carrying out large-scale technical assistance activities for the environment. For a period of three years, over twenty consultants will be dispatched to BAPEDAL, but most likely this is on a test-case basis only. It should be understood that positive results are seldom borne in connection with technical assistance (in the form of consultants dispatched from advanced countries) often provided by international organizations which is limited to a short time and a specified field.

As of late, the voice of representatives of developing countries who participate in a wide variety of international conferences has become more prominent than before. However, it seems that there is an inadequate level of discussion in regard to the feasibility of carrying out the policies which are discussed or otherwise necessary. A discussion must be made which focuses on the feasibility as to whether developing countries can carry out the necessary policies.

In discussions made regarding technology transfers, using Indonesia as an example, few of the people from developing countries are interested in the experiences of how such transfers have been conducted by the United States, Japan, or Germany. This owes to the fact that the gap between these nations and developing countries is too great, and transfers cannot be realized in the same manner, so the experiences sound like a fairy-tale. However, people from developing countries can be expected to show a lot of interest concerning discussions of how technology transfers have been conducted in countries such as Malaysia, or Thailand.

In non-governmental organizations (NGOs) and the mass media, how to approach decision-makers and the importance of enlightenment programs have been discussed at many conferences. But these are not fields which easily produce results. A request for some innovative ideas is in order. Normally, the methods by which international organizations conduct technology transfers include workshops, seminars, study tours, case studies, other research activities, and small-scale technology transfers conducted by the dispatch of consultants.

The large-scale assistance furnished by the JICA in the form of financial donations and project-type technical assistance is not carried out by United Nations organizations. Moreover, the World Bank and Asian Bank do not provide support for OECF and other soft loans, so assistance will depend as before on small-scale project activities. Therefore, it is important to consider how to make these small-scale projects more effective.

The most effective means to conduct these projects is by limiting the purpose, focusing on problems in a specified, narrow field, restricting the number of persons to whom the project is geared, planning detailed activities, and widely announcing to the public the results thereof. When the purpose is limited, it is difficult to focus both on the project results and also on the activities which constitute long-term goals. Finally, concerning the importance of widely announcing results to the public, if only 300 copies of a report are issued then no impact can be expected. Some type of positive effect is likely if, at the least, one copy of a report is distributed to and carefully read by all of the bureau heads, department chiefs, and section managers in a single administrative organ of a developing nation.

(Translated from original manuscript in Japanese. ILEC Secretariat is responsible for translation.)

Chapter 4

◆

Deterioration of Lakes and Reservoirs

(This text is based on *Survey of the State of World Lakes*, Vols 1-5 (ILEC/UNEP, 1988-93), and *The pollution of Lakes and Reservoirs* (UNEP, 1994) and other sources.)

Freshwater on the earth

The world's lakes and surface water reservoirs are probably the planet's most important freshwater resource. They provide water for domestic use for a large part of the world's population. They are one of the major sources of the water used to irrigate the one-third of the world's crops that cannot be produced by rain-fed agriculture. They also provide an essential resource for industry and are a major source of renewable energy in the form of hydropower.

These direct uses are matched by important indirect ones. Lakes and reservoirs are a source of essential protein in the form of fish which provide 25 percent of the protein intake of many people in developing countries. They are important resources for tourism and recreation, and are home to significant elements of the world's biological diversity—one-third of all fish species live in lakes and reservoirs. They also play an important role in flood control. Finally, lakes and reservoirs are culturally and aesthetically important for people throughout the world.

Yet lakes and reservoirs and the environment of which they form a part—are in grave danger. Since lakes attract human settlement, pollution from agricultural run-off and toxic chemicals is increasingly common. Irrigation schemes are causing major fluctuations in water levels in many lakes and reservoirs, and deforestation—which encourages soil erosion—is leading to rapid siltation, thus shortening the lifespans of many major reservoirs. Acid rain has killed many forms of life in lakes in North America and north-west Europe, and the introduction of non-indigenous species of plants and animals has disrupted many lake ecosystems. Luckily, solutions exist to most, if not all, these problems. However, major and long-lasting improvements to the lake environment depend on people understanding the real value of their lakes and reservoirs, and the factors that affect these values.

There are nearly 14×10^8 cubic kilometres of water on the planet but 97.5 percent of this is saltwater. Fresh water accounts for only 2.53 percent of the total. Many people depend on freshwater lakes and rivers for their water supplies, and these sources contain respectively only 0.26 and 0.006 percent of the total volume of fresh water. More than 68 percent of all surface fresh water is locked away in continental ice. Figure 1 summarizes the world's water distribution, showing availability in terms of the percentage of total volume of fresh and salt water on the planet.

The availability of fresh water depends more on the rate at which it is recycled by the hydrological cycle than on the amount that is available for use at any moment in time. For example, while groundwater supplies are very large, they are recycled only slowly—on average, every 1400 years or so. The average retention time of water in lakes and rivers is much shorter: 1.2 years for lake water and 12 days for rivers.

In most parts of the world, the finite supply of fresh water is put to heavy use. Industrial wastes, sewage and agricultural run-off can overload rivers and lakes with chemicals, wastes and nutrients, and poison water supplies. Sediments from eroded land can silt up dams, rivers and hydroelectric schemes. Ill-conceived irrigation projects can suck dry irreplaceable

Annual runoff from endogenous precipitation in selected countries.

	Total (km³)	Per land surface (km³/ha)	Per capita (1,000m³/person)		Total (km³)	Per land surface (km³/ha)	Per capita (1,000m³/person)
Water-Rich countries				**Water-Poor Countries**			
Iceland	170	16.96	685.48	China	2,800.00	3.00	2.58
New Zealand	397	14.78	117.53	India	1,850.00	6.22	2.35
Canada	2,901	3.15	111.74	Peru	40.00	0.31	1.93
Norway	405	13.16	97.40	Haiti	11.00	3.99	1.59
Nicaragua	175	14.74	49.97	South Africa	50.00	0.41	1.47
Brazil	5,190	6.14	36.69	Poland	49.40	1.62	1.31
Ecuador	314	11.34	31.64	Netherlands	10.00	2.95	0.68
Australia	343	0.45	21.30	Kenya	14.80	0.26	0.66
Cameroon	208	4.43	19.93	Singapore	0.60	10.53	0.23
former USSR	4,384	1.97	15.44	Barbados	0.05	1.16	0.21
Indonesia	2,530	13.97	14.67	Saudi Arabia	2.20	0.01	0.18
United States	2,478	2.70	10.23	Egypt	1.00	0.01	0.02

ground-water reserves. Unlike the rapidly flowing water in rivers, water remains in lakes for months or years, and therefore is more easily polluted. Water quality in lakes can be quickly degraded if human activities are intensified and population increases in the drainage basin around them. Much attention must therefore be paid to maintaining lake environments in good condition and using their resources in a sustainable way. This means that not only the lake itself but also its watershed or 'catchment area' must be carefully managed.

The state of the world's fresh water is also closely linked to human health. Every day 25 000 people die as a result of poor water quality. Some 1700 million people—more than one-third of the world's population—are without safe drinking water. As a result, there are an estimated 900 million cases of diarrhoea annually, which kill more than 3 million people, mostly children, every year. Some 1200 million people lack proper sanitation facilities and at any one time more than 200 million people are suffering from schistosomiasis —a debilitating and sometimes lethal water-borne disease.

Surface area of selected freshwater and salt lakes

	(km²)
Freshwater lakes	
Superior (Canada/USA)	82,367
Victoria (Kenya/Uganda/Tanzania)	68,800
Ontario (Canada/USA)	59,570
Michigan (USA)	58,016
Tanganyika (Tanzania/Zaire/Burundi/ Zambia)	32,000
Baikal (Russia)	31,500
Great Bear (Canada)	31,153
Erie (Canada/USA)	25,821
Leman (Switzerland/France)	584
Salt lakes	
Caspian Sea (Russia/Iran/Turkmenistan/ Kazakhstan/Azerbaidjan)	374,000
Aral Sea (Kazakhstan/Uzbekistan)	64,500*
Balkhash (Kazakhstan)	17,301
Maracaibo (Venezuela)	13,010
Dead Sea (Israel/Jordan)	940

* before shrinking

Benefits of lakes and reservois

Lakes are important not only for their mass but also for their stability. Since river water flow tends to fluctuate widely, man-made lakes called surface water reservoirs are created by damming rivers, providing stable water sources for domestic use, irrigation and hydroelectric power, and reducing flooding in downstream areas. The number of reservoirs continues to increase. Japan, for example, has some 100 natural lakes with areas larger than 1 square kilometres but nearly three times as many reservoirs in the same size range.

Natural lakes are most common in the north of the North American and Eurasian continents, surrounding the Arctic Ocean: there are several million in Siberia and Canada alone. Most, including the famous Great Lakes of North America, were created by the scouring action of continental glaciers during the glacial period some 12 000–13 000 years ago. In addition, many shallow coastal and river lakes were formed along large rivers after the glacial period, particularly along the Yangtze River in China and the Atlantic coast of South America.

The largest lake in the world is the salty Caspian Sea. Lake Superior has the largest area of any freshwater lake. Lake Baikal has the largest volume and contains about 20 percent of the planet's surface fresh water. With a maximum depth of 1637 metres, Lake Baikal is also the deepest lake in the world (the Caspian has a maximum depth of 1025 metres.) Compared with these gigantic lakes and the other Great Lakes, most others are small.

However, the importance of a lake is not related solely to its size. For example, Inba-numa, situated in the metropolitan area of Tokyo, is important because it supplies domestic and industrial water to the city even though its volume is several million times smaller than that of Lake Baikal. The socio-economic importance of a lake determines the care needed in using it and managing its water quality.

As a rule, deep lakes with large volumes tend to be very transparent while small lakes often appear turbid because they are easily stirred up by the wind and overloaded by nutrients which results in excess growth of algae. It is obviously much harder to restore the quality of a large lake than a small one. Once the water quality and ecology of a large lake has been degraded, restoration is difficult because the lake water takes so long to be renewed. The value of lakes and reservoirs

Apart from their value as water sources, freshwater lakes have always been important to human life for other reasons. They serve as fishery grounds, recreation sites and avenues of transport. They also provide many other practical and aesthetic benefits. Salt lakes, which comprise about one-quarter of the world's large lakes, also play important roles in fishery, navigation and other areas.

Volume of selected lakes and reservoirs	
	Volume (km³)
Natural lakes	
Baikal (Russia)	23,000
Tanganyika (Tanzania/Zaire/Burundi/ Zambia)	17,800
Superior (Canada/USA)	12,221
Nyasa/Malawi (Malawi/Tanzania)	8,400
Michigan (USA)	4,871
Victoria (Kenya/Uganda/Tanzania)	2,750
Great Bear (Canada)	2,236
Ontario (Canada/USA)	1,638
Toba (Indonesia)	1,258
Leman (Switzerland/France)	89
Reservoirs	
Owen Falls (Uganda)	204
Bratsk (Russia)	169
Aswan High Dam (Egypt/Sudan)	169
Kariba (Zimbabwe/Zambia)	160

Mean residence time* of selected lakes/reservoirs	
	Residence time (year)
Natural lakes	
Titicaca (Peru/Bolivia)	1,343
Tahoe (USA)	700
Baikal (Russia)	380
Superior (Canada/USA)	191
Great Bear (Canada)	124
Michigan (USA)	99.1
Vattern (Sweden)	55.9
Victoria (Kenya/Uganda/Tanzania)	23
Biwa (Japan)	5.5
Balaton (Hungary)	2
Tai-hu (China)	0.65
Reservoirs	
Kariba (Zimbabwe/Zambia)	3
Volta (Ghana)	4.3

(mean water volume/mean annual flux of outflowing water)

Water uses

One of the most important roles of lakes and reservoirs is as a source of water for direct human consumption, agriculture, industrial use and hydropower. Human beings always choose to live, if they can, in places where fresh water is easily available. For example, in Japan, Lake Biwa and the river that drains it supplies drinking water to 14 million people. Much water is also used by industry, particularly in the production of iron, steel, paper and chemicals.

Freshwater use for irrigated agriculture accounts for about 70 percent of total world use. Since 1950, the world's irrigated and area has nearly tripled, to about 270 million hectares. One-third of the world's food is grown on irrigated lands, even though they comprise only 18 percent of total cropland areas.

Lake water is also a potential source of hydropower. For example, the Aswan High Dam began to produce electricity in 1967 and by 1984 it had reached 88 percent of its theoretical total electricity production (about 8000 million kilowatt-hours a year). In 1986 Aswan power provided more than one-third of the electricity used in Egypt—after reaching a peak of 53 percent in 1974, before other power stations were built—and provided the power for a new fertilizer plant with a 200 000-tonnes per year capacity and other chemical installations at Aswan.

Fisheries

Both natural lakes and reservoirs are important sources of food for local people, especially in developing countries. In Africa, fish comprise 20 percent of the animal protein in the average diet.

IMPACT OF THE ASWAN HIGH DAM ON FISH PRODUCTION

In Egypt, the combined fish production in the Mediterranean and the Aswan High Dam Lake has been significantly larger than that from the Mediterranean alone before the Aswan Dam was built. Accordingly, the overall impact of the Aswan Dam on fish production in Egypt has been overwhelmingly positive, and not negative as some environmental literature suggests. The HAD Lake Authority, charged with developing the potential of the lake and its environs, is now encouraging former residents to return to the area and helping develop the fishing and farming industries. Fish production through hatcheries and intensive fish farming is seen as having a major potential. Already there are about 7,000 fishermen on the lake. The main problem is industry and marketing.

In many lake areas, water transport is efficient, easy and environmentally sound. In some areas, it is the only practical means of transport. It is important not only for passengers but also for supplying goods to local markets and for moving bulk cargo, agricultural and lake products over longer distances.

Tourism and recreation

The UNEP/ILEC publication Survey of the state of world lakes, which covered 215 world lakes and reservoirs,showed that many world lakes and reservoirs could be developed for tourism.

This potential is increased if a lake has rare or threatened plant and animal species, unusual ecosystems, landscapes and natural processes, a high diversity of habitats and significant altitude changes across the site. Recreation and tourism contribute significantly to local, regional and national economies, both in developed countries (for example Loch Ness in the United Kingdom and thevEverglades in the United States) and in developing countries (for example Lake Kariba in Zimbabwe and Zambia, Lake Toba in Indonesia, Lake Nakuru in Kenya and Dal Lake in India).

UPGRADING TOURISTIC VALUE OF XI-HU LAKE

With the interfusion of picturesque hills, Xi-hu (West Lake), a shallow lake close to Hangzhou City in China, has been famous for its scenic beauty since Tang Dynasty (618-907 AD). Efforts has been made to maintain the beautiful lakeshore, and the lake has attracted many tourists. In 1983, an overall plan of the city was adopted, which defined tourism as an important function. Integrated countermeasures were taken by the local environment agencies to prevent the progress of eutrophication and to protect the world-famous beautiful landscape of the lake, which included: 1) construction of waste water treatment plants, 2) diversion of a nearby clean river water into the lake, 3) remove out or close down of industrial pollutant sources, 4) dredging of bottom sediment, 5) building of block stone banks to prevent the inflow of silts and nutrients by storm runoff, 6) replacement of diesel engine pleasure boats by battery driven ones, 7) removal of N and P through fishery and ban of baiting, 8) control of pollution caused by a large number of tourists. The interception of waste water and the diversion of clean water have fundamentally changed the balance of N and P in the lake, and the artificial nutrient loads were reduced by 71 % and 74 %, respectively.

⬆ Lakeshore of Xi-hu Lake, China

Biological diversity

Freshwater fish comprise about one-third of all fish species. The diversity of fish species in old lakes is particularly striking. In Lake Tanganyika, one of the world's oldest lakes, more than 250 fish species have been found, of which more than 80 percent are endemic. Since lakes are semi-closed systems, fish have no means of escaping from lake deterioration, and are therefore vulnerable to ecosystem disturbances.

The shore or littoral zone has the highest biological activity and productivity in a lake ecosystem, thus contributing greatly to the biological resources of the entire lake, particularly in shallow small lakes. On the other hand, human activities tend to be concentrated on lake shores, with the result that littoral ecosystems are exposed to disturbance and destruction. Moreover, because lake shores are frequently used by migratory birds, lakes can play a significant role in the ecosystems of remote areas in other regions.

Fish species in old lakes

Lake(Area)	Lake age (million yrs)	Number of fish Species	Ratio of endemic species
Tanganyika (Africa)	5-20	>250	>80%
Victoria (Africa)	0.75	>240	>80%
Malawi (Africa)	2	>260	>80%
Baikal (Asia)	20-30	40*	50%*
Biwa (Asia)	2	60*	20%*

* approximate value

Flood control

Tonle Sap, the Great Lake of Cambodia, is fed in the rainy season by water and sediment from the Mekong River draining the mountainous areas of Thailand, Laos and the Chinese border. Thus the lake, by retaining flood flows, maintains a constant flow regime downstream into Vietnam, preserves water quality there and enhances biological productivity for both the aquatic life of the river and for the human communities of the region.

In South America, activities in the Brazilian catchment of the Parana River, in particular deforestation, water diversion and mining, are causing concern for the future of the Pantanal, the world's most extensive wetland, which straddles the frontiers of Brazil, Paraguay and Bolivia. Furthermore, changes in land use within the Pantanal itself, including reduction in forest cover and expansion of cropland, have altered the flooding regime of the Parana further downstream along much of its course in central Paraguay and Argentina.

Cultural heritage and aesthetic significance

Lakes are often key components in the landscape of the region that surrounds them, providing diversity and a focal point for viewing the landscape. Landscape and its associated aesthetic values are difficult to recreate once destroyed.

Many lakes, large and small, have for centuries played a central role in the economies of their respective regions. Lakeside communities follow the natural cycle of the lakes closely, adjusting to the seasonal movements of fish, to vegetation growth and to changing water levels. In almost all lake systems, the local population uses a diversity of resources, including fish for consumption or sale, vegetation for livestock and construction, and the moist shoreland on which to grow vegetables and other crops.

PEOPLE AND LAKE TITICACA

Despite its altitude (3,810 m), people have lived around Lake Titicaca since pre-Incan times. Prior to the arrival of the Europeans, it supported a healthy economy based principally upon raising of alpacas and llamas, as well as fishing and commerce. Today an important population continues to live around the lake, and relies closely upon the wetland environment. The domestic herds are now composed of vicunas and cattle, and trout have been introduced. Submerged aquatic vegetation, "Yacco", is collected as cattle feed. Similarly Totora reed is used for making boats and floating crop beds, in handicrafts and as food. The fish biomass of the lake is estimated as 80,000 tons of which some 5,000-6,000 tons is harvested annually for direct consumption and local sale on the Peruvian side.

⬆ Totora stands and Totora boats at Lake Titicaca

Many communities use distinct sites for religious and spiritual activities, or value a site for some religious or spiritual occurrence that they believe took place there. This devotion to a site may be so integrated into the way of life of a community that it is not immediately apparent to outside observers. Lakes often serve as such sites. In addition, local inhabitants may have a strong spiritual attachment to a site because their family or community has used the site for many generations, or because it is associated with aspects of their culture. In many cases it is impossible to compensate for the loss of such sites which are, by definition, unique.

Lakes of the world abound in legends. What characterizes these legends is the fact that for humans water is something that is indispensable. They deal with animism - of spirits still alive - and a rare reflection of the old world where souls, ghosts, giants, dwarfs and goblins exist and in which the black art is believed. Legends, while they might be plausible, are different from historical facts. Nevertheless, legends are pierced with people's hopes and emotional logic and pull at the heartstrings of listeners.

LEGEND OF LAKE TANGANYIKA (Zaire side)

High on a mountain there was a rock mass with no grass and no trees. Birds would come to rest there. It was not clear what kind of birds they were, but they were big birds. As the bird felt thirsty they searched for water. They pecked at the rock with their beaks using great force and these broke with a snap. The birds died. When other birds came there, they did the same and also died. One day a little bird came and pecked at the rock softly. He demolished the rock speck by speck. After some time a drop of water came out. The little bird drank it. The bird kept pecking. Then, water suddenly gushed out in a torrent. The bird flew away and sang. People and villages that were not on mountains were all consumed by the water.

⬆ Lake Tanganyika

Six major problems

The report of the UNEP/ILEC joint project Survey of the State of World Lakes identifies six major problems that are confronting the world's lakes and reservoirs. In view of the growing importance of lakes and reservoirs as sources of fresh water, these problems represent a serious ecological disaster, comparable in importance to the destruction of tropical forests and desertification. The resultant deterioration of water quality and aquatic ecosystems as well as the decreasing amount of available fresh water is a global environmental problem in the sense that it is taking place simultaneously over much of the world.

Eutrophication

Eutrophication—a process of water quality degradation caused by excessive nutrients —is depriving lakeside residents of good quality water in many densely populated areas of the world. The development of treatment plants for sewerage and waste water have reduced eutrophication in many lakes in the industrialized countries. The recovery of water quality is not yet complete, however, because of the difficulty of controlling diffuse sources of nutrients such as run-off water from agricultural land and urban areas.

Percentage of lakes/reservoirs with indications of eutrophication problems in 215 lakes/reservoirs covered by the UNEP/ILEC survey.

Asia and the Pacific	54 %
Europe	53 %
Africa	28 %
North America	48 %
South America	41 %

In developing countries, most cities have no or limited sewerage systems. Enormous investments of money and time are needed to construct these systems. Some lakes in developing countries are now so eutrophic that many of the native plants and animals they once supported have now died.

EUTROPHICATION OF DIANCHI LAKE

In Dianchi Lake near Kunming City, the capital of Yunnan Province of China, heavy blooms of the blue-green algae, *Microcystis*, cover the lake surface almost all the year round, killing 90 % of native waterweed, fish and molluscan species and destroying fish culture industry because of the oxygen deficiency in lake water. Ironically, city water supply for 1.2 million residents of Kunming are running short, and the city began to take this hypertrophic lake water as a source of tap water in 1992. The first sewage treatment plant also started working in this summer, but its capacity covers only 10 % of the city's population. To rehabilitate the lake, the World Bank funded projects are going to start from mid 1990s. (see World Bank)

Proliferation of water hyacinth ➲
due to eutrophication

Water level fluctuations

Taking too much water from a lake or its tributary rivers results in a decrease in lake area and volume, temporary eutrophication symptoms and concentration of minerals in the water. This can damage industries that depend on lake resources and even destroy the lake ecosystem. The case of the Aral Sea, which has lost one-third of its area, two-thirds of its water and almost all its native organisms during the past 30 years, is a well-known example. Similar symptoms are said to be common in other arid zone lakes such as Balkhash (Kazakhstan), Chinghai (China) and Mono (United States). Increased use of water for hydroelectric power generation and irrigation led to a drop in water level of 18 metres and dramatic eutrophication in Armenia's Lake Sevan between 1935 and 1976. There are indications that even a drop in water level of a few metres can cause water quality degradation (as in Erhai Lake in Yunnan, China). Further studies, however, are needed. Two further examples of water level fluctuations are described below.

CASPIAN SEA

Although not so distant from the Aral Sea, the water level of the Caspian Sea is rising quickly in recent years. There is much evidence of the large water level oscillation of the gigantic closed lake in the historic past. A very drastic drop in the water level occurred from 1932 to 1945. The area of the lake decreased by 37,000 square kilometres, mainly at the expense of the shallow northern part of the Sea. All ports had to be adjusted to the lower water level. The fish spawning grounds reduced causing loss in the fish production. Salty deserts appeared in place of the lake bottom.

Since the end of the 1970s the water level started to grow quickly exceeding the lowest level by about 1.5 meters. Apparently, the main reason for the growth was increased precipitation in the basin. The economy has to adjust again to the higher and still increasing water level. Protection of the cities and other settlements are on the agenda as well as protection of railways and roads. Exploitation of the oil fields is also a problem. The case of the Caspian Sea indicate the need of long-term monitoring for basin planning. Were it not for the record of water level over a century, the interpretation of recent water-level rise could have been different.

◑ The Iranian town of Anzali inundated as a result of water level rise

LAKE CHAD

The shallow closed Saherian freshwater lake, is also suffering from water level lowering due to climatic change. As exemplified by the remains of sand dunes in the lake, the lake has experienced expansion and shrinking historically. The lake size was five times its present size several thousand year ago, while the drought years in 1970s made the northern half of the lake completely dry and turned the southern basin into a densely vegetated area with scattered swamps and open pools. The lake which until the 1960's occupied an area of up to 25,000 square kilometres has had its area reduced to about one tenth by the end of the 1970s.

O Lake Chad

THE ARAL DISASTER

The Aral Sea, once the world's fourth largest lake, now ranks only sixth. Since 1960 the Amu and Syr rivers which flow into the lake have had so much of their water diverted for agriculture that there is not enough remaining to counteract evaporation from the lake surface. As a result water levels has fallen and salinity increased. At present rates of inflow the Aral will continue to shrink and by the year 2000 will be reduced to two-thirds of its present size.

A half of the investments in agriculture in the Aral Sea basin over the last thirty years went into the irrigation. However, the irrigation canals are mostly unlined. The Sea has been shrinking since the beginning of 1960s while the salt concentration of lake water has been increasing. The former lake bottom is now a salty desert and serves as a source of salts spread out by wind. The environmental degradation, namely unacceptable drinking water quality, high salt contents of the air and, apparently, high level of the pesticides residue applied to prevailing cotton fields make direct impacts on the state of human health in the Aral Sea basin.

In the lower reaches of Syr River the morbidity has increased 20 times over the last 20 years. The infants mortality in a number of districts exceeds 110 per 1,000, that is three times more than the average for the former USSR and comparable to the figures for the least developed countries. That in Autonomous Republic of Karakalpakya is 7 times the all-Union level. Over 90 % of the population there suffer from anemia, the number being 60 times more than the average for the former USSR. In the Autonomous Republic 46 percent of women have genetic disorders of different kind and in its capital, Nukus, the breast milk of all the 35 mothers sampled was unsuitable for feeding. Clearly, the area close to the lake is in the state of the environmental catastrophe and the whole of Aral Sea basin is no much better.

Strict measures directed to water economy in the basin would allow the liberation of 35-50 km3 of water per year. Such measure include 1) reconstruction of inadequate irrigation systems, 2) reduction of irrigation standards, 3) removal of low-productivity lands from irrigation, 4) introduction of modern irrigation methods and systems of water management, and 5) decrease of the areas containing the most water-consuming crops. It is suggested this is the minimum quantity of water sufficient to preserve the Aral Sea as an integral productive ecosystem in its present condition.

Siltation

Many lakes in developing countries, both natural and man-made, are suffering from siltation caused by accelerated soil erosion from the overuse or misuse of arable, grazing and forest lands within their catchment basins.

Percentages of Lakes and Reservoirs with Eutrophication Phenomenon or Critical Sedimentation Problems

Region	Eutrophication
Asia and Oceania	54%
Europe	53%
Africa	28%
North America	48%
South America	41%

This occurs mainly because traditional forms of sustainable land use are rapidly disappearing with increasing numbers of people and the invasion of the cash economy, even in remote rural areas. In fact, the concentration of suspended solids in lake water is often closely correlated with the percentage of land in the catchment basin that is devoted to agriculture.

Lakes and reservoirs can diminish the destructive onslaught of flood crests downstream by storing precipitation and releasing run-off evenly. For example, Poyang Lake, China's largest freshwater lake, is surrounded by extensive wetlands and can store one-third of the annual flood waters from Jiangxi Province. It reduced the peak of the June 1954 flood by one-half. Dongting Lake and its wetlands provided a similar reduction for Hunan Province. Siltation of these lakes now prevents them from controlling floods so effectively.

SHRINKING OF LAKE DONGTING

Lake Dongting in Central China, which receives flood water from the Chiang-Jiang (Yangtze River) every summer, was much bigger (6,200 square kilometres) 150 years ago than it is now (2,740 square kilometres). The rapid progress of sedimentation and land reclamation works have since reduced its size, resulting in the formation of three more or less separate lakes, West, South and East Dongting. In the summer flooding season, however, the three lakes unite into a single water body of about 3,900 square kilometres surface area. The lake is now accumulating new sediments at a rate of 5 - 6 cm per year as the result of extensive hill-slope cultivation in the upper reaches of the river in recent years. This means that the lake with an average depth of 6.7 m may be filled up within some 100 years. This is essentially a symptom of disorder of the socio-economic system concerned which is especially difficult to cope with by technical measures alone.

○ Large-scale dike construction to prepare for water level fluctuation ranging more than several meters

SOIL EROSION AT SAGULING RESERVOIR

Saguling Dam was constructed in a densely populated area in central Java, Indonesia. A large number of households were affected by the project; about 3,000 households had to be displaced while other 7,000 households lost all or part of their livelihood bases, such as farmland and/or places of work due to inundation. The policy responses to the affected local population are, however, said to have been implemented in a haphazard manner as they were not properly integrated in the project plan. While the project proponent, the national electric power development company, was responsible only for the construction of dam and other related facilities, necessary measures for the affected people were entirely left to be undertaken by the provincial government.

The most serious issue to emerge as a result of this displacement was a further increase in the risk of soil erosion in the catchment areas of the Sagling reservoir. A large number of displaced people opted for resettling in the upstream mountainous areas, thus augmenting the already extremely high population pressures on the land. One of the consequences of this process has been the increased rates of siltation in the reservoir, which might have become much greater than originally estimated, thus reducing the effective water storage capacity of the reservoir.

Some strategic measures are being taken to assist the displaced population by generating income-earning opportunities through promoting non-land-based or less-land-consuming productive activities such as freshwater aquaculture, sericulture, and agro-based industries.

◑ Saguling Dam suffering from erosion and polluted inflowing water

Contamination with toxic chemicals

The toxic contamination of lake water, sediments and organisms is one of the problems that have not yet been overcome in industrialized countries in which it started, as typically shown by the case of North American Great Lakes, where eating fish is locally controlled because of the contamination with chlorinated hydrocarbons such as PCB and certain pesticides, heavy metals, etc. There are ample evidences that similar contamination has now spread in many developing parts of the world, but very little information has yet been obtained from lakes of developing countries. More efforts have to be made urgently to fill the information gap by a global network.

Contamination by oil is a particularly insidious form of pollution which fortunately occurs on a large scale only in those relatively few lakes where oil is transported in bulk or whence it is extracted.

TOXICANTS CONTAMINATION IN THE GREAT LAKES

Large amount of organic pesticides are used around the world. The main foci of use in the northern hemisphere are the United States, Europe west of the Urals, and the Far East. In North America a major database on concentrations and fate of pesticides in aquatic ecosystems is in the Great Lakes. In these lakes, in spite of their dimensions, organic pesticides are found in all compartments.   Highest concentrations are associated either with bottom lake sediments or with predator fish. Due to bioaccumulation of persistent toxicants, very high concentrations of specific toxicants have been recorded in a variety of biota. Because of this, human consumption guidelines for certain fish have been developed.

The concentrations of most organic pesticides in the sediments and biota of the Great Lakes declined, often dramatically, over the last twenty-five years. Nevertheless, for some organochlirine compounds, these declines have leveled off. Part of the reason is that the atmosphere has become a major source of some organochlorine compounds, now that terrestrial point- and non-point sources have been controlled.

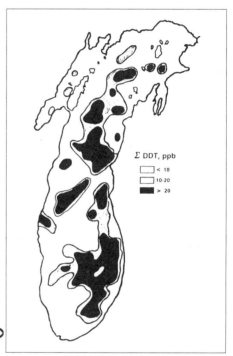

Distribution of total DDT in sediments (0-3cm) of ◐
Lake Michigan (after Frank et al., 1981)

USE OF COPPER SULFATE AT LAKE MENDOTA

One of the treatments to reduce blue- green algal blooms is the application of copper sulfate to surface waters. Copper in ionic (Cu^{++}) form is a general biological poison; however, by judicious application in relatively low concentrations it can bring about the death of algae without detriment to fish or aquatic invertebrates. This was the method used between 1912 and 1958 to reduce the incidence of blue- green algal blooms in the chain of lakes at Madison, Wis., U.S.A. There, Lake Mendota, Lake Monoma, Lake Waubesa and Lake Kegonsa are linked in a row from upstream to downstream of the Yahara River. Thousands of tons of copper sulfate were used over the 46-year period to create clear-water conditions in lakes. Between 1926 and 1936, 27-45 tons of copper sulfate were applied annually to reduce algal growth. These additions now lie buried in copper-rich layers of sediment - a useful reminder to future scientists of the futility of trying to solve man-made eutrophication   problems without cutting off the supply of nutrient-rich wastes.

OIL SPILL IN LAKE MARACAIBO

There are more than 5,000 oil wells in Lake Maracaibo, a large brackish lake in Venezuela, and the lake has repeatedly suffered from enormous oil spillages. The risks of spillages inherent to the oil industry arise from varied activities: perforation, extraction, transportation and the oil related industries, affect in many ways the Lake Maracaibo ecosystem. The lack of data from the time span before and during the history of oil exploitation, hinders the possibility of an evaluation of the effects that natural and accidental oil spills may have had on the ecosystem. Official actions for solutions have been so far ineffective,   since they are not supported by scientific data. Six decades have passed away without effective measures and concern to protect the lake basin.

Acidification

Acidification and the death of fish and other animals which it causes are so far confined to the lakes of north-western Europe and the north-east of the United States and adjacent parts of Canada. These symptoms are not yet apparent in other parts of the world which receive rainwater of similar acidity. The reason for this is probably related to the nature of the soil in the regions concerned, which has a high buffering capacity and is able to neutralize the acidity of rainwater before it reaches streams and lakes. However, the buffering action of soil may not last forever in such regions; eventually, the materials in the soil that buffer acidity may be exhausted if acid precipitation continues. Scientists are now trying to predict when this can take place in different types of soil.

Swedish and Norwegian lakes and rivei, were the first habitats to suffer visibly from extensive acid rain damage. More than one-fifth of Sweden's 85 000 medium and large lakes are now acidified, 4000 of them seriously. In Norway, fish populations had disappeared from an area covering 13 000 square kilometres by 1980 and been depleted in a further area of 20 000 square kilometres.

ACIDIFICATION OF LAGO D'ORTA AND ITS RECOVERY BY LIMING

The pollution of Lago d'Orta began at the end of 1926 when a factory producing artificial silk (rayon) with the cupro-ammoniacal method was established at the southern (upstream) end of the lake. Within a few years the chemistry of the lake water was showing clear signs of becoming uninhabitable for most of the organisms present. In 1958 a recovery plant was set up, and the copper load from the factory was significantly reduced. However, the factory was continuing to dump loads of untreated ammonium sulfate in the lake. It was not until the beginning of the eighties that there was a real breakthrough in the recovery of the lake by setting up a treatment plant. Also, a plan for a direct recovery intervention through spreading of natural limestone powder into the lake was formulated. The results so far confirm that the liming is bringing about positive changes in the lake chemistry and is also contributing to the re-establishment of a structurally more complex biological community. It is therefore essential to continue the operation until the permanent recovery of the lake is guaranteed.

⬆ Lago d'Orta recovering from acidification

The disruption of lake ecosystems

Lake ecosystems, and the fauna and flora they contain, normally evolve slowly over time. The sudden introduction of new species, however, can quickly upset an ecosystem that has been stable for centuries or even millennia. Equally disrupting effects can occur when lake conditions are changed—for example, as a result of excess nitrogen in agricultural run-off—causing a sudden eruption in the population of one or more species that were previously in balance with other members of the ecosystem.

IMPACT OF THE ZEBRA MUSSEL ON THE GREAT LAKES ECOSYSTEM

In North America the zebra mussel, a tiny bivalve species of European origin that sticks to any substrata forming dense colonies, was first recorded in St. Clair Lake in June, 1988. During 1989 and 1990, the zebra mussel was reported in all five of the Great Lakes. By 1991 zebra mussels had spread down the St. Lawrence River into New York's Hudson and Mohawk rivers via the Erie Canal and into the Illinois River via the Chicago Sanitary Canal. In heavily infested areas, dense colonies have clogged water intakes and delivery systems for municipal and industrial water supplies and electric power generation stations. They have fouled boat hulls and water intakes of boat motors and converted sandy beaches into piles of shells. In addition, zebra mussels can colonize and disable sensitive recording instruments such as pH and DO probes, causing serious problems for in-lake environmental sensing. The U.S. Fish and Wildlife Service estimates that Zebra mussels may cause $5 billion damage to factories, ships, power plants, fisheries and water supplies in the United States and Canada over the next decade.

To eliminate ships' ballast water as a means of preventing further introductions of the exotic nuisance species, the Canadian coast Guard first introduced voluntary guidelines for controlling ballast water discharges into the Great Lakes in May 1989.

◑ Colonies of Zebra Mussels clogging up a water pipe

ABNORMAL WEED GROWTH IN LAKE ROTORUA

Prosperous growth of water weeds causes serious obstacles for navigation and transportation during the growing season and, when drifted ashore, decomposing plants causes foul smell and deterioration of water quality in the lakeshore regions widely. In Lake Rotorua of New Zealand, the nuisance weed beds of Lagarosiphon major reached a peak in the mid-1960s. At present, L. major and Elodea canadensis grow in some sheltered areas and near stream outlets. Some danger exists that L. major and E. canadensis might be replaced by Egeria densa, which can thrive at lower light levels. Alternatively, reduction of phytoplankton populations because of reduced nutrient inputs may lead to a resurgence of growth by L. major and E. canadensis. The very recent arrival of Ceratophyllum demersum at L. Rotorua is likely to complicate matters further. It is possible that their spread and excessive growth have occurred coincidentally with enrichment and pollution in New Zealand lakes, rather than because of it.

INTRODUCTION OF EXOTIC FISH SPECIES AND INVASION WATER HYACINTH INTO LAKE VICTORIA

In Lake Victoria, following the introduction of an exotic Tilapine fish and piscivorous Nile perch, serious damage has occurred to the native fish community. The situation has become so severe that along almost all shores of the lake native fishes have not been caught during the past 10 years, and all endemic Haplochromine fishes are facing extinction. In official fisheries statistics, however, the present fishery yield is several times greater than that of previous years. Some cautioned against the future stocking of exotic fish species to any natural bodies of water; whereas others strongly favoured such introduction in order to increase protein resources. A researcher says that, formerly, small-sized native fishes could be caught by most native persons themselves, but that the exotic Tilapia and Nile perch are too big for the average fisherman to catch and are presently too expensive for native people to buy.

The latest nuisance of the lake is the invasion of Water hyacinth *(Eichhornia crassipes)*. Without its natural enemies, it has expanded explosively around tropical and sub-tropical regions of the world causing severe problems in rivers, lakes and canals. The rate of growth varies with nutrient availability and ambient conditions, but relative growth rates of 68% weight/day in the Nile delta and 2.5-20.5% plant numbers in Sudan have been recorded.

Water hyacinth affects lake ecosystems and lives of people in a number of ways. The first is that mats change environmental conditions beneath them primarily the reduction in dissolved oxygen levels, and thus limit the area available to the fish. In small water bodies this can destroy a fishery completely. In larger bodies it can destroy spawning sites e.g. Tilapia, and change the species composition of the water. On the other hand, there are cases fish food supply is enhanced at the edge of the mat by the provision of a habitat for shrimps and other fauna. The weed blocks waterways hindering navigation. It can reduce water flow by 40-95% and seriously affects irrigation distribution.

The weed originates from the northern rivers of South America. In Africa Water Hyacinth was first reported in Egypt in 1880. It was introduced in South Africa in 1910 and spread to Zimbabwe (1937) Mozambique (1942) Zaire river (1952) White Nile (1956) and Senegal (1963). In East Africa the weed was first noted in the Mukungwa River (Rwanda) in 1987; in Lake Kyoga (Uganda) in 1988; and Lake Naivasha (Kenya) in 1988, and was first noted in Lake Victoria in December 1989.

In Lake Victoria, water hyacinth has now colonized in the form of large mats mainly along the Ugandan shores which are shallow, sheltered and have a muddy bottom (that supported papyrus populations). It is also seen at Kenyan shores but is not so serious at Tanzanian side. The weed obstructs fish landing sites and village washing areas, fouls fishing nets, endangers hydro-electric power generation (Owen Falls in Uganda). There is widespread concern amongst fishermen and fisheries researchers that the weed will damage fish breeding sites. Preliminary investigations carried out by the Uganda Freshwater Fisheries Research Organizations (UFFRO) support these concerns. The situation seems worse in Lake Kyoga, the second largest lake in Uganda.

The invasion of the weed into East Africa has been so recent that no attempts have been made to control its spread. Though there is a general consensus that the weed is a serious problem, views on the solution to the problem are divergent and a general strategy for its control has not emerged.

In 1991 Ugandan government and FAO launched a short-term project to assess the situation of water hyacinth invasion in the Uganda Sector of Lake Victoria and Lake Kyoga. Global Environmental Facility (GEF) also justified its funding to the weed control projects as it fulfills two of GEF's criteria; protection of biodiversity and protection of international waters. The control projects include the following components:

- **SURVEY AND MONITORS :** Analysis of satellite images on a 6-monthly basis.
- **INSECT REARING AND DISTRIBUTION :** Setting up of five national centre for rearing, distribution and monitoring of bio-control agents.

- **AWARENESS CAMPAIGN AND COMMUNITY INVOLVEMENT :** Campaign involving political leaders, local authorities and beach leaders appointed by the fishermen. Information and training programmes for staff directly involved in the control process.
- **SUPPORT FOR CURRENT PHYSICAL REMOVAL OPERATIONS :** Provision of floating booms, tools, protective clothing and other equipment to assist and improve the current operation at those fishing beaches most seriously affected.
- **ADAPTIVE RESEARCH TO DEVELOP MONITORING INDICATORS FOR WEED CONTROL :** Quantifying the impact of water hyacinth on wetland ecology within Lake Victoria, and in particular its effects on fish breeding and nursery areas.

In East Africa an integrated approach using both biological and physical controls might be most effective, and the most promising uses of harvested weed appear to be as mulch, compost and fuel. Attempts have been made to interest people to utilize the weed for fodder, compost and mulch, but foregoing attempts show little success in terms of costs and benefits.

⊙ Nile perch at Lake Victoria

Prevention and restoration

Monitoring

The Global Water Quality Monitoring programme (GEMS/WATER), a joint UNEP, WHO, WMO and UNESCO programme begun in 1977, was the first of its kind to address global issues of water quality through a network of monitoring stations in rivers, lakes, reservoirs and groundwater on all continents. Technical cooperation with developing countries was the main focus of the programme's first phase, and this resulted in the establishment and expansion of national water quality monitoring systems in many countries.

Phase Two of the programme is concentrating, during the period 1990–2000, on data interpretation, assessment of global and regional water quality issues, and water quality management options. The number of monitoring stations will be increased and categorized as: Baseline Stations (located in headwater lakes or undisturbed upstream river stretches to establish background conditions); Trend Stations (located in major river basins, lakes and aquifers to follow long-term changes in water quality in relation to industrial, agricultural and municipal pollution and various land-uses); and Global River Flux Stations (located at the mouth of major rivers to determine annual fluxes of critical pollutants and nutrients from river basins to the ocean).

The long-term objectives of Phase Two include providing governments, the scientific community and the public with water quality assessments and information relating to the health of human populations, aquatic ecosystems and the global environment; and to strengthen national water quality monitoring networks in developing countries, including the improvement of their analytical capabilities and the quality of the data they produce.

Environmental impact assessment

Environmental impact assessment (EIA) is an essential policy instrument for incorporating environmental considerations into development projects. EIA involves a scientific and inter-disciplinary assessment of the possible environmental impacts that investments and development projects may have before they are undertaken. EIA is an important tool in making rational policy decisions. EIAs should be used whenever projects are likely to affect the lake environment.

The following issues, among others, have to be considered in EIAs on the lake environment: water quality and quantity, water input and output changes, changes in water level fluctuations, physical shoreline changes, vegetation, soil degradation, siltation, wildlife habitats, irreversible changes to cultural and historic sites, changes in water and land use, and population resettlement. As a guiding principle, it is important to remember that prevention is cheaper than treatment.

While EIAs have been made compulsory in many countries, their use in developing countries is still limited. This is partly because EIA methodology is difficult to apply in areas where there is limited expertise, resources, data and time. The OECD Specialist Project Group on Environment Assessment and Development Aids has estimated that 0.01 to 1.1 percent of project costs are spent in preparing EIAs in developing countries.

Sustainable management

Basin-wide land-use management is needed for the sustainable management and development of river basins, including the control of non-point source pollution. Strategies used to control water quantity and quality should be combined. Basin-wide management requires improvements in soil management (to reduce erosion and salinization, for example) which, in turn, require sound land-use planning for the basin as a whole.

This cannot be done without proper regard for the natural features of the basin, including an analysis of the processes that lead to environmental problems. Nor can it be done without considering the objectives and goals of socio-economic development in the basin.

AFFORESTATION AND SUSTAINABLE FOREST USE IN LAKE BIWA BASIN

In the southern part of Lake Biwa basin, gradual population pressure for centuries led the farmers to over-harvest their common forest lands. The impact on countryside forests was such that some were turned into bare slopes almost devoid of green vegetation. This was especially the case with the Tanakami mountains to the southeast of Lake Biwa where deeply weathered fragile granite prevailed as bedrock. The national government established with the inauguration of the Meiji era (1868) undertook to restore this area by introducing erosion control technology from Western Europe as early as in the 1870s. The work referred to as 'SABO', though still being continued today, has been largely successful, allowing pine forests to recover steadily. A considerable part of the existing pine forests is a result of his long-term effort.

◑ Bold mountains a century before

◑ Stepping for planting

In the northern part of the basin, deciduous forests distant from villages had been used to supply local people and urban residents with firewood and, above all, charcoal as an industrial and domestic energy source. The forest was cut once every 20-30 years for charcoal production, and left for natural regeneration by suckers sprouting from stumps. Repeated cuttings over the centuries led to the survival only of tree species with vigorous sprouting habits. Regeneration was permanently assured, and took place so rapidly that soil erosion and degradation remained negligible even on steep slopes. This was therefore an ideal type of sustainable energy forest in that it could be used permanently and protected the watershed slopes from devastation, though the use of charcoal and firewood as energy source is now negligibly small in present-day Japan.

◑ Charcoal wood forest sustainably used for hundreds years

Physical and legislative restoration measures

The deterioration of lake and reservoir environments occurs in both advanced and developing countries. Moreover, a feature of these problems is that they not only occur in industrial zones and densely populated zones but also in areas not heavily touched by human economics. Nearly all regions of the world there are lakes and reservoirs caught up in some sought of environment problem.

For these problems, various physical measures and waste water regulations are not only implemented by advanced countries but also by developing countries too. A general view of these measures is shown below. They are just a very small portion of the effort being made around the world, nevertheless, the action content of both advanced and developing countries have the following features.

- Sewage treatment is a fundamental way of water quality conservation in all countries.
- Water conveyance and sewage watercourse alterations are being carried out in some way even by developing countries.

- Afforestation as a base for basin action is being tested even by developing countries; however, it is not clear whether the scale of planting is enough to gain results.
- There are attempts to apply ecological engineering in both developed and developing countries; however, these actions all seem to be at the experimental stage.
- Water hyacinth measures can only be seen in developing countries as this problem is peculiar to tropical lakes and reservoirs.
- Acid lakes and reservoirs are limited to advanced countries.
- Overall countermeasure, like those for Lake Valencia in Venezuela, that include basinwide management, are being planned at some lakes in developing countries. However, a basic problem with developing countries is the failure to realize these plans.

Example of physical and legislative restoration measures for lakes and reservoirs.

	Developing countries	Developed countries
"EXTERNAL" CONTROL MEASURES		
1) Protection of catchment area		
a) Control of hydrological cycle and soil erosion		
• afforestation in upstream areas	Dian-chi(China) Chao-hu (China)	
• hillside work (Sabo)		Biwa (Japan)
• installation of buffer-zone between agricultural land and watershore	Broa Res. (Brazil)	Swedish lakes
• contour cropping	Barra Bonita Res.(Brazil)	Swedish lakes
b) Land use regulation		
• stringent regulation of land use		Tahoe(USA)
• moving of pollutant sources out of the basin	Feitsui Res. (Taiwan)	Balaton (Hungary)
• ban of reclamation		Constance (Germany)
• closedown of pollutant-emitting factories		Baikal (Russia)
c) Sewage treatment		
• construction of large-scale treatment plant	Dian-chi (China)	Maggiore (Italy)
• construction of oxidation pond	Ya-er (China)	
• small-scale wastewater treatment plant		Nakaumi (Japan)
• use of septic tank		Biwa (Japan)
• diversion of sewage outlets	Dong-hu (China) McIlwaine (Zimbabwe)	Washington (USA) Tahoe (USA)
• livestock waste treatment facilities		Furen (Japan)
• methane fermentation of domestic waste-water	Chao-hu (China)	
• regulation of the use of agrochemicals	Kinneret (Israel)	
• ban on toxic substance discharge		Great Lakes (USA) Orta (Italy)

2) Nutrient control in inflowing river waters

• use of wetlands for wastewater treatment	Victoria (Uganda)	Balaton (Hungary)
• establishment of coordination units for international river/lake basin countries		Rhine River basin
• ban on phosphate-containing detergent		Great lakes (USA)
• control of waste discharge from enterprises		Myosa (Sweden)
• embankment for prevention of polluted water inflow.	Xi-hu (China)	Rotorua (New Zealand)
• effective use of agricultural fertilizers	Tota (Columbia)	Shinji (Japan)
• recycling of treated water to afforested areas	San Roque Res. (Argentina)	
• nightsoil treatment facilities		Biwa (Japan)

"INTERNAL" CONTROL MEASURES

1) Physical Manipulations

a) Mixing and thermal destratification

• improvement of lake water turnover	Bled (Slovenia)	
• introduction of clean water to lakes	Xi-hu (China)	Ijsell (Netherland)

b) Aeration, hypolimnetic oxygen inflation

• Lake bottom aeration		Baldeggar (Switzerland)
• Forced vertical mixing of reservoir water		Sagami (Japan)

c) Release prevention form sediments

• Sediment removal by dredging	Beira (Sri Lanka)	Trumen (Sweden)
• Sediment sealing with sand layer		Biwa (Japan)

2) Biological measures

a) Mechanical and chemical removal

• harvesting water weeds	Sagling Res. (Indonesia)	Leman (Switzerland)
• harvesting blue-green algae		Inba-numa (Japan)
• killing algae		Mendota (USA)
• killing water hyacinth	Kariba (Zimbabwe/Zambia)	

b) biomanipulation and protectionl

• manipulation of food chain		small lakes in Europe
• release of grazing fish for water weed control	Dong-hu (China)	
• use of grasshoppers for water hyacinth control	Kariba(Zimbabwe/Zambia)	
• water-level control for vegetation protection	Chao-hu (China)	
• lake shore vegetation protection	Victoria (Uganda)	Neusiedler (Austria)
• restriction of navigation for protecting lakeshore vegetation		Taupo (New Zealand)

c) Chemical measures

• liming		Orta (Italy)

• Not all of the measures are successful. Some turned out to be ineffective, and others too costly or experimental.

• Division of advanced countries and developing countries depends on the criteria of the OECD Development Assistance Committee.

○ Lake Maggiore recovered by diversion of sewarage system

EUTROPHICATION MEASURES AT LAKE KASUMIGAURA

Lake Kasumigaura, the second largest lake in Japan (surface area 220 sq.km, maximum depth 7m) located about 60 km northeast of Tokyo and not far from Tsukuba Science City, is a typical case of eutrophication and efforts for rehabilitation.

An increase in population and industrialization around the basin places a high demand on the water resource. Therefore, the Kasumigaura development project started in 1971 for water resources development and flood control. Now the lake supplies water to the Kashima Coastal Industrial Zone and the Tokyo metropolitan area.

Rapid water quality deterioration of the lake started around 1970, followed in 1973 by an unusual bloom of *Microcystis*. This disturbed filtration in clearing beds, foul smelling tap water, and depressed fish production (carp aquaculture). It has been proposed that the construction of salinity barrier during the above development project accelerated eutrophication.

The lake experienced two peaks of water quality deterioration in 1973 and 1978. The major pollutant sources were domestic effluents and discharges from industries, municipal nightsoil disposal facilities, pig farms, and carp aquaculture. The first peak was overcome by enforcement of stringent effluent standard in 1974 while construction of sewage and animal waste treatment facilities were among measures taken after the second peak. In 1981, the Eutrophication Prevention Act was enforced by the Ibaraki Prefectural Government l. In 1985 the lake became a 'designated lake' under the 'Clean Lakes Law'.

In response to such efforts, nutrient loading gradually declined with a decrease of 30% in COD loading between 1979 and 1991. Nevertheless, the COD value of the lake in 1992 (7.4mg/L) was above the national environmental standard (3mg/L for this type of lake). From 1992 the lake again indicated deteriorating signs. In order to control the problem, the coverage of public sewage will increase from 33.4% in 1992 to 58.7% by the year 2000. Another point is to connect more households with the already-constructed system because households already equipped with treatment septic-tanks are often not willing to put their share of expenses into sewage construction.

In areas without a public sewage system, septic-tank treatment is the alternative. However, the treatment efficiency of the conventional type which receives only human waste is far from satisfactory, and moreover, those tanks are often not maintained properly. It has been proposed to replace them with the new combined-type which also collects domestic wastewater.

Among COD loading in 1990, domestic waste occupies 44%, non-point sources 33%, industries 4%, animal (pig) husbandry 12.0%, and carp aquaculture 7%, respectively. To reduce fishery loading, the Prefecture recommends to transfer the aquaculture ponds outside the lake by constructing new ones at abondaned paddy fields.

Reduction of non-point loadings: Even before deterioration become serious, the lake was already eutrophic (COD 3mg/L) and most of loadings were probably from non-point sources. Appropriate use of fertilizers and irrigation water is required to agricultural sectors. For example, some measures are needed to lotus cultivation which is becoming popular as a substitute for rice farming at muddy areas, because the former requires 10 times more fertilizers than the latter. Studies are also being made to utilize abandoned rice paddy as nutrient trap wetlands.

The Ministry of Construction has been engaged to dredge 7.2 million cubic meters of sediments (out of total 40 million) from the lake and estuaries of main inflowing rivers by year 2000, hence reducing COD loading by 0.9mg/L. Dilution by introducing clean water to the lake from rivers is also made. The Ministry has also begun incorporating ecological considerations such as conservation of reed beds into their embankment work to maintain the biodiversity of the lakeshore.

In the basin, a few dozens of citizen groups are active with conservation activities. They are promoting nature observations, bio-monitoring, cooperation in ecological census by national and local government. In 1981 a coalition of these groups was established. Local private firms are also cooperating in their activities by establishing a foundation in 1992 to subsidizing citizens' activities. In order to make the public more aware, campaigns are being carried out jointly by the prefectural government and the Association of Kasumigaura Basin Municipalities. A few of the campaigns are as following:

- Promotion of non-phosphorus detergents and demonstration on making home soap from wasste food oil.
- Citizen's participation in lakeshore cleanup (in 1992 total 160,000 citizens participated in the half-yearly cleaning events)
- Lakeshore municipalities designate each 10 specialists to watch water quality and illegal garbage dumping. Training on simple monitoring techniques is given to them.
- A campaign organized to address the importance of small efforts in daily life such as the use of fine-mesh strainer and, not disposing of cooking garbage and oil as sewage.
- A long-distance swimming meet is held every year in the lake to encourage people to experience the real lake water quality.

As a part of the awareness effort, Ibaraki Prefectural Government jointly with ILEC is to hold the 6th International Conference on the Conservation and Management of Lakes (Kasumigaura '95) on the shore of the lake in October 1995. In addition to the participating sectors (administrators, residents and scientists) of foregoing conferences, business sectors are newly involved in the 6th Conference. Moreover, both environment and development sides (Environment Agency and Ministry of Construction) are actively supporting the Conference, thus making the conference an arena for stakesholders' dialogue.

↟ Citizens participating in shore clean-up

Ecotechnology

The pollution of lakes is a complex problem and can rarely be solved by the use of a single method. Ecotechnology—also named ecological engineering—has emerged as an alternative technological approach during the past decade, due to the failure of conventional environmental technology. Ecotechnology exploits the self-purification capabilities of lakes and their immediate environment—for example, wetlands can be used to purify polluted water and forests to stabilize erosion and an erratic water regime. Ecotechnology offers a wide spectrum of possibilities, but it must be used hand-in-hand with environmental technology to achieve the best possible result. This approach can be used to deal with non-point sources of pollution or to return degraded lakes to their natural balance.

USE OF WETLANDS FOR WASTEWATER TREATMENT

The water quality of Lake Balaton deteriorated in the last few decades through eutrophication. To reduce nutrient loading, a reservoir (wetland) was constructed on the Zala River in 1985, which has a surface area of 18 square kilometres, a mean depth of 1.14 m and a water retention time of 44 days. The load reduction efficiencies of the reservoir were the following: suspended solids 12-82 %, total nitrogen 16-25 %, NO_3-N 57-69 %, total phosphorus 38-52 %, PO_4-P 57-90 %, by summer denitrification, direct adsorption to the sediment and incorporation into macrophytes. Construction of the second reservoir downstream from the first one is in preparation.

In Lake Kinneret (Sea of Galilee) in Israel, in the past, the main stream flowing into the lake used to pass through the papyrus swamps of the Hula valley which trapped sediments and stripped nutrients from the water. Since reclamation of the swamps for agriculture, a delta of sediment has developed in Lake Kinneret, and turbidity has increased. With loss of the filtering capacity of the swamp and release of nitrogen from the mineralized peat, concentrations of nitrates are also rising.

In Uganda, the National Sewerage and Water Corporation is supporting conservation of papyrus swamps and other wetlands in the Kampala area because of the role that these play in nutrient trapping. The cost of replacing the tertiary wastewater treatment services provided by marshes in Massachusetts has been calculated at about US$123,000/ha, and for the removal of phosphorous alone, US$47,000/ha.

⬆ Artificially constructed wetland at a river-mouth flowing into Lake Balaton

Appropriate technologies

While technology transfer is generally thought of as having a North-South focus, much more needs to be done to improve international communication between all scientists and managers in both the northern and southern sectors. The opportunities to apply this knowledge more widely also need to be enhanced. For example, lake management experiences in China may be applicable to other developing countries.

The Hungarian experience of using wetlands for nutrient retention in place of costly treatment plants may benefit countries with large areas of cheap land. However, some measures that are effective for one lake may not be applicable to others. Technologies should be selected carefully according to the economic, technical and cultural conditions of the area concerned.

AQUATIC AGRICULTURE - AN EXPERIMENTAL ECOTECHNOLOGY FOR SUSTAINABLE LAKE USE

Tai-hu Lake, the third largest freshwater lake in China, is facing two serious and difficult requirements to increase both the aquatic productivity and water quality of the lake, to meet the growing population of the basin. For optimizing the food chain, AQUATIC AGRICULTURE, integrated fish culture methods with complex composition of fish species and integrated food feeding, have been developed by Chinese researchers. Some selected submerged plants cultured in surrounding area are used as the food for fish in the fish-pen. The places for plant culture and fish culture may be alternatively changed year by year for water quality conservation, because nutrient-rich sediments under fish-pen serves as fertilizers for aquatic plants. Aquatic plants also help reducing wind wave, improving water quality by absorbing nutrients and increasing dissolved oxygen in water. The annual productivity of 22-30 ton/hm2 is estimated as an economically reasonable value at this moment.

Biomanipulation

The structure of the food-web has a decisive influence on the water quality of ponds, lakes and reservoirs. Biomanipulation is a kind of biological engineering which attempts to reconstruct the ecosystem by using biological as well as, or instead of nutrient reduction to reduce the algal crops. The hope to possess a simple and cheap solution for the complicated and expensive pollution problem of eutrophication was certainly one of the reasons for the tremendous increase in biomanipulation research during the last fifteen years.

A HISTORY OF SUCCESS AND DISAPPOINTMENT

Analysis of 33 examples indicates that the basic assumptions of the biomanipulation concept have general validity in all types of standing waters, although experiments in small and shallow lakes are more likely to be successful:

- enhancement in standing stocks of fish-eating fish
- decrease in the standing stocks of plankton-eating fish
- increase of macrophyte standing stocks in shallow lakes
- increase in water transparency
- reduction of total phosphorus concentration

Nevertheless, success and disappointment are not widely separated, because every top-down mechanism is accompanied by a counteracting bottom-up effect, creating a complex system of structures and nonlinear processes which is difficult to control:

- the creation and stabilization of a strong population of piscivorous fish is difficult and time-consuming
- the population of planktivorous fish is sometimes difficult to control and tends to reestablish high standing stocks
- except for poisoning the fish community, the food-web impulse established by manual removal of zooplanktivorous fish and/or introduction of piscivorous fish is sometimes too weak to evoke strong reactions
- the extent to which planktivorous fish have to be removed depends considerably on the species and size composition of the fish community

- due to very different turnover times of the organisms a new and stable equilibrium may require several years to develop
- phytoplankton is usually treated as a homogeneous group. Differences are only considered with respect to the nutritional value for suspension feeding zooplankton;
- as the grazing pressure increases, the phytoplankton community tends to develop several defense mechanisms
- with increasing phosphorus concentration, the probability for successful biomanipulation decreases ;

Comparing the encouraging results with the disappointing ones, it sometimes seems that biomanipulation as a lake management concept is lost before it matures. To prevent biomanipulation being lost as a lake management concept, the only way to reach this aim may be the reunilication of the loading and the biomanipulation concept and the integration of indirect mechanisms. From an ecological point of view it is a careful method and it needs little additional energy to function, because sunlight is the main driving force.

Publicizing the benefits of lakes

While many people benefit from lakes and reservoirs, few appreciate their real value. Unless this is changed, and people are made aware of the actions needed to maintain these benefits, preventive and remedial measures may not be taken. As no two lakes share the same natural and socio-economic circumstances, the prescriptions for sustainable lake use also differ for each lake. The exchange of information about successes and failures in lake management are therefore of great importance.

SCHOOL TEACHERS' TRAINING IN NATURAL LABORATORIES

The University of Sao Paulo in Brazil started the training of school teachers in 1986 with the aim to reinforce their understanding of sustainable watershed management and to exploit the possibilities to use their local watersheds as a natural laboratory. During a 10 day field and laboratory work groups of 20-25 school teachers were trained in recognizing sub-systems (watershed-rivers, reservoirs, wetlands, gallery forest, impacts (mining, deforestation) and human uses of the watershed). A strong emphasis was placed on processes and techniques during this training period in such a way that the school teachers could develop creative observations in their local watersheds. The second project started in 1991. It consists in training school teachers in measurements of water quality and interrelating this water quality with the watershed uses. A specially designed "water quality kit" was designed and provided to make several kinds of determinations. Continuous observation and experimentation will yield results that can be useful in interpretation of watershed inputs into the aquatic system. The kit was distributed to schools in 20 towns of S. Paulo State.

❶ Broa Reservoir, a base for school teachers' training

Information transfer needs to be promoted at all levels of society: among young people, their teachers, the general public, users of local lake resources and decision makers. Publications, training courses, conferences and improved education in schools are all greatly needed if the world's lakes are to be better managed and, hence, better used.

THE FLOATING SCHOOL ON LAKE BIWA

Since 1983 Shiga Prefectural Government, one of 47 autonomies in Japan, has been offering an overnight school for 5th grade elementary school pupils at Lake Biwa on a study boat called "Uminoko". Through this program, the pupils gain an experience that can be rarely obtained in normal classroom situations including: microscopic observation of planktons, measurement of lake water transparency, lakeshore clean up activities, rowing practice on one of Uminiko's row boats. It fosters social adaptability, love for their home province and a sense of romanticism in those boys and girls who come to spend a night on the boat with their classmates. "Uminoko" offers 100 cruises a year, and by 1993 accumulatively 185,000 children participated in the study navigation.

⬆ The floating school study boat "Uminoko"

↑ Elementary and Secondary school children planting fodder plants of waterfowl at Izunuma Lake, one of Ramsar Sites in Japan

Sources

Abu Zeid, M. 'Environmental Impacts of the High Aswan Dam: a case study', In Environmentally-sound water management, Delhi, Oxford University Press, pp 247-270, 1990.

Allan, R.J. 'Organic pesticides in aquatic environments with emphasis on sources and fate in the Great Lakes'. In Guidelines of lake management Vol. 4: Toxic substances management in lakes and reservoirs, Nairobi/ Otsu, UNEP/ILEC, pp. 87-111, 1991.

Biswas, A.K. 'Objectives and concepts of environmentally-sound water management', In Environmentally-sound water management, Delhi, Oxford University Press, pp 30-58, 1990.

Brotoisworo, E. 'Environmental Management of the Sagling Dam Project'. In Report of the expert group workshop on river/lake basin approaches to environmentally sound management of water resources, Otsu andNagoya, UNCRD and ILEC, pp. 40-41, 1988.

Calderoni, A. et. al. 'Lago d'Orta ecosystem recovery by liming', In Guidelines of lake management Vol. 5: Management of lake acidification, Nairobi/Otsu, UNEP/ILEC, pp. 105-144, 1993.

David, H., Speidel & A.F. Agnew. 'The world water budget', In Perspectives on water uses and abuses, New York, Oxford University Press, 1988.

Davis, J and C.F. Claridge(eds.) 'Wetland benefits: the potential for wetlandsto support and maintain development'. Kuala Lumpur, Asia Wetland Bureau, 1993.

D'Itri, F.M. & C. McNabb. 'Impact of the zebra mussel on the Great Lakes ecosystem', ILEC Newsletter (22):7-9 1993

Dugan, P.J.(ed.) 'Wetland conservation: a review of current issues and required action', Gland, IUCN, 1990.

FAO 'Lake Victoria Environment Management Project', Project Preparation Report, 1993.

Golubev, G.N. 'Environmental problems of large central Asian lakes', In Proceedings of symposium on water resources management with the views of global and regional scales, Nairobi and Otsu, UNEP and ILEC, pp 55-63, 1991

Golubev, G.N. 'Sustainable water development: implications for the future', Water Resources Development, 9(2):127-154, 1993.

Iide, M. 'World legends Vol. 7: lake and fountain', Tokyo, Gyosei, 1979.

IIED/WRI "World Resources" 1987 Basic Books, New York, 1987

ILEC & Lake Biwa Research Institute (eds.) 'Survey of the State of World Lakes Vol I-V', Otsu/Nairobi, ILEC/UNEP, 1988-1993

Jørgensen, S.E. 'Management and modelling of lake acidification'. In Guidelines of lake management Vol. 5: Management of Lake Acidification, Nairobi/Otsu, UNEP/ILEC, pp.79-104, 1993.

Jørgensen, S.E. & R.A.Vollenweider. 'Remedial techniques', In Guidelines of lake management Vol. 1: Principles of Lake Management, Nairobi/ Otsu, UNEP/ILEC, pp 99-114, 1988.

Kasprzak, P. 'Objectives of biomanipulation'. In Guidelines of lake management Vol. 6: Biomanipulation, Nairobi/Kusatsu, UNEP/ILEC, 1995.

Kira, T. 'State of the environments of world lakes: from the survey by ILEC/UNEP', In Proceedings of symposium on Water resources Management with the views of global and regional scales, Nairobi and Otsu, UNEP and ILEC, pp 48-54, 1991

Kira, T. 'Lake Biwa in Global Environment', Kyoto, Jinbun-Shoin, 1990.

Kurata, A. Comparative stydy on the data of lake environments of Lake Biwa and world lakes. Annual Report of Lake Biwa Research Institute, 5:17-37, 1987

Lake Biwa Research Institute (ed.). 'World Lakes', Kyoto, Jinbun-Shoin, 1993.

Mahmood, K. 'Reservoir sedimentation, impact, extent and mitigation', World Bank Technical Paper No.71, Washington, D.C., World Bank, 1987.

Rubec, C.D.A., P. Lynch-Stewart, G.M. Wickware and I. Kessel-Taylor. "Wetland Utilization in Canada", In Wetlands of Canada, Polyscience Publication, pp 381-412, 1988.

Nakayama, M. 'Application of remote sensing technologies to monitor lakes/ wetlands in developing countries', In "Towards wise use of Asian wetlands", Otsu, ILEC, 1993.

Tundisi, J.G. et.al. 'ILEC Environmental Education Project in Brazil', In ILEC Environmental Education, Otsu, ILEC, pp 9-14, 1993.

Vallentyne, J.R. 'The algal bowl - lakes and man', Ottawa, Department of the Environment Fisheries and Marine Service, 1974.

White, E. 'Eutrophication of Lake Rotorua - a review', DSIR Information Series No.123, 1977.

White, G.F. 'The environmental effects of the High Dam at Aswan', Environment, 30(7):4-40, 1988.

Yuma, M. 'Nature conservation of Lake Tanganyika', In Fishes of Lake Tanganyika, Tokyo, Heibonsya, pp 224-239, 1993.

Chapter 5

◆

Ninety Lakes and Reservoirs in Developing Countries and Countries with Economic Transition

Lake name*

A : Location of the lake

B : Description of the lake

C : Physical dimension of the lake

* Index numbers correspond to those in *Survey of the State of World Lake Environments* Vols. 1-5, 1988 - 1993, ILEC/UNEP

Contents

Asian Developing Countries

ASI-02 LAKE SONGKHLA

A. LOCATION
- Phatthalung, Songkhla and Nakhon Si Thammarat, Thailand.
- 7°08'-7°50'N, 100°07-100°37'E ; ca. 0 m above sea level.

B. DESCRIPTION

Lake Songkhla, a coastal lagoon produced by sandbar formation includes three lakes, Thale Noi (2,800 ha), Thale Luang (78,280 ha) and Thale Sap Songkhla (17,600 ha), from north to south, which are interconnected by narrow channels. A narrow strait (minimum width 380 m) connects Thale Sap with the sea (Gulf of Thailand) at its southeastern end. A gradient of salinity exists, therefore, between the brackish water of Thale Sap and the pure freshwater of Thale Noi. The middle lake, Thale Luang, approaches a freshwater condition during the rainy season (October -January), but is influenced by the invasion of seawater in other months.

The lakes are shallow throughout and moderately eutrophic, with a mean water depth of 1.2-1.3 m in relatively dry seasons, but the water level rises by about one meter during the winter months. Thale Sap is known for its production of fish, shrimp and crabs, and is also intensively utilized for the aquaculture of seabass (Lates calcarifer). The fry produced and supplied by the National Institute of Coastal Aquaculture in Songkhla is grown in net cages by fishermen families. Thale Noi and the eastern branch of Thale Luang, called Kukut, have been designated as an area for waterfowl protection.

The catchment area of about 8,020 sq. km consists mostly of lowland rice fields, rubber plantations and forest-covered hills, and contains such rapidly growing cities as Hat Yai and Songkhla. The waste water from certain manufacturing and freezing factories has caused local pollution of the lake and some damage to the fisheries, but the complete and rapid turnover of water in the rainy season seems to prevent severe problems.

C. PHYSICAL DIMENSIONS
- Surface area [sq. km]   1,082
- Volume [cubic km]   1.6*1-3.8*2
- Maximum depth [m]   2.0
- Mean depth [m]*3   1.4
- Luang   1.8
- Sap Songkla   1.4
- Water level   Unregulated
- Normal range of annual water level fluctuation [m]   0.6-2.2
- Residence time [yr]   0.3-0.5
- Catchment area [sq. km]   8,020

*1 Mean surface level.
*2 1.5 m mean surface level.
*3 The depth of the channels connecting Thale Sap with the Gulf of Thailand and with Thale Luang is approximately 6m. The average of monthly water depth observations at 35 stations in Thale Sap and Thale Luang (Oct. 1976-Sep. 1978) was 1.53 m.

ASI-03 LAKE RARA

A. LOCATION
- Mugu District, Nepal.
- 29°24'N, 82°05'E ; 3,000 m above sea level.

B. DESCRIPTION

Lake Rara is situated in the western part of Nepal, at about 300 km northwest of Kathmandu, the capital of Nepal. It is a warm, oligotrophic lake with a monomictic type of water circulation. It is surrounded by hills and mountains from which more than 30 brooks flow into the lake. It has only one outlet,

Khater Khola, on its western shore (khola =stream). Khater Khola forms a deep gorge at about 7 km downstream from the outlet and finally joins Karnali River, a tributary of the Ganga.

Lake Rara is somewhat oval in shape. It has relatively large maximum depth for its surface area. It has two basins. The main basin, occupying the western part of the lake, covers about 80% of the total surface area. It is characterized by a steep margin and vast flat bottom. The area below 160 m accounts for about 27% of the lake area. The eastern sub-basin has a gently sloping margin and a small bottom. Lake Rara is a part of 'Rara Lake National Park and Wildlife Conservation Area'.

C. PHYSICAL DIMENSIONS
- Surface area [sq. km]   10
- Volume [cubic km]   0.98
- Maximum depth [m]   167
- Mean depth [m]   100
- Length of shoreline [km]   14.3

ASI-04 LAKE PHEWA

A. LOCATION
- Pokhara, Nepal.
- 28°10'N, 83°55'E ; 742 m above sea level.

B. DESCRIPTION

Lake Phewa is one of the largest lakes of Nepal. It is situated in Pokhara Valley in the western part of the country. The main inflows into this lake are two perennial spring-fed streams, Harpan Khola (khola =stream) and Seti Khola. In addition, several temporary streams drain into the lake during the rainy season. This lake has a single outflow which joins Phusre Khola. The lake belongs to a warm monomictic type with thermal stratification. The lake water has very low electrical conductivity.

Lake Phewa is very young in geological terms as tree trunks are still standing in water down to 6 m depth. There are two versions about the formation of this lake. According to Hagen (1969), there was a "Paleo-Pokhara Lake" filling whole Pokhara basin and the existing lakes are the remains of the former huge lake. But Gurung (1970) and several other workers agree with the view that this lake was formed by damming of tributaries by sediments of Seti River.

Lake Phewa is one of the main sources of recreation, natural beauty, drinking water, hydroelectricity, fisheries and irrigation in Pokhara Valley.

C. PHYSICAL DIMENSIONS
- Surface area [sq. km]   5
- Volume [cubic km]   0.039
- Maximum depth [m]   21
- Mean depth [m]   8.6
- Water level   Regulated
- Normal range of annual water
  level fluctuation [m]   1
- Length of shoreline [km]   18
- Catchment area [sq. km]   110

ASI-07 CHAO-HU (LAKE CHAO)

A. LOCATION
- Anhui Province, P.R. China.
- 30°25'-31°43'N, 117°17'-117°52'E.

B. DESCRIPTION

Lake Chao is located 15 km southeast from Hefei City, the capital of Anhui Province. It is one of the five largest freshwater lakes in China, and is the largest lake in the Province. The life of the lake is about 10 thousand years.

The lake is famous for its beautiful landscape and historic sites, and is extensively used as water sources for drinking, irrigation, fishery and transportation. About 5 million people live around the lake. In 1962, a dam was built at the only outflowing river. Control of water level has brought about some merits for irrigation and transportation, but at the same time it resulted in some demerits. The most evident effect was the reduction of fish production.

Owing to the rapid development of industry, fast increase of population and establishment of water conservancy facilities, the lake has suffered from eutrophication and silting in recent years.

C. PHYSICAL DIMENSIONS
- Surface area [sq. km]   756
- Volume [cubic km]   1.7
- Mean depth [m]   7.5-7.8
- Water level   Regulated
- Length of shoreline [km]   185
- Catchment area [sq. km]   10,430

ASI-08 MIYUN RESERVOIR

A. LOCATION
- Beijing, P.R. China.
- 40°13'-40°48'N, 116°40'-117°30'E ; 75 m above sea level.

B. DESCRIPTION

Miyun Reservoir, located 100 km northeast of Beijing City, is a mountain valley reservoir. It was built in September,1960, and is the largest reservoir in Beijing area. Two main rivers, Chaohe and Baihe, flow into Miyun Reservoir. The catchment is about 15,788 sq. km, consists of mountains and piedmonts and lacks large industrial enterprises. Sediments and nutrients from agricultural, pastoral and forestry lands that enter the reservoir with overland flow make the main pollution sources.

The initial purpose of building Miyun Reservoir was flood control, irrigation and fishery, but it has become more and more important as a main drinking water storage for Beijing area. The water quality is therefore of great importance.

Recently, the nutrient concentration and the number of phytoplankton in the Reservoir are constantly rising to arrest the attention of Beijing municipality. A project for keeping the water clean is being put into effect.

C. PHYSICAL DIMENSIONS
- Surface area [sq. km]   188
- Volume [cubic km]   0.4375
- Maximum depth [m]   43.5
- Catchment area [sq. km]   15,788

ASI-09 LAKE KINNERET (SEA OF GALILEE)

A. LOCATION
- Israel.
- 32°50'N, 35°35'E ; -209 m above sea level.

B. DESCRIPTION

Lake Kinneret (The Biblical Sea of Galilee) is a warm, monomictic lake, located at the northern end of the Afro.Syrian Rift Valley in Northern Israel with a surface area of 170 sq. km, a maximum depth of 40 m and a mean depth of 24m. The climate is hot in summer, with winter rains from November through April. There is extensive agriculture in the catchment area especially in the Hula Valley (cotton, alfalfa, agricultural ponds) and around the lake shores (bananas, dates, cotton). Lake Kinneret serves as the major reservoir for Israel's National Water Carrier System and supplies approximately one third of the country's annual water requirements. It is also an important tourist and vacation area, famous for antiquities and historical sites especially those associated with the New Testament accounts of Jesus and his disciples. As in Biblical Times, there is a significant commercial fishery on the lake with annual yields of 1,500-2,000 tons.

Over the past twenty years, extensive limnological studies have been carried out on this lake, mainly at the Kinneret Limnological Laboratory which has recently set up an International Centre for Warm Freshwater Research.

C. PHYSICAL DIMENSIONS
- Surface area [sq. km]   170
- Volume [cubic km]   4
- Maximum depth [m]   43
- Mean depth [m]   25.6
- Length of shoreline [km]   53
- Residence time [yr]   4.8
- Catchment area [sq. km]   2,730

ASI-10 DANAU TOBA (LAKE TOBA)

A. LOCATION
- North Sumatra Province, Indonesia.
- 2°21'-2°56'N, 98°26'-99°15'E ; 905 m above sea level.

B. DESCRIPTION

Lake Toba lies in the northern part of Barisan Mountain Range, which is volcanic and traverses Sumatra Island from northwest to southeast as its backbone.

The lake trough is surrounded by precipitous cliffs 400-1,200 m high. Based on the topographic feature and the wide distribution of volcanic ejecta around the lake, some geologists and valcanologists have considered it to be a giant caldera or cauldron.

The water surface of L. Toba is 905 m above sea level and about 1,100 sq. km wide. The total area of the lake, including the areas of Samosir and Paradapur Islands, amounts to 1,780 sq. km. The mountains around the lake are called Batak Highlands. The only draining river from L. Toba, the Asahan, flows southeastwards dissecting the gentle slopes of the pyroclastic plateau.

C. PHYSICAL DIMENSIONS
- Surface area [sq. km]   1,100
- Volume [cubic km]   1,258
- Maximum depth [m]   529
- Water level   Unregulated
- Normal range of annual water
  level fluctuation [m]   1.5
- Catchment area [sq. km]   3,440

ASI-11 DONGTING-HU (LAKE DONGTING)

A. LOCATION
- Hunan Province, P.R. China.
- 28°30'-30°20'N, 111°40'-113°10'E ; 33.5 m above sea level.

B. DESCRIPTION

Lake Dongting, in northeastern Hunan, is the second largest freshwater lake of China, with an extensive catchment area including the whole of Hunan and parts of the neighboring provinces, Hubei, Sichuan and Guizhou. It serves as a great retarding basin for the Chang Jiang (Yangtse River), from which flood water pours into the lake in July-September. The inflow from the Chang Jiang amounts to more than a half of the total water influx to L. Dongting, and carries with it a tremendous sediment load of 140,000,000 m³/yr on average.

One hundred and fifty years ago, the lake was much bigger (6,200 sq. km) than it is now (2,740 sq. km), but the rapid progress of sedimentation and land reclamation works have since reduced its size, resulting in the formation of three more or less separate basins, West, South and East Dongting. In the summer flooding season, however, the three lakes unite into a single water body of about 3,900 sq. km surface area. The water from the Chang Jiang flows mainly into the West and East Lake through three channels, and is drained from the northeastern corner of East Lake at Yueyang directly into the Chang Jiang again. The annual range of water level fluctuation in normal years ranges between 6.5 m (W. Lake) and 17.8 m (E. Lake).

The greatest environmental problem for L. Dongting is the rapid sedimentation fat a rate of ca. 5 cm/yr on a whole lake average) that causes trouble for surface transportation by boats, diminishes the lake's capacity for water storage and flood control, and affects fishery production through changes in the aquatic ecosystem. The Provincial Ordinance for Environmental Protection formulated in 1981, therefore, allows for no further reclamation work in or around the lake.

The heavy application of pesticides to rice fields as well as industrial development in recent years has caused local contamination of rivers and small attached lakes with BHC, heavy metals and organic wastes, but the main lake as a whole maintains fairly good water quality, with a mesotrophic nutrient level.

C. PHYSICAL DIMENSIONS

- Surface area [sq. km]   2,740*
- Volume [cubic km]   17.8
- Maximum depth [m]   30.8
- Mean depth [m]   6.7
- Water level   Unregulated
- Normal range of annual water
  level fluctuation [m]   6.5-17.8
- Catchment area [sq. km]   259,430

  * At the low water level.

ASI-12 DONG-HU (LAKE DONG)

A. LOCATION

- Hubei Province, P.R. China.
- 30°33'N, 114°23'E ; 20.5 m above sea level.

B. DESCRIPTION

Dong (east) -hu (lake) is a small lake in the Wuchang Ward of Wuhan City, the capital of Hubei Province. It obtained its name from being located at the eastern end of this big city. Dong.hu is a natural dammed lake formed in the early Holocene as a so-called "lateral lake" attached to the right bank of the Chang Jiang which flows through Wuhan, and is only five kilometers away from the river.

The lake area, especially the northwestern coast, is a park and recreation area for the citizens of Wuhan, with museums, a botanic garden, observation towers, restaurants, sanatoria, beautiful groves of exotic swamp cypress, swimming sites and sightseeing boats. The Wuhan Institute of Hydrobiology established by the Academia Sinica in 1954 is located on the westernmost shore of the lake. Its research activity made Dong-hu one of the most familiar lakes of China to world limnologists.

It is also intensively utilized for fish production. Many small bays are separated from the main lake by causeways for artificial stocking of fish. Introduction of such planktophagous fishes as the silver carp and the bighead carp, increased the fish production by more than four times in a seven-year period. The increasing density of fish as well as the inflow of waste water from the city and industrial factories, however, has caused a rapid change in the lake's biota. Accelerated eutrophication is producing noxious effects which now hinder the utilization of lake water and recreational activity. A plan for establishing a waste water treatment plant for domestic sewage and the diversion of treated water to Chang Jiang, is now being carried out by the Municipality of Wuhan.

C. PHYSICAL DIMENSIONS

- Surface area   [sq. km]28
- Volume [cubic km]   0.062
- Maximum depth [m]   4.8
- Mean depth [m]   2.2
- Water level   Regulated
- Normal range of annual water
  level fluctuation [m]   0.5
- Length of shoreline [km]   9.2
- Residence time [yr]   0.4
- Catchment area [sq. km]   97

ASI-13 LAGUNA DE BAY (LAKE BAY)

A. LOCATION

- Luzon, the Philippines.
- 14°02'-14°05'N, 121°00'-121°05'E ; 1.8 m above sea level.

B. DESCRIPTION

Laguna de Bay (Lake Bay) is often erroneously called the "Laguna Lake". It is the largest lake in the Philippines. On the lake, there are an island, Talim, and two peninsulas jutting out a long way from the north coast. The lake is considered to have once been a branch of Manila Bay but later became separatedfrom the bay by volcanic deposits and the upheaval of land. Water flows out from the northwestern end of the lake to Manila Bay. Since, the difference of water level between the lake and the sea is so small, the adverse tides occur frequently during the dry season from January to April.

Vast paddy fields, sugar cane fields and coconut plantations spread over the alluvial plain around the lake. Cash products like vegetables, fruits and poultry are also raised for consumption in neighboring big cities as Manila and Quezon City. The Laguna Lake Development Authority established in 1970 is mainly responsible for promoting development and conservation works in the lake and its drainage basin.

C. PHYSICAL DIMENSIONS

- Surface area [sq. km]   ca. 900
- Volume [cubic km]   ca. 3.2
- Maximum depth [m]   7.3
- Mean depth [m]   2.8
- Water level   Regulated
- Length of shoreline [km]   ca. 220
- Catchment area [sq. km]   ca. 3,820

ASI-15 TASEK BERA (SWAMP LAKE TASEK BERA)

A. LOCATION

- Pahang State, Malaysia.
- 3°05'N, 102°38'E ; >30 m above sea level.

B. DESCRIPTION

Tasek Bera is an alluvial blackwater swamp lake located in the southern part of Malay Peninsula at uppermost reach of the southern branch of River Pahang. It occupies an area of about 25 km×35 km on the forest-covered peneplain that stretches over the low east-west watershed of the peninsula. A narrow channel drains its water northward to River Pahang and eventually eastward into South China Sea.

The lake is a complex dendritic system consisting of extensive swamp forests that account for nearly two-thirds of its area, littoral swamps overgrown by Pandanus shrub or sedges (mostly Lepironia), network of flowing channels and

scattered small open waters. The open water area constitutes less than 1.5% of the whole system. The water is poor in calcium and magnesium contents, and is acidic and brown-colored due to dissolved humic substances. The decomposition of plant detritus is thus remarkably inhibited resulting in the accumulation of peat several meters thick on the lake bottom. The vigorous growth of insectivorous Utricularia in open waters and the occurrence of the other insectivores, Nepenthes spp., along the lake shore suggest oligotrophic nature of the habitats. However, the nitrogen and phosphorus contents of lake water and the biological productivity are not very low.

The catchment area has been inhabited for centuries by a Malayan aboriginal tribe, Semalai. Their subsistence depended on the shifting cultivation of upland rice and cassava, fishery in the lake and gathering forest and swamp products. The slash-and-

burn agriculture has turned an extensive area of original vegetation of mixed rain forest into low secondary forest in the northern half of the catchment. In recent years, they were given a chance to go beyond their traditional subsistence economy by growing rubber trees and wetland rice, which may gradually affect the lake environment.

An integrated ecosystem research on Tasek Bera was carried out during 1970- 1974 at Pos (Fort) Iskander, within the framework of the International Biological Program by the Joint Malaysian-Japanese Team of 19 scientists. The program contributed much to the knowledge of the swamp ecosystem of this type, which once widely occurred throughout the lowlands of equatorial Southeast Asia but has almost disappeared. As its valuable relics that escaped exploitation, it is desirable to preserve the peculiar biota and natural physiognomy of Tasek Bera as a nature reserve (Editor).

C. PHYSICAL DIMENSIONS

- Surface area [sq. km]   62
- Maximum depth [m]   7
- Mean depth [m]   2-2.5
- Water level   Unregulated
- Normal range of annual water
  level fluctuation [m]   1-5
- Catchment area [sq. km]   ca. 550

ASI-19 BUNG BORAPHET (BORAPED RESERVOIR)

A. LOCATION

- Nakhon Sawan Province, Thailand.
- 15°50'N, 100°10'E ; 23.8 m above sea level.

B. DESCRIPTION

Bung (= big pond) Boraped is a half man.made reservoir originating from a natural retarding basin situated close to the city of Nakhon Sawan, where the two rivers, Mae Nam Nan and Mae Nam Ping. unite into Mae Nam Chao Phraya (sometimes erroneously called the Menam River). The lake area had been a vast retarding basin known as the Boraped Swamp, which formed a big lake of 600 sq. km in seasons of high water level while turning into a grass-covered plain with scattered ponds and swampy depressions during the dry season. A dam was built at the head of the main outflowing channel (Klong Boraped) by the Fishery Department of Thailand in 1926-30 mainly for increasing fish production. Part of the swamp thus turned into a lake which has since been known as Bung Boraped. The present lake area is about 106 sq. km at the spill level, but it varies extensively owing to the water level fluctuation, amounting to as much as 300 sq. km in time of floods.

The majority of some 30,000 people living around the lake gain their livelihood from both farming and fishing. Since the lake is the largest source of fishery products for central Thailand, the Nakhon Sawan Fishery Station was established at Klong Boraped for the study of fish biology and for stocking the lake with artificially grown fry. Bung Boraped and surrounding swampy areas form one of the non-hunting nature reserves established by the Royal Thai Forest Department. Two development projects have been drafted for tourism development, upgrading aquaculture and utilizing the lake as sources of irrigation and domestic water supply.

C. PHYSICAL DIMENSIONS

- Surface area [sq. km]   106
- Volume [cubic km]   0.2764
- Maximum depth [m]   5.8
- Mean depth [m]   2
- Water level   Regulated
- Normal range of annual water
  level fluctuation [m]   1-1.2
- Length of shoreline [km]   53-62.5*
- Catchment area [sq. km]   4,200
  * Minimum-maximum.

ASI-20 LAKE BUHI

A. LOCATION

- Camarines Sur, the Philippines.
- 13°05'N, 123°05'E.

B. DESCRIPTION

Lake Buhi is a unique tropical lake serving as home of the world's smallest commercial fish The lake provides for many uses such as fishery, navigation, water reservoir for irrigation, hydroelectric power and domestic water supply. This 1,800 hectare freshwater lake sits in the valley between two ancient volcanos, Mt. Malimas and Mt. Iriga. The lake was formed in 1641 when a strong earthquake caused the side of Mt. Iriga to collapse, forming a natural dam on small streams.

C. PHYSICAL DIMENSIONS

- Surface area [sq. km]   15-18
- Maximum depth [m]   18.2
- Mean depth [m]   6.8

ASI-26 TAI-HU

A. LOCATION

- Jiangsu Province, P.R. China.
- 30°56'-31°34'N, 119°54'-120°36'E ; 3.1 m above sea level.

B. DESCRIPTION

Tai (great)-hu (lake) is the third largest freshwater lake of China, below in size Lakes Poyang and Dongting, situated about 100 km from the east coast of the Chang Jiang delta in central China. The whole lake is under the administration of Jiangsu Province, though its southern coast belongs to the neighboring province, Zhejiang. It is located in the densely populated fertile plain of the delta known for its complicated network of small lakes, ponds, streams and man-made canals, including the Grand Canal built in the 7th century to connect Beijing with Hangzhou in Zhejiang.

The inflowing water comes mainly from mountains to the west and southwest of the lake, while the draining rivers start mostly from the east coast of the lake. Several rivers and channels connect the lake with Chang Jiang, but the water flux is controlled by dams to maintain the lake water level within a range of fluctuation of 2-3 meters.

The lake is famous for its abundant production of fishes and crabs, and the aquaculture farms on the coast that apply skillful techniques. In addition to supporting heavy boat traffic, Tai-hu provides some of the best known water- side scenery in China for domestic and foreign sightseeing visitors.

Tai-hu and its effluent rivers are important sources of water for the inhabitants and rapidly increasing industrial factories in Shanghai, Wuxi, Suzhou and other neighboring cities, so that the pollution of the lake is a serious social concern. The pollutants originate mainly from home sewage of the vast number of inhabitants, agricultural pesticides applied over fields in the drainage basin, and the industrial sewage of more than 700 factories and mines. The Film Studio, Tanshan Ore Dressing Plant, West-hill Mines and the Wuxi No.3 Instrument and Metal Plant discharge 2,750 tons per day of waste water directly into the lake. Phenol, mercury, chromium etc. are widely detected over the lake, but at fairly low concentrations. The lake water is also highly eutrophic, with frequent blooms of blue-green algae even in late autumn.

C. PHYSICAL DIMENSIONS

- Surface area [sq. km]   2,428
- Volume [cubic km]   4.3

- Maximum depth [m]   2.6
- Mean depth [m]   1.9
- Residence time [yr]   <0.8

ASI-27 OZERO BAYKAL (LAKE BAIKAL)

A. LOCATION

- Buryat A.S.S.R. and Irkutsk, Russia
- 51°29'-55°46'N, 103°40'-109°55'E ; 456 m above sea level.

B. DESCRIPTION

Lake Baikal is the deepest lake in the world. The bottom of the lake lies 1,285 m below sea level, and is the deepest continental rift on the earth. Its water volume is approximately equal to the total volume of the Great Lakes of North America, or to about 20% of the total freshwater on the earth. It is also known as one of the most ancient in geological history, and there are few lakes in the world to compete with this lake in biotic diversity. As many as 852 species and 233 varieties of algae and 1,550 species and varieties of animals have been known to inhabit L. Baikal. The world-famous Baikal seal, the only mammal living on the lake, is found throughout the whole area of the lake to this day.

The lake is completely surrounded by mountains, and there are 22 small islands over the lake. The lake water is fed by some 300 inflowing rivers, and is drained through the single outlet, the Angara River. The climate of the drainage basin is extremely continental with long, very cold and dry winters and short cool summers. The climax vegetation under the climate is the coniferous forest largely dominated by larch. The nutritional level of the lake water is typically oligotrophic as indicated by the highest transparency in the world, though an industrial pulp complex built in the early 1960's near the lake's southern end is said to have caused considerable pollution.

C. PHYSICAL DIMENSIONS

- Surface area [sq. km]   31,500
- Volume [cubic km]   23,000
- Maximum depth [m]   1,741
- Mean depth [m]   740
- Water level   Unregulated
- Length of shoreline [km]   2,000
- Catchment area [sq. km]   560,000

ASI-38 DAL LAKE

A. LOCATION

- Jammu and Kashmir, India.
- 34°18'N, 74°91'E ; 1,583 m above sea level.

B. DESCRIPTION

Dal is a Himalayan urban lake which is mainly used for tourism. Fishery is of secondary importance. The lake comprises five basins and a myriad of inter-connecting channels. It is one of the most beautiful lakes of India and the second largest lake in the State of Jammu and Kashmir. The lake is surrounded by mountains on its three sides. A large number of gardens and orchards have been laid along the shores. Dal Lake is unique in having hundreds of house boats which afford an opportunity to tourists to reside on the lake in an atmosphere of peace and tranquility. The boats are served by Shikaras which more or less resemble the gondolas of Venice but are smaller in size and are tastefully decorated. Besides the Moghul monuments the campus of the University of Kashmir is also located along the shores of the lake. Overlooking the lake are two hillocks which house the famous temples of Shankaracharya and Hari Parbat. A perennial inflow channel enters the lake from the north and supplies about 80% of the water. Towards the southwest side an outflow channel drains the lake water into a tributary of the River Jhelum. Parallel to this exit is a stone-lined canal which connects the lake with the tributary. This channel is used for movement of boats in and out of the lake and prevents inundation of floating gardens during high floods.

The famous Moghul gardens around the lake have been laid during 16-17th century and their number was about five hundred but now only a few of these have survived. The origin of the lake has remained unresolved. It is believed by some geologists that the Dal Lake is the remnant of a Pleistocene oligotrophic lake which once covered the entire valley of Kashmir. There are other geologists who believe Dal to be a flood plain lake.

The lake water is being used for irrigation of vegetable fields which have grown in number and extent during recent years. The present maximum depth of the lake is 6 m (Nagin basin). Many aquatic plants growing in the lake are used as food, fodder and compost.

The water quality of Dal Lake has deteriorated considerably in the last two decades. Large peripheral areas have been reclaimed and converted into floating gardens. With the increase in the tourist influx a large number of residential buildings, restaurants and hotels have come up along the lake front. The number of house boats has also been increasing at an alarming rate. As a result of rapid and unplanned urbanization, large quantities of raw sewage are discharged in the lake water, which might pose health problems in the near future.

The main environmental issues are excessive weed growth, reduction in water clarity, enrichment of waters and high microbial activity. A Dal Development Project was formulated in 1978 and the State Government of Jammu and Kashmir adopted it with some modifications. The main thrust of the project is to improve the lake environment by using both physical and biological approaches. The work is in progress.

C. PHYSICAL DIMENSIONS

- Surface area [sq. km]   21[*1]
- Volume [cubic km]   0.00983
- Maximum depth [m]   6
- Mean depth [m]   1.4[*2]
- Water level   Regulated
- Normal range of annual water
  level fluctuation [m]   0.7
- Length of shoreline [km]   15.5
- Catchment area [sq. km]   316

    [*1] Including Floating Gardens.

    [*2] Nagin Basin.

ASI-39 LAKE SAGULING

A. LOCATION

- Jawa Barat, Indonesia.
- 107°25'E, 6°50'S ; 643 m above sea level.

B. DESCRIPTION

The Saguling is an artificial lake. It is located about 40 km from Bandung city, or about 12 km to the south of the main road from Bandung to Jakarta, and about 90 km at the upstream of the Jatiluhur Lake. The lake was built on the Citarum River, the largest river in West Java Province, in February 1985.

Originally, the Saguling was planned for a single purpose dam to generate electricity. At the first stage the plant was built with an installed capacity of 700 MW, but if the demand of electricity might increasing in the future the plant could be extended to produce 1,400 MW. The responsible body in charge of construction is "Proyek Induk Pembangkit Hidro" abbreviated as PIKITDRO (Main Project of Hydroelectric Development) of the State Electrical Company, of the Ministry of Mining and Energy. Later, considering the environmental problems of the area, the Saguling was re-planned as a multipurpose dam, which included the use of the lake created by the project for other development purposes such as fisheries, agri-aquaculture, tourism and their multiple effects. But, at present, the lake is also used for domestic purposes such as bathing and washing, or also for toilet.

The surrounding area of Lake Saguling is hilly, while the river has many tributaries at this location. This makes the shape of Lake Saguling very irregular or dendritic, with many extended bays. The lake area was formerly densely populated by farmer population with extensive agricultural lands. The catchment areas of the lake or the upper Citarum River basin are faced with high population pressure. This is because over 50% of the population consists of farmers with a high annual growth rate (2.34% is the national average). The growth of farmer population has caused the decrease of landholding and this condition forced them to extend their agricultural land by forest clearing and utilize marginal lands. As a consequence, there is a prevailing problem of floods accompanied by accelerated soil erosion in rainy seasons. The Institute of Ecology at Bandung has been studying the area since 1978, dealing with basic conditions of the area and also environmental monitoring and management for enhancing the living standard of the population.

Due to the high population density in the upper catchment of the lake, extensive agricultural land, soil erosion and the presence of industries,the lake water became polluted and eutrophic. The growth of aquatic weeds has been accelerated,with frequent blooms of Microcystis algae. The water is also contaminated by heavy metals, pesticides, etc. An extensive growth of water- hyacinth is maintained by fencing to reduce pollutant contents of water at inlets of the Citarum River.

C. PHYSICAL DIMENSIONS

- Surface area [sq. km]   53
- Volume [cubic km]   2.75
- Maximum depth [m]   92
- Water level   Regulated
- Normal range of annual water
  level fluctuation [m]   20
- Length of shoreline [km]   417
- Catchment area [sq. km]   52

ASI-45 PARAKRAMA SAMUDRA (LAKE PARAKRAMA)

A. LOCATION
- North Central, Sri Lanka.
- 7°55'N, 81°00'E ; 58.5 m above sea level.

B. DESCRIPTION

Parakrama Samudra, the Sea of King Parakrama as the name literally means, is a shallow reservoir with a surface area of 22.6 sq. km. It consists of three separate reservoirs connected only by narrow channels at low water. The northernmost reservoir is the oldest and referred to as Topa wewa (Sinhalese wewa=lake or reservoir). The middle section is Eramudu wewa and the southernmost portion at the highest elevation is Dumbutula wewa. Topa wewa was built around A.D. 386. The other sections were added and the reservoir expanded during the reign of King Parakrama Bahu the Great (A.D. 1153-1183).

Lake Parakrama forms one of the larger reservoirs of an ancient, intricate and sophisticated water storage system for the irrigation of rice fields in Sri Lanka. During the twelfth century A. D. it was situated in the capital of Sri Lanka and in a densely populated area, judging from the extensive ruins of a magnificent civilization. Later the area was abandoned, the city reverted to jungle, and the lake was drained due to damage to the dam. The reservoir was restored to its present status about thirty years ago, and the surrounding area has attracted increasing numbers of immigrants, mainly rice cultivators and more recently fishermen.

Lake Parakrama has a catchment of about 75 sq. km. This consists mainly of a forest reserve which is limited by high ground in the west. The reservoir is supplied by water from rainfall in its catchment carried by small streams and also by a channel running north from a small river. Water from the river traverses a distance of about 8 km before reaching the lake. Considerable amounts of silt are deposited in the channel and do not reach the reservoir. The stored water is supplied mainly for the irrigation of rice fields. There has been encroachment on the forest reserve by fishermen in the last twenty years.

Human use of water for domestic purposes has grown with settlement of a large number of immigrants in the vicinity of the lake. The lake receives a considerable load of faecal pollution from the human population in the vicinity. During the low water season when large areas of the lake bed are exposed, cattle graze on the lush growth of grass and leave considerable quantities of faeces behind, enriching the lake.

C. PHYSICAL DIMENSIONS
- Surface area [sq. km]   23
- Volume [cubic km]   0.1273
- Maximum depth [m]   12.7
- Mean depth [m]   5.0
- Water level   Regulated
- Normal range of annual water
  level fluctuation [m]   ca. 4.4
- Catchment area [sq. km]   ca. 75

ASI-46 LAKE FATEH SAGAR

A. LOCATION
- Rajasthan, India.
- 24°35'N, 73°37'E ; 578 m above sea level.

B. DESCRIPTION

Lake Fateh Sagar is a medium-sized perennial storage reservoir constructed in the year 1678 A. D. by the rulers of former Mewar State. Although primarily constructed for irrigational purpose, this water body has lately formed a second major source of drinking water for the city of Udaipur.

The main feeder canal of the lake comes from Madar tank situated at a higher altitude about 15 km from Udaipur City.

Lake Fateh Sagar is also connected to the adjoining Lake Pichhola through a canal having gates. This (former) lake has somewhat pear-like shape and is surrounded by hills except on its eastern side where a straight masonry dam of about 800 m length is located. The lake lies on the northwest of main Udaipur city. The runoff emerging from surrounding hillocks drains into this lake. Along the eastern shore line runs a beautiful serpentine road which has a stone wall on the lake periphery. This lake has got three prominent islands. The largest is developed into a public park. The second island is situated on the northern side and has an installation of solar observatory. The smallest island on the western side near shore supports a jet fountain. The western bank of lake is occupied by marginal agricultural field. The vegetation cover around the lake is scanty. However, several species of plants are found along the undulating roads and hillocks around this lake.

Leaching of nutrients from the catchment area and agricultural activities in the marginal areas of the lake has influenced the nutrient level of this water body. Similarly, incoming silt has also reduced the water holding capacity of this lake.

Lakes are focal point for social and economic activities of Udaipur people. Every year thousands of tourists from India and abroad come to this 'City of Lakes'. Yet this water body is facing acute shortage of water sometimes due to scanty rains. For checking loss of water through evaporation, Public Health Engineering Department (PHED) has been using cetyl alcohol (hexadecanol) during drought period. In the year 1972 the lake exhibited heavy bloom of blue green algae Microcystis. In 1978, local citizen groups and environmental conservation organizations undertook desilting operation through human labour wherein about 10 thousand truck loads of silt were removed from the shallow basin of this lake.

C. PHYSICAL DIMENSIONS

- Surface area [sq. km]   4
- Volume [cubic km]   0.0121
- Maximum depth [m]   13.4
- Mean depth [m]   5.4
- Water level   Regulated
- Normal range of annual water
  level fluctuation [m]   3-4
- Length of shoreline [km]   8.5
- Catchment area [sq. km]   54

ASI-47 LOWER LAKE

A. LOCATION

- Madhya Pradesh, India.
- 23°16'N, 77°25'E ; 495 m above sea level.

B. DESCRIPTION

The findings indicate that the lake is highly eutrophicated and grossly polluted by continuous inflow of large amount of sewage badly affecting aquatic life. The lake gets high nutrient loading both from the bottom and the surface which creates complete anaerobic conditions in many parts even at a depth of one meter. The water remains very turbid throughout due to permanent algal blooms specially of Microcystis spp. In summer, water gets stratified with a difference of 9.8°C but without well defined thermocline. Nutrients N & P ; chlorophyll contents have increased many folds within a period of about ten years. Fecal bacteria population is very high indicating a high degree of contamination, with low fish production. The lake has a basic defect in its construction of the lower dam wall which is without a sluice gate and only aerated surface water continuously overflows the dam wall. Since, the lake is surrounded by the rows of houses within a hilly terrain the water remains stagnant without any

circulation and mixing of the aerated and anaerobic bottom water and increases the sinking rate of the silt particles into the bottom. The whole lake is thus converted into a large septic tank making the lake shallower and shallower day by day. It has been recommended that all the sewage inflows should be diverted immediately to save its life span. The lake has great importance to local people, who take bath and wash their clothes because of scarcity of water. Water is also used forgardening but there is no well developed tourism because of the fowl odour of decaying algae.

C. PHYSICAL DIMENSIONS

- Surface area [sq. km]   1
- Volume [cubic km]   0.008
- Maximum depth [m]   10.7
- Mean depth [m]   6.2
- Water level   Regulated
- Normal range of annual water
  level fluctuation [m]   No record
- Length of shoreline [km]   6.3
- Residence time [yr]   N.A.
- Catchment area [sq. km]   N.A.

ASI-48 QIONGHAI-HU (LAKE QIONGHAI)

A. LOCATION

- Sichuan Province, P.R. China.
- 27°48'-27°52'N, 102°16'-102°21'E ; 1,508 m above sea level.

B. DESCRIPTION

Lake Qionghai, the second largest lake of Sichuan Province, is located in Xichang City, Liangshan Yi Nationality Autonomous Region. The tectonic lake measures 11.5 km from northwest to southeast. It is a semi-enclosed fresh water lake and has only one outlet, Haihe River, on the north. It flows into Anning River, one of the subtributaries of Changjiang River.

Since a chemical fertilizer factory in the north was moved away in 1979, there are almost no industry sites around Lake Qionghai. Domestic sewage and industrial wastewater from Xichang City discharge into Haihe River, without impact on the lake water. So the main pollution source is farmland runoff, and sewage from schools, hotels and a hospital nearby.

In the lake, with good water quality, there are plenty of flora and fauna. More than 30 fish species have been described. The maximum annual fish catch was up to 680 tons, including fish 450 tons, shrimp 20 tons and crab 110 tons.

C. PHYSICAL DIMENSIONS

- Surface area [sq. km]   31
- Volume [cubic km]   0.32
- Maximum depth [m]   34
- Mean depth [m]   14
- Water level   Unregulated
- Normal range of annual water
  level fluctuation [m]   2
- Length of shoreline [km]   35
- Residence time [yr]   2.7
- Catchment area [sq. km]   300

ASI-49 SANCHA-HU (LAKE SANCHA)

A. LOCATION

- Sichuan Province, P.R. China.
- 30°20'N, 104°15'E ; 465 m above sea level.

B. DESCRIPTION

Sancha-hu (Lake Sancha) is a man-made lake. The construction work was designed by the Sichuan Survey and Design Institute for Water Resources and Electric Power, and implemented by the government of Jianyang County. The work was started in March 1975, and completed in February 1977.

The site of the reservoir is a transitional zone between Longyuan Mountains and the hilly area covered by terra rossa which belongs to an inland lake sedimentary phase of Upper Jurrasic and Cretaceous Periods. The surrounding hills have gentle slopes and are made of relatively hard rocks. The quality of air and water comes up to No. 1 grade of National Environmental Standards.

The purpose of damming was to store water for irrigating farmlands, now amounting to 39,700 hectares. Meanwhile fish culture and uses for recreation/tourism have been developed. The reservoir with its natural scenic beauty and nearby historic sites is now a famous touristic site in the western part of Sichuan Basin.

C. PHYSICAL DIMENSIONS

- Surface area [sq. km]   27
- Volume [cubic km]   0.2235
- Maximum depth [m]   32.5
- Mean depth [m]   8.2
- Water level   Regulated
- Normal range of annual water
  level fluctuation [m]   4.5
- Length of shoreline [km]   240
- Residence time [yr]   0.7
- Catchment area [sq. km]   161

ASI-50 CHANGSHOU-HU (LAKE CHANGSHOU)

A. LOCATION

- Sichuan Province, P.R. China.
- 29°56'-30°12'N, 107°12'-107°24'E ; 338.15 m above sea level.

B. DESCRIPTION

Changshou-hu (Lake Changshou) is a man-made lake with another name Shizitun (Lion Beach) Reservoir. For generating electric power, four hydraulic power stations were built after damming in the 1950's. Since then a state farm was set up for fishery and horticulture as well as animal husbandry. The irrigation area amounts to 24,800 hectares.

C. PHYSICAL DIMENSIONS

- Surface area [sq. km]   60
- Volume [cubic km]   0.745
- Maximum depth [m]   34
- Catchment area [sq. km]   3,020

ASI-51 LAKE HUBSUGUL

A. LOCATION

- Hubsugul Aimag, Mongolia.
- 50°27'-51°37'N, 100°51'-101°47'E ; 1,645 m above sea level.

B. DESCRIPTION

Lake Hubsugul is the largest freshwater lake in Central Asia. The landscape complex around the lake is unique and inimitable in its beauty. The lake basin consists largely of highlands, where underground permafrost layers, sometimes as deep as 100-200 m, are widespread.

The climate is severely continental with 300-430 mm of mean annual precipitation. Between the lake shore and the top of high mountains reaching 3,491 m in altitude, there is a series of alternating vegetation zones from steppe, through forest-steppe, forest and forest-tundra, to alpine tundra zone. Forests of larch, cedar, pine and birch predominate on permafrost, together with tundra. The lake basin supports 60 species of mammals including 32 game animals and 800 species of plants of which more than 50% are grasses and herbs.

The lake has three tributaries, while a single river, the Egyn-gol flows out toward Lake Baikal. There are petroleum fields in Hatafal and Hanh on the north and the south side of the lake. More than 30 phosphorite beds have also been exploited.

It is of prime importance for this lake as a natural treasure how to maintain its crystal-clean water against the impact from industrial developments. The exploitation of phosphorite beds may disrupt surrounding environments, Lake Hubsugul, and eventually Lake Baikal via the Egyn. Local authorities are making efforts to cope with the problem, but the processes and extent of industrial influence on the environment still remain unknown because of the lack of comprehensive ecological research on the complex system of the lake, its surroundings, rivers and springs.

C. PHYSICAL DIMENSIONS

- Surface area [sq. km]   2,770
- Volume [cubic km]   381
- Maximum depth [m]   267
- Mean depth [m]   138
- Water level   Unregulated
- Normal range of annual water
  level fluctuation [m]   0.5-2.0
- Length of shoreline [km]   414
- Catchment area [sq. km]   4,940

ASI-53 XI-HU (THE WEST LAKE)

A. LOCATION

- Zhejiang Province, P. R. China.
- 30°18'N, 120°07'E ; 7.2 m above sea level.

B. DESCRIPTION

Xi-hu (West Lake) is a small freshwater lake situated close to the city of Hangzhou in the southeastern coastal area of China. The scenery of the lake has been famous for its picturesque interfusion of hills and water since the age of Tang Dynasty (618 907 A.D.). The lake originated from an estuary and evolved into the present-day freshwater lake through ages. According to historical records, dredging had been conducted in the lake more than 23 times; thus human activities played an important role in the formation and protection of the lake.

It is divided into five sections by artificial causeways. The Outer (Wai) Lake is the main body which accounts for 82.4% of the total lake volume. The annual inflow of natural runoff water into the lake from its small drainage basin is only 1.5 times the lake volume, so the retention time of lake water is relatively long.

The drainage basin consists mainly of eroded limestone hills. Being favored by a subtropical monsoon climate with abundant rainfall, up to 70% of the basin area is covered by forests of mixed evergreen and deciduous broadleaf trees and conifers. A spell of hot sunny days prevails through July and August, and the average winter temperature is well above the freezing point.

Tourism makes the largest contribution to the basin s economy. The number of tourists visiting Xi-hu amounts to 7 millions in recent years. Traditional tea plantation is the leading type of local agriculture. Eutrophication is a serious threat to the lake, although the rainwater and wastewater from the urban area of Hangzhou do not enter the lake. A series of such control and remedial measures have been taken by responsible authorities as the interception of inflowing wastewater, diversion of clean water from the Qiantang River into the lake through a canal, control of point sources of pollution, dredging of sediments, construction of protection bank, use of electric leisure boats, controlled fishery, etc.

C. PHYSICAL DIMENSIONS

- Surface area [sq. km]   5.6
- Volume [cubic km]   0.0110
- Maximum depth [m]   3.1
- Mean depth [m]   2.0
- Catchment area [sq. km]   26.6

ASI-54 LAKE BALKHASH

A. LOCATION

- Kazakhstan.
- 44°45' 46°44'N, 73°21' 79°30'E ; 341.4 m above sea level.

B. DESCRIPTION

The closed Lake Balkhash is situated in a land depression of tectonic origin. The orography of its drainage basin is very complex: there are high mountain systems, low mountains, plains, and sands partly bordering the lake.

The Balkhash depression is under the influence of arid continental climate with annual precipitation less than 150 200 mm. There is semi-dessert vegetation along the lake shore.

The area and water volume of the lake vary considerably in due course depending on the large amplitude of long-term and secular fluctuations of its water level. For example during our century its water surface has changed from 15,730 sq. km (1946) to 23,464 sq. km (1910) and its water volume from 82.70 cubic km to 163.9 cubic km.

The difference between the eastern and the western parts of the lake basin is essential. There are 58% of the total water surface and 46% of the lake water volume in the western part. The mean depth of the eastern part is 1.7 times more than those of the western part. The western part of the lake has fresh or slightly salty water (0.5% 1.5%) depending on the secular fluctuation of its water level, while the eastern part is characterized by rather high concentration of dissolved solids (up to 7%). The main reasons for such a difference are the inflow of a huge river to the western part and the retarded exchange of water between the two parts.

Balkhash is very important for its utilization. The water resources of the lake and its tributary rivers are used for irrigation, municipal and industrial water supply (including the supply for the Balkhash Copper Melting Plant). The fish catch in the lake is also very important for the Kazakhstan.

During the latest years, the problem of Balkhash Lake became more explicit because of the start of the filling of Kaptchagayskoye Reservoir (with a volume of 29 cubic km) on the River Ili. The filling of the first 14 km has resulted in negative consequences on the water level, water-salt balance and ecology of the lake. The main problem is how to harmonize natural-ecological conditions of this lake with the need of a reservoir for irrigation, water supply and hydropower production.

C. PHYSICAL DIMENSIONS

- Surface area [sq. km]   18,200
- Volume [cubic km]   106
- Maximum depth [m]   25.6
- Mean depth [m]   5.8
- Water level   Unregulated
- Normal range of annual water level fluctuation [m]   1.6
- Length of shoreline [km]   2,385
- Residence time [yr]   6.8
- Catchment area [sq. km]   413,000*

*Fifteen percent is in the territory of China.

ASI-55 LAKE ISSYK-KOOL

A. LOCATION

- Issyk-Kool Region, Kirgizstan.
- 42°30' 43°20'N, 76°10' 78°20'E ; 1,606 m above sea level.

B. DESCRIPTION

According to the study of its 3,000 m-thick lake deposits, Lake Issyk-Kool (Issyk Kul) was born 20 million years ago in early Miocene, when an isolated intermountain depression was formed by intensive tectonic movements and was filled with water. The freshwater lake which existed in Pliocene was larger than the present lake.

Currently, Issyk-Kool is located at an altitude of 1,606 m (in 1990) in an oval-shaped basin surrounded by steep slopes on its periphery. The catchment area measures 252 km x 146 km and is bordered by high mountain ridges reaching 4,000 5,200 m in altitude on both the northern and the southern side. There are 834 glaciers on the alpine slopes of the basin, which supplies water of about 48×10^9 cubic m annually. In accordance with the gradient of climatic aridity, different landscape types, desert, semi-desert and steppe from west to east, alternates on the flat part of the catchment (exceeding 3,000 sq. km).

The basin of the lake itself has a rather simple shape like a truncated cone inverted. The lower base of the cone, 1,357 sq. km wide, is almost flat ranging between 600 m and 668 m in depth. The shelf zone down to 300 m depth consists of several old terraces indented by 40 50 m deep canyons. Issyk-Kool never freezes even in severe winters. Water temperature does not fall below the temperature of maximum density (2.75°C at the mineral concentration of 6) except in shallow inlets.

The coastal zone of the Issyk-Kool has undergone continuous changes due to the gradual sinking of the lake water level during the present century (at a rate of about -5/cm yr). Shoals have dried up, and bars, spits, islands and littoral banks have newly appeared. The area already dried up during the last 25 years amounted to more than 55 sq. km.

The interaction of east and west winds, which often act simultaneously within the catchment basin, creates a cyclonic vortex with its divergence zone at the lake center and the convergence zone in the lake's periphery, causing the upwelling of cool deep water in the central part of the lake as well as the sinking of warm surface water in the sublittoral zone. As the result, the lake accumulates a large amount of heat during the warm season. Every fourth day is stormy on Issyk-Kool, and this explains the occurrence of a dome of cool water at the lake center, the prevalence of cyclonic current system and the absence of freezing. This dynamics of the lake water causes another feature an extremely high transparency at the center of the dome. Secchi disc reading reached 53 m in that very place in the stormy winter of 1985.

C. PHYSICAL DIMENSIONS

- Surface area [sq. km]   6,236
- Volume [cubic km]   1,738

- Maximum depth [m]　　　　　　668
- Mean depth [m]　　　　　　　270
- Water level　　　　　　Unregulated
- Normal range of annual water
  level fluctuation [m]　　　　　0.2
- Length of shoreline [km]　　　688
- Residence time [yr]　　　　　305
- Catchment area [sq. km]　　15,844

ASI-56 KRASNOYARSKOYE RESERVOIR

A. LOCATION

- Krasnoyarsky District, Russia.
- 53°40' 56°00'N, 90°50' 92°35'E ; 243 m above sea level.

B. DESCRIPTION

Krasnoyarskoye Reservoir on the Enisei River is one of the largest man-made lakes of river origin in Siberia. It is situated at a distance of 2,502 km from the Enisei mouth. The construction of the reservoir started in 1967 and its live storage was filled in 1970. The cost of the project development and the construction of hydroelectric power plant and the reservoir was 802.66 million rubles including 132.56 million rubles for the lake itself. The back- water from the dam extends for a distance of 386 km. The Krasnoyarskoye Reservoir is of the channel type and a long-term storage regulation.

The drainage basin of the reservoir covers three natural zones, forest, forest-steppe and steppe, located in the eastern part of the Sayan Altai mountain range. Mountains are built with ancient crystalline and metamorphic rocks. The drainage network of the basin mainly consists of mountain rivers with narrow valleys, of which 35 enter Krasnoyarskoye Reservoir. The recharge water from the rivers is formed by melting snow and precipitation of summer- autumn period. The annual inflow to the reservoir changes from 60 to 120 cubic km/yr.

The water resources of the reservoir are used for electric power generation at the Krasnoyarsk hydro-electric power station (capacity 6×10^6 kWh). Annual power production is 20×10^9 kW. Navigation and transportation are carried out on the reservoir and its main tributaries (Enisei, Tuba and Abakan) during the ice free period. Timber rafting, commercial fishing and recreation are also among important uses of the reservoir. Further, its water is used for irrigation in the steppe region of the basin. The water supply for domestic needs is mainly met by underground water and only small remote villages utilize water from the lake.

The pollution of the reservoir is caused by the wastewater from mining industry and domestic sewage of the cities Abakan and Tchernogorsk. The projects to cope with the problems of lake shore erosion and water pollution are as follows: bank reinforcement, removal of floating and sinking timbers, sewage treatment, and filling shallow parts of the lake for agricultural development.

C. PHYSICAL DIMENSIONS

- Surface area [sq. km]　　　　2,000
- Volume [cubic km]　　　　　73.3
- Maximum depth [m]　　　　　105
- Mean depth [m]　　　　　　　37
- Length of shoreline [km]　　1,560
- Residence time [yr]　　　　　0.81
- Catchment area [sq. km]　287,000

  All the values corresponds to mean water level.

ASI-57 MANASBAL LAKE

A. LOCATION

- Jammu and Kashmir, India.
- 34°15'N, 74°40'E ; 1,583 m above sea level.

B. DESCRIPTION

Manasbal Lake is located about 30 km north of Srinagar, the summer capital of Jammu and Kashmir State. It has predominantly rural surroundings with three villages, Kondabal, Jarokbal and Gratbal overlooking the lake. Manasbal is considered as the 'supreme gem of all Kashmir lakes' with lotus (Nelumbo nucifera) nowhere more abundant or beautiful than on the margins of this lake during July and August. It is the deepest lake of Kashmir valley and perhaps the only one that develops stable summer stratification. Manasbal is classified as warm monomictic lake and circulates once in a year for a short time. The other lakes in the region either have weak stratification or are polymictic. Close to the northern shore are the ruins of a fort which was built in 17th century by a Moghul king to cater the needs of caravans that used to travel from Panjab to Srinagar. On the south, overlooking the lake is a hillock-Ahtung which is used for limestone extraction. The eastern part is mainly mountainous and towards the north is an elevated plateau known as 'Karewa' consisting of lacustrine, fluviatile and loessic deposits.

The lake has no major inflow channels and the water supply is maintained through spring water inflow and precipitation. An outlet channel connects the lake with the Jhelum River. The outflow of water is regulated artificially.

The local population uses the lake as a source of water, for fishing and for obtaining food and fodder plants. Many people are involved in harvesting and marketing of lotus rootstocks which are extensively eaten in the State. In recent years, tourism has caught up with the Manasbal Lake in a big way and as a consequence there are lots of pressure on the terrestrial ecosystem which is being exploited at many places.

The origin of the lake is still unresolved but there is no denying the fact that Manasbal is very ancient. The local people believe in the legend that the lake is bottomless.

Over the years as a result of human pressure the lake has become eutrophic. The water body is virtually choked with submerged weeds particularly during summer which is the high tourist season. The deep water layers become anoxic with considerable accumulation of hydrogen sulphide.

C. PHYSICAL DIMENSIONS

- Surface area [sq. km]   2.81
- Volume [cubic km]   0.0128
- Maximum depth [m]   13
- Mean depth [m]   4.5
- Water level   Regulated
- Normal range of annual water level fluctuation [m]   1.5-2.0
- Length of shoreline [km]   10.2
- Residence time [yr]   1.2
- Catchment area [sq. km]   33

ASI-58 LAKE TAAL

A. LOCATION

- Batangus Province and Luzon, Philippines.
- 14°00'N, 121°19'E ; 2.5 m above sea level.

B. DESCRIPTION

Lake Taal, formerly known as Bombon Lake, is 60 km south of Manila. It is the deepest lake in the Philippines (172 m) and the third largest in area (234.2 sq. km).

It is a caldera lake, having been formed partly by the collapse of a large volcanic crater and partly by subsidence. Subsequent volcanic activity has modified the morphometry of the lake. During the 10th century, it was connected to the sea at Balayan Bay by a wide channel, but an extremely powerful eruption of the Taal Volcano in 1754 rearranged the shape of the lake and narrowed the outlet to form the present day Pansipit River, the lake's only outflow, which leaves the lake in its southwest corner and travels about 10 km to the sea.

A high ridge, part of the crater wall, rises to 640 m above sea level to the northwest of the lake, upon which is located the chief town in the catchment area, Tagatay City. To the south and east, the land is more gently sloping.

The region is still volcanically active an island of 4,537 ha in the lake contains a crater lake of about 30 ha formed by an eruption in 1911, and a crater about 2 km away from the crater lake was formed by an eruption in 1967.

There are about 4 species of endemic fish in the lake. The most important is clupeid (Harengula tawilis), which is the basis of an important subsistence fishery. The fish fauna also includes important migratory components composed mainly of mullets (Mugilidae) and jacks (Carangidae) which move up the Pansipit River when juvenile and spend their lives in the lake until they are sexually mature, at which time they return to the sea. These fishes also support valuable fisheries, but the indications are that their numbers have been declining due to over-fishing in the Pansipit River. In addition, there is some floating cage culture of Oreochromis nilotica in sheltered bays.

The catchment area is largely deforested and given over to agriculture. Coconut cultivation is important, with additional crops such as coffee, cocoa and cassava grown underneath the coconut trees. Other areas are dominated by grassland (Imperata cylindrica) and there is some livestock raising.

There is very little industry in the catchment area at present. Major threats to the lake include over-exploitation of fishery resources, inappropriate development for tourism and plans to use the lake water for irrigation and domestic water supply.

C. PHYSICAL DIMENSIONS

- Surface area [sq. km]   234.2
- Maximum depth [m]   172
- Mean depth [m]   100
- Water level   Unregulated
- Normal range of annual water level fluctuation [m]   2.0
- Length of shoreline [km]   ca. 82.5
- Catchment area [sq. km]   380

ASI-60 UST-ILIMSKOYE RESERVOIR

A. LOCATION

- Irkutsk Region, Russia.
- 56°25' 58°00'N, 101°25' 104°00'E ; 296 m above sea level.

B. DESCRIPTION

The Ust-Ilimskoye Reservoir is the third reservoir (after Irkutskoye and Bratskoye) of the Angara cascade of reservoirs. It is situated 837 km from the Angara mouth and consists of two parts which are located on the rivers Angara and Ilim.

The general planner of this reservoir was the Institute "Hydroproject" (Moscow). The man-made lake was filled in October 1974. The Ust-Ilimskoye Reservoir is of the channel type and has seasonal storage regulation. Its water resources are widely used for electric power production, transportation and navigation, fisheries, timber-rafting and recreation.

The drainage basin of this man-made lake is situated on the Sredne-Sibirskoye plateau. The sedimentary cover of the plateau consists of the Paleozoic, Mesozoic and Cenozoic rocks. The volcanic rocks are widely spread on the reservoir's coasts.

The total cost of the power plant with the reservoir was 1,257 million rubles, the cost of the reservoir being 127.89 million rubles (in current prices at 1974).

C. PHYSICAL DIMENSIONS

- Surface area [sq. km]   1,920
- Volume [cubic km]   58.9
- Maximum depth [m]   97
- Mean depth [m]   30.7
- Water level   Regulated
- Normal range of annual water
  level fluctuation [m]   2.43
- Length of shoreline [km]   4,000
- Residence time [yr]   0.58
- Catchment area [sq. km]   785,080 (49,000*)
  * The part of the catchment area between the dams of Bratsk and Ust-Ilim hydroelectric power plants.

ASI-61 BRATSKOYE RESERVOIR

A. LOCATION
- Irkutsk Region, Russia.
- 52°45' 56°15'N, 100°35' 103°50'E ; 402 m above sea level.

B. DESCRIPTION

Bratskoye Reservoir is situated at the upper part of the Angara River. It was formed in 1961 1967 by damming the Angara River near Bratsk City. The general planner of this reservoir and hydroelectric power plant was the Saint Petersburg Department of the Institute "Hydroproject". The cost of this project development and construction was 789.2 million rubles including 213.63 million rubles for the reservoir

construction. Bratskoye Reservoir is of the channel type with long-term storage regulation.

The water resources of this man-made lake are widely used for hydroelectric power generation, navigation and transportation, fisheries, recreation and timber-rafting. The capacity of the Bratsk hydroelectric power station amounts for to 4.5×10^6kWh. This reservoir operates in a cascade with the reservoirs Irkutskoye (upstream) and Ust-Ilimskoye (downstream).

The drainage basin of Bratskoye Reservoir includes the drainage basins of Lake Baikal, Irkutskoye Reservoir and its own partial drainage basin between the dams of the Irkutsk and Bratsk hydroelectric power plants. The partial drainage basin accounts for 22% of the total drainage area and consists of two parts; north-eastern plain and south-western mountains. The plain part is situated on the Siberian Plateau formed by thick sedimentary rocks of Cambrian, Ordovician and Silurian systems. The mountain part is characterized by the presence of rocks from Archean to Quaternary period with mass intrusions of gneiss, crystalline slate with seams of quartzite and marble.

C. PHYSICAL DIMENSIONS

- Surface area [sq. km]   5,478
- Volume [cubic km]   169.3
- Maximum depth [m]   150
- Mean depth [m]   31.1
- Water level   Regulated
- Normal range of annual water
  level fluctuation [m]   3.75
- Length of shoreline [km]   7,400
- Residence time [yr]   1.8
- Catchment area [sq. km]   757,200 (157,530*)
  * Part of the catchment area between the dams of Irkutsk and Bratsk hydroelectric power plants.

ASI-62 HO TAY (WEST LAKE)

A. LOCATION
- Hanoi City, Viet Nam.
- 21°04', 105°50'E ; 6.0 m above sea level.

B. DESCRIPTION

Ho (= lake) Tay is located in the western part of Hanoi City, and is the largest of the lakes of the Red River (Song Koi R.) delta. It is horseshoe- shaped and may be divided into two parts; the upper part is small and shallow with a surface area of 176 ha and the lower part is longer and deeper (237 ha). Its surface area has been progressively reduced, from 466 ha in 1960 to

413 ha in 1992, owing to the filling by human population encroaching the lake.

The lake had originally been a segment of the course of the Red River, but is now a semi-closed water body with only small inflow- and outflow-channels. It receives a daily amount of wastewater of about 10,000 cubic m from surrounding urban areas. The increase of population around the lake resulted in moderate eutrophication. The growth of water hyacinth extensively covers the southern shore side of the lake, causing a serious trouble. Mud deposits 50 80 cm in thickness are found on the flat lake bottom.

Ho Tay provides the highest scenic spot in Hanoi. Lake-front open spaces are being developed for various recreational activities including fishing, boating and sightseeing for the citizens as well as for tourists.

C. PHYSICAL DIMENSIONS

- Surface area [sq. km]   4.13
- Volume [cubic km]   0.008
- Maximum depth [m]   .5
- Mean depth [m]   1.7
- Normal range of annual water
  level fluctuation [m]   0.8
- Length of shoreline [km]   1.4
- Catchment area [sq. km]   4

ASI-63 KANHARGAOV RESERVOIR

A. LOCATION

- Madhya Pradesh, India.
- 22°05'N, 78°45'E ; 717 m above sea level.

B. DESCRIPTION

Kanhargaov Reservoir is located in Chhindwara district near the southern boundary of the province of Madhya Pradesh, Central India. The district is well known for its coal mines which have been producing coal during the past half century. This area is hilly with undulating topography, belonging to Mahadeo Range of Saptura Mountains and reaching a height range of 1,000 1,500 m above sea level both to the north and in the southern part of the district.

The reservoir, the largest one in the district, was constructed in 1986 at a cost of 14 million rupees by impounding the River Kulbehra which is a tributary of the Pench River (in the Godavari River system) originating from the central plateau of the district. The dam site is at a distance of 25 km from Chhindwara town, and the reservoir serves as the main source of drinking water for the town.

C. PHYSICAL DIMENSIONS

- Surface area [sq. km]   6.1
- Volume [cubic km]   0.0281
- Maximum depth [m]   20.9
- Water level   Regulated
- Normal range of annual water
  level fluctuation [m]   2 4
- Length of shoreline [km]   18.6
- Catchment area [sq. km]   108

ASI-64 LAKE BA BE

A. LOCATION

- Ba Be District and Cao Bang Province, Viet Nam.
- 22°23' 22°26'N, 105°36'E ; 145 m above sea level.

B. DESCRIPTION

The freshwater Lake Ba Be is the only significant natural upland lake in the North of Viet Nam. It was formed by combined tectonic force and severe erosion in karst area. Surrounding limestone hills rise to 500 600 above sea level. There are a number of caves in this limestone area: the most famous is Puong Grotto through which the Nang River flows.

The lake consists of three parts, Pe leng, Pe lu and Pe lam; hence the name Ba (three) Be (sea). It measures 9 km in total length, with the width between 0.2 km and 1.7 km. The average depth varies from 17 m to 23 m, the maximum depth reaching 29 m. Ba Be is connected with the Nang River by Be Cam Channel, to which the lake water drains during the dry season. The lake thus serves as a natural reservoir for the Nang River system, while Dau Dang Waterfall plays a role of natural dam for the lake.

The beautiful and magnificent scenery of Ba Be and its surroundings has considerable potential for both national and international tourism. The lake and forests around it are designated as a protected area by the government. The lake is also important for the life of the local people belonging to an ethnic minority group Tay (total population 1,283 in 184 families in 1990) as the source of water, navigation and transportation routes, and fishing ground.

C. PHYSICAL DIMENSIONS

- Surface area [sq. km]   4.5
- Volume [cubic km]   0.090
- Maximum depth [m]   29
- Mean depth [m]   18
- Normal range of annual water
  level fluctuation [m]   2.8
- Length of shoreline [km]   22
- Catchment area [sq. km]   454

European Countries with Economic Transition

EUR-04 LAKE BALATON

A. LOCATION
- Somogy and Veszprem, Hungary.
- 46°42'-47°04'N, 17°15'-18°10'E ; 104.8* m above sea level.
  - * Adriatic.

B. DESCRIPTION

Lake Balaton was formed mainly by tectonic forces 12,000-20,000 years ago. Prior to the opening of Sio-canal in 1863, its water level was 3 m higher and its surface was about twice larger than at the present. With its surface area of 593 sq. km, Lake Balaton is the largest lake in Central Europe, but its mean depth is only 3.2 m. The main inflow, the Zala River, empties into the southwestern end of the lake, while the Sio-canal drains the water from the eastern basin into the River Danube. The lake is covered by ice in winter. In summer the average water temperature is 23°C. The strong waves swirl up much sediments, rendering the transparency low. The major ions of the water are Ca^{2+}, Mg^{2+} and HCO^{3-}. The pH is 8.4, rising to higher values during intensive primary production. Oxygen deficiency is formed only temporarily in the western part of the lake in calm summer periods with algal blooms. The distribution of macrophytes is restricted by strong waves to a relatively narrow belt. Only 3 percent of the lake surface is covered by reeds, and even less by submerged macrophytes. The major primary producers are phytoplankton. Zooplankton is not abundant. Zoobenthos represents an important food for the fish. The annual commercial fish catch is 1200 tons. The southern shore of the lake consists of sandy beach, while on the northern shore there are mountains of volcanic origin with old ruins on their tops and vineyards on their slopes. The picturesque landscape and the water ideal for swimming and other water sports attract 2 million tourists annually. The sewage discharge from rapidly developing towns in the watershed, the growing use of fertilizers in agriculture and large animal farms increased the nutrient loading to the lake in the last decades. A rapid eutrophication became apparent by increased production and biomass of phytoplankton. Blooms of blue-green algae are frequent in the most polluted western part of the lake. A eutrophication control program has been formulated, based on intensive scientific researches. Most of the municipal sewage is now diverted from recreational areas. Phosphorus removal was introduced at other sewage treatment plants. A reservoir was constructed to retain the nutrients carried by the Zala River. Pollution due to liquid manure was reduced. Construction of more reservoirs on major tributaries of the lake and a soil protection program are in progress.

C. PHYSICAL DIMENSIONS
- Surface area [sq. km] — 593
- Volume [cubic km] — 1.9
- Maximum depth [m] — 12.2
- Mean depth [m] — 3.3
- Water level — Regulated
- Normal range of annual water level fluctuation [m] — 0.3
- Length of shoreline [km] — 236
- Residence time [yr] — 2
- Catchment area [sq. km] — 5,181

EUR-09 LAKE SKADAR

A. LOCATION

- Yugoslavia; and Albania.
- 42°10'N, 19°20'E ; 5 m above sea level.

B. DESCRIPTION

Lake Skadar is the largest lake in the Balkan district, situated at the southern end of the Dinaric Alps on the border of Yugoslavia and Albania. It lies about 100 km to the southeast of the famous scenic town of Dubrovnik on the coast of the Adriatic Sea. To the southwest of the lake rise high mountains, while to the northeast stretches a wide swamp. There are many islands in the western part of the lake and a number of spots where ground water spouts up from the bottom (Okos). The lake is considered to have been formed by dissolution of limestone in a tectonic basin during the Tertiary or Quarternary period. It is a shallow lake with 8 m maximum depth and 5 m mean depth.

The Moraca River, which is the largest inflowing stream with cold water heavily loaded with suspended solids, has a great influence upon the transparency and water quality of this lake. The Bojana River flows out from the south end and drains into the Adriatic Sea. The phosphate concentration in the lake water is low, and the low transparency is attributed to the large amount of suspended solids in the inflowing water. The lake is rich in fish and waterfowl fauna.

C. PHYSICAL DIMENSIONS
- Surface area [sq. km] — 372

- Volume [cubic km]   1.93
- Maximum depth [m]   8.3
- Mean depth [m]   5
- Water level   Regulated
- Normal range of annual water
  level fluctuation [m]   2
- Length of shoreline [km]   207
- Catchment area [sq. km]   5,490

EUR-30 LAKE SNIARDWY

A. LOCATION

- District of Great Masurian Lakes, Poland.
- 53°45'N, 21°45'E ; 116.1 m above sea level.

B. DESCRIPTION

Lake Sniardwy is the largest lake in Poland. It receives the water from an area about 2,400 sq. km, i. e. two-thirds of the basin of Great Masurian Lakes, the most important lake district in Poland, which contains about 10% of all lake area in Poland and in turn is part of Baltic lakelands in Europe. Lake Sniardwy watershed belongs to the River Pisa and finally - the River Vistuala drainage basin.

The whole Lake Sniardwy region was formed during the last glaciation about 12,000 years ago as the melting product of "dead" ice block. Hilly relief is formed by moraines, ramparts and out-wash plains; sand, gravel and clay dominate substrata. Lake Sniardwy is the central part of Masurian Landscape Protective Area formed to protect the postglacial relief, forest and swamps with boreal and subarctic vegetation, as well as many lakes and pools. In the Protective Area several reserves occur with the stands of rare plant species and old forest; there are also waterfowl reserves like Lake Luknajno biosphere reserve with the colony of mute swan. The area including Lake Sniardwy is a popular study site for botanical, zoological and ecological researches. The Great Lakes area is one of the most important touristic centres in Poland, and Lake Sniardwy offers main sites for navigation and yachting.

C. PHYSICAL DIMENSIONS

- Surface area [sq. km]   110
- Volume [cubic km]   0.6509
- Maximum depth [m]   23.4
- Mean depth [m]   5.8
- Water level   Unregulated
- Normal range of annual water
  level fluctuation [m]   0.2-0.8*
- Length of shoreline [km]   91.3
- Residence time [yr]   .4
- Catchment area [sq. km]   14
  * 1950-1970

EUR-31 LAKE STECHLIN

A. LOCATION

- Potsdam, Germany.*
- 53°10'N, 13°02'E ; 59.7 m above sea level.
  * Place names are not updated.

B. DESCRIPTION

Lake Stechlin with its large number of bights was formed by deep melting of dead ice blocks and erosion of melt water channels after the Weichselian stage of the last glaciation. It is situated in the outwash plain immediately to the south of the terminal moraine of the Furstenberger Staffel. Formations of gravel and sand deposits reaching heights up to 84.5 m above the sea level and approaching the shores are towards the northeast of the lake.

Lake Stechlin has an area of 4.3 sq. km, a maximum depth of 68 m, and is stratified in summer with small hypolimnetic oxygen depletion. Towards the west and southwest, a sand plain follows at heights of 70-80 m above the sea level bordered on the east by a ground moraine. Before 1750, surface in- or effluents were virtually absent. The natural real surface catchment area amounts to 12.4 sq. km of which 80% are covered by forests. The actual sub-surf ace catchment area amounts 26.0 sq. km. The actual water level is 59.7 m above the sea level. Before 1750, it was 60.7 m.

The lake is locally cut deeply into its environs with considerably steep shores on the northwest and northeast sides of the north bay. The Fenchelberg, the highest point (84.5 m a.s.l.) of the Lake Stechlin area, is situated immediately on its northeast shore.

The lake is divided in four basins or bays: the north basin with the maximum depth of the whole lake (68 m); the relatively shallow central basin, 59 m deep; the west basin influenced directly by the cooling water circuit, 41 m deep and separated from the south basin (35 m) by a nearly 1.2 km long peninsula stretching from west to east. During the stagnation phases the hypolimnion of the different basins is not changeable mutually. The volumes of the four basins are: west basin 19,000,000 cubic m, north basin 37,000,000 cubic m, south basin 13,000,000 cubic m, central basin 28,000,000 cubic m.

The shore of Like Stechlin is bounded by a more or less closed large zone of mixed forests mainly consisting of pines, beeches, willows and alders. Allochthonous input of organic matter - mostly leaves, twigs, pollen and fruits from the surrounding trees - are potentially significant for material balance and production in the lake. Open land borders on the shores up to 4.8% only and the trophic level of the lake water is still oligotrophic. Now the input of cooling water circuit from a nuclear power plant and the man-made surface run-in of water from Lake Dagow influence mainly the ecosystem.

C. PHYSICAL DIMENSIONS

- Surface area [sq. km]   4
- Volume [cubic km]   0.0969
- Maximum depth [m]   68
- Mean depth [m]   22.8
- Water level   Regulated
- Length of shoreline [km]   16.1
- Catchment area [sq. km]   26

EUR-35 VARNA LAKE

A. LOCATION

- Varna, Bulgaria.
- 43°10'N, 27°38'E ; 0.05 m above sea level.

B. DESCRIPTION

The Varna Lake, a lagoon formed at the mouth of the Provadijska River, is the biggest lake on the Bulgarian Black Sea coast. It is separated from the sea by a continuously enlarging sand strip 2 km in width. The southern bank of the lake is high and steep, while the northern bank is slanting. The valley bottom in which the lake is located is covered by a thick (10-30 m) mud deposit. The lake is a tectonic unit formed by the rise of sea-level at the end of Pleistocene. The nearby district is characterized by the occurrence of many fault valleys, 30-120 m wide and favored with rich sources of water.

A navigation channel was constructed across the sand strip in 1909, resulting in the invasion of sea water into the lake. Later on in 1976, the lake was dredged along the river course to put another new navigation route into operation, which is 12 m deep with underwater bank slope. The linkage of the lake with Varna Bay by the two channels enhanced the exchange of water by generating slow currents between the two water bodies, and caused changes in the thermal regime, water quality and ecosystem of the lake.

The lake water level is mainly determined by the change of sea level, and partly by the inflow from the Provadijska and the Devnja River. The salinity of lake water is 1.1-1.2% on an average, and the density increases downward from the surface value of 1.0076 to 1.0114 in bottom water. H_2S gas is released from bottom layers under 4-5 m depth in summer, owing to decomposition processes and strong thermal stratification.

The completion of the new channel led to the establishment of a large industrial and electric power generation complex and a railway-port-ferry boat centre on the northern bank of Lake Varna. Their impacts on the lake environments are now under study, and some changes such as the increase of anthropogenic sediments have already been recorded. A large amount of silt, containing rich organic matter, pesticides and other pollutants, are supplied via the channels to the bay causing eutrophication and spoiling sand beach recreational areas.

C. PHYSICAL DIMENSIONS

- Surface area [sq. km]   17
- Volume [cubic km]   0.165
- Maximum depth [m]   19
- Mean depth [m]   9.5
- Water level   Unregulated
- Normal range of annual water
  level fluctuation [m]   0.3
- Length of shoreline [km]   32
- Residence time [yr]   0.8
- Catchment area [sq. km]   2,680

EUR-36 LAKE ONEGO

A. LOCATION

- Karelian ASSR, Leningrad and Vologda regions of RSFSR, Russia
- 60°55'-62°55'N, 34°14'-36°30'E ; 35 m above sea level.

B. DESCRIPTION

Lake Onego is the second largest lake in Europe next to Lake Ladoga. The lake basin is situated on two contrasting parts of the earth crust with different geological histories, Baltic shield and Russian plate. The boundary runs approximately along the line connecting the mouths of the Vodla River and the Shuja River. To the north of the boundary, the shoreline is extremely jagged, and the greater part of islands and numerous fjord-type bays are found. The northern basin is surrounded by hills and cliffs consisting of crystalline rocks. There, land relief forms are oriented from northwest to southeast, following the direction of ice flow during glacial periods. Deep hollows (90-100 m deep) are interspersed with ridges only 1-2 m below the water surface. The southern basin is relatively shallow with a mean depth of 30 m and more or less flat bottom. Shorelines are less jagged, and are frequently covered by marsh.

Tectonic processes in the pre-glacial period, combined with glacial erosion and transport, formed the specific hydrographical network. The history of Lake Onego experienced several glacial periods, when its flora and fauna were exterminated. The last glaciation ended 11,000-12,000 years ago. The lakeshore became inhabited some 9,000 years ago. Some 800 rock drawings or so-called petrogliffs, which were made from the end of the third to the beginning of the second millennium B. C., are invaluable heritage in the history human culture. On the lake shore, there are also a number of wood architectures of 17-18th centuries including world-famous Kizhi-ensemble.

Lake Onego is now the source of freshwater of high quality (total mineral concentration 34-36 mg l-1). It also forms part of the major waterborne transport system in Russia, and serves as a reservoir for hydroelectric power generation and an important fishing ground.

C. PHYSICAL DIMENSIONS

- Surface area [sq. km]   9,890
- Volume [cubic km]   280
- Maximum depth [m]   120
- Mean depth [m]   30
- Water level   Regulated
- Normal range of annual water level fluctuation [m]   0.5
- Residence time [yr]   12
- Catchment area [sq. km]   51,540

EUR-37 LAKE LADOGA

A. LOCATION

- Karelia, Russia
- 59°54'-61°47'N, 29°47'-32°58'E ; 4.8 m above sea level.

B. DESCRIPTION

Lake Ladoga is the largest freshwater body in Europe with a surface area of 18,135 sq. km including the islands area of 460 sq. km. The volume of the lake is 908 cubic km, its average and maximum depths being 51 and 230 m, respectively. The shallowest southern part has a mean depth of 13 m (the lake is divided into four zones taking depth distribution into account).

Lake Ladoga is situated on the borderline between the crystalline Baltic shield and Great Russian Plain, and the geological history of its drainage basin (250,600 sq. km) is very complicated (1). Differences in the geological structure of the watershed are reflected in the structure of both shores and depressions of the lake. Seven types of bottom sediments were distinguished (2); blocks, boulders, pebbles and gravel, sand of various grain size, coarse- grained aleurite silt, fine-grained aleurite silt, and clayey silt. Clayey silt accumulates in the deepest areas of the lake. The other types of bottom sediments are characteristic of littoral and declinate zones.

The principal components of water balance are inflow and outflow, accounting for 86 and 92% of the total inputs and outputs, respectively. Since 1981 the annual inflow has varied between 77.8 and 89.0 cubic km (3). Lake thermic regime is characterized by the existence of thermal bar in periods of spring warming and autumn cooling. Thermal bar divides the lake into two regions - thermoactive and thermoinert, whose water masses differ one from another by physicochemical characteristics (4). Lake Ladoga is influenced by wind waves. The maximal measured wave height amounts to 5.8 m and the maximal length to 60 m (3).

Ladoga water is poorly mineralized - average value of mineralization is 62 mg/L. Once favorable oxygen regime is now getting worse under the influence of anthropogenic eutrophication during the last 10 years. Great attention is being paid to the preservation of water quality in Lake Ladoga. In 1984 the Council of Ministers of USSR adopted a resolution on protecting measures for Lake Ladoga and its basin. Implementing this resolution, a large pulp and paper plant in Priozersk was closed. The governmental program "Ladoga" has been elaborated and is being carried out by cooperation of several different institutions.

C. PHYSICAL DIMENSIONS

- Surface area [sq. km]   18,135
- Volume [cubic km]   908
- Maximum depth [m]   230
- Mean depth [m]   51
- Water level   Unregulated
- Normal range of annual water level fluctuation [m]   0.7
- Length of shoreline [km]   1,570*
- Residence time [yr]   12.3
- Catchment area [sq. km]   70,120

    * Not including the catchments of upstream lakes.

EUR-38 MOZHAYSK RESERVOIR

A. LOCATION

- Moscow Region, Russia.
- 55°30'N, 35°50'E ; 183 m above sea level.

B. DESCRIPTION

Mozhaysk Reservoir was formed by the construction

of Mozhaysk Dam (1955-1960) in the upper reaches of the Moskva River 94 km downstream from its source, within the framework of the Hydroproject Scheme commanded by the Water Supply and Sewerage Board of Moscow Municipality Executive Committee. After its completion in 1961, this small reservoir forms, together with similar three reservoirs (Rouza, Ozerna and Istra Lake), the Moskva River System which provides about 50% of water for municipal and industrial uses by more than nine million inhabitants of the capital city Moscow.

The reservoir stores runoff water from the Moskva River and its two tributaries, the Koloch and the Lousyanka River. The Koloch is dammed at its mouth to protect the old field of Borodino Battle (1812) from submergence, the river water being pumped up to the Mozhaysk Reservoir. Another tributary, the Bodnya, is also dammed to reduce flooded areas and its flow is diverted into an adjacent basin by a canal.

According to the morphogenetic classification of man-made lakes, Mozhaysk Reservoir is referred to as the morphologically simple reservoirs of flood plain/ valley type. Its bed is part of a very old (formed more than 100 million years ago) valley filled up by glacial deposits 30-50 m in thickness, in which a narrow (2 km wide) and deep (up to 25 m) trench was dug by the Moskva River. The mean gradient of the valley bed is 6 m km-1.

The water quality of the reservoir satisfies the requirements of USSR state standards for potable water. Water is discharged through the surface and bottom outlets at a mean rate of 9.4 m3 sec-1 (range from 1.5 to 350-400 cubic m/sec). The rate of water exchange is not large, being larger in spring than in summer.

The catchment extends over the southwestern slopes of Smolensk-Moscow Hills and is characterized by gentle hilly relief with a maximum height of 310 m above sea level. The catchment area is covered by podsols under mixed spruce- birch forests, meadows and arable lands. There are neither cities nor towns and the construction of industrial plants is prohibited. Thanks to these conditions, the water quality of tributaries remains more or less stable, though nutrient loads from arable lands and livestock farms have increased during the last ten years.

The Mozhaysk Reservoir is intensively used for recreational activities of Muscovites and local residents. Within the catchment of the reservoir, sport- fishing is popular and there are a lot of hunting bases, sanatoriums, holiday homes, children's summer camps and country cottages. For the protection of water resources, it is of prime importance to control eutrophication, recreational load, fish fauna composition and fishing activities.

C. PHYSICAL DIMENSIONS

- Surface area [sq. km]   31
- Volume [cubic km]   0.235
- Maximum depth [m]   22.6
- Mean depth [m]   7.7
- Water level   Regulated
- Normal range of annual water level fluctuation [m]   4.8*[1]
- Length of shoreline [km]   119
- Residence time [yr]   0.5*[2]
- Catchment area [sq. km]   1,335
  *[1] Range 2.7-6.6 (1961-1988).
  *[2] Range 0.36-1.03 (1961-1987).

EUR-39 LAKE SLAPY

A. LOCATION

- Bohemia, Czecho.
- 49°37'N, 14°20'E ; 271 m above sea level.

B. DESCRIPTION

Lake Slapy is a multipurpose reservoir built on the Vltava River about 40 km south of Praha, the capital of Czechoslovakia. It represents the third major step of the Vltava Cascade of Reservoirs (Lipno, Orlik and Slapy) built primarily for power generation. Orlik Reservoir (volume 0.722 cubic km, 75 km long, 70 m deep, completed in 1960) with its re-regulation step (volume 0.013 cubic km) is located immediately upstream of Slapy. After its completion in 1954, the Slapy area became recreational and, because of the lack of natural lakes in the country, is heavily visited during summer.

The underlying geological formation is a plutonic massif, the bed being formed by granodiorite from the younger Paleozoic with the inclusion of Algonkian paleo-volcanites. The reservoir is riverine in its shape, with an average width of about 300 m and a length of 44.5 km, and is rather through-flowing. Due to the peak power generation at both Slapy and Orlik reservoirs, the water level fluctuates daily in addition to the seasonal variation with winter minima. Characteristic is the brown water color resulting from the paper mill industry in the upper reaches of the Vltava (some 200 km upstream from Slapy) and also from natural fulvic acids supplied by bogs in the Black Forest Mountains. Other sources of pollution are municipal sewage containing wastewater from food industry and agricultural non.point runoff.

During its history the reservoir water quality has changed several times: due to "reservoir aging" in 1954-58 when heavy water blooms of blue-greens were observed, in 1960 due to construction of Orlik Reservoir immediately upstream, and in 1966 due to stopping the operation of old paper mills in the upper reaches which reduced the load of resistant organic matter and decreased the brown water colour. Also, the use of motor boats and houseboats has been prohibited since 1970. Most profound effects were due to the construction of the upstream reservoir, which resulted in lowering the load of phosphorus due to its retention by Orlik Reservoir and resultant shifting of the blooms to that reservoir. Also, the stratification structure in Slapy changed: until the construction of Orlik, Slapy were fed by a river with a natural temperature regime, whereas afterwards the inflow is mainly hypolimnic water of Orlik. A continuous water quality trend is related to the development of agriculture in the watershed (about 50% of the watershed is agricultural land). During the last thirty years the amount of fertilizers applied to the drainage area has been gradually increasing and field meliorations were carried on in the upper reaches of the river. This is mainly reflected in the concentration of nitrogen compounds (annual mean values up to 5 mg/L N), but also of chlorides and sulphates. Concerning limnological research Slapy Reservoir is, on a long term basis, one of the most intensively studied reservoirs.

C. PHYSICAL DIMENSIONS

- Surface area [sq. km]   13
- Volume [cubic km]   0.27
- Maximum depth [m]   53
- Mean depth [m]   20.7
- Water level   Regulated
- Normal range of annual water
  level fluctuation [m]   5-25*
- Length of shoreline [km]   150
- Residence time [yr]   0.1
- Catchment area [sq. km]   12,900
  * Exceptional.

EUR-41 LAKE BALTA ALBA

A. LOCATION

- Buzau and Braila Districts, Romania.
- 45°17'N, 27°20'E ; 22.66* m above sea level.
  * 1983.

B. DESCRIPTION

The Lake Balta Alba is located in the Ramnic Plain just south of the highway between the cities of Ramnicu-Sarat and Braila. The southern lake shore - loessial bluff up to 24 m in height - contrasts sharply with the almost flat surrounding landscape. Seen from the bluff top, the lake displays a rich- coloured palette: the yellow of loessial bluff, the white of saline efflorescences on the beach, different shades of green belonging to reed, algae and aquatic weeds dominating, the lake water mass in summer, ...

From the limnogenetic standpoint, the lake is a fluviatile "liman" formed by the alluvial damming up of an old Ramnic river bed at its confluence with the Buzau River, as a consequence of Holocene neotectonic subsidence. After the freshwater accumulation, the setting and abrasion of loess-like deposits (Upper Pleistocene - Lower Holocene) modelled the existing lake basin. The present lake, brackish, shallow, dimictic, eutrophic, and pelogenous (= with unctuous, rich-organic, therapeutical muds) is strongly influenced by freshwater inputs from precipitation and Boldu Brook, in connection with the fluctuations of steppe climate. It has only one tributary, Boldu Brook, and no outlet stream.

The sapropelic mud therapy dates back to as early as 1840, the year of the beginning of such treatments in Romania. Recent multi-disciplinary researches characterized the lake as one of the important Romanian sources of therapeutical sapropelic mud, which is recommended for the treatment of some rheumatic, articular and dermatological diseases. The therapy uses the mud itself (either by outdoor application in the camping "la Plaja" or by indoor treatments in Balta Alba Spa located ca. 2 km west of the lake) or the "Pell-Amar" extract (= saline interstitial) solution obtained by squeezing the mud.

C. PHYSICAL DIMENSIONS

- Surface area [sq. km]   11
- Volume [cubic km]   0.0118
- Maximum depth [m]   2
- Mean depth [m]   1.1
- Water level   Unregulated
- Normal range of annual water
  level fluctuation [m]   0.4-0.7
- Length of shoreline [km]   17.5
- Residence time [yr]   1.1*
- Catchment area [sq. km]   91.6
  * 1955-1974.

EUR-43 LAKE PAANAJARVI

A. LOCATION
- Karelian ASSR, Russia
- 66°15'-66°17'N, 29°48'-30°20'E ; 135 m above sea level.

B. DESCRIPTION

Sharp broken forms of tectonic relief with large breaks and vertical displacements dominate in the Lake Paanajarvi region. A lot of picturesque lakes connected by swiftly flowing rivers and brooks with waterfalls and rapids are distributed among relatively high mountains.

The lake basin is situated in large tectonic break which were not exposed to the influence of geological remarking or exogenous processes. The lake is surrounded by rocks, boulders or boulder-pebbles; sometimes banks are sandy. The lake is latitudely orientated; this feature with specific coast forms define original wind conditions and microclimate in the lake region.

The flora of Paanajarvi region is notable for its richness and variety. There is plenty of rare plant species which require national protection. A number of species are on the area boundary.

Lake Paanajarvi is one of the rare regions in Soviet Karelia where ecological systems of exceptional importance are still remaining in natural conditions. The creation of a national park with domestic and international tourism development may be the best perspective for Lake Paanajarvi.

C. PHYSICAL DIMENSIONS
- Surface area [sq. km]   24
- Volume [cubic km]   0.89
- Maximum depth [m]   128
- Mean depth [m]   37.8
- Water level   Unregulated
- Normal range of annual water
  level fluctuation [m]   2.5
- Length of shoreline [km]   50.5
- Residence time [yr]   0.4
- Catchment area [sq. km]   5,295

EUR-44 LAKE G. DIMITROV

A. LOCATION
- Kazanlak, Bulgaria.
- 42°36'N, 25°19'E ; ca. 800 m above sea level.

B. DESCRIPTION

The man-made lake "G. Dimitrov" has been built 7 km upstream from the town of Kazanlak on the Tundja River in the Rosa Valley, which separates the Balkan mountain chain from the Sredna Gora mountains. The rock-filled dam is provided with thick concrete cover on the lake side and a road on its crest. The construction was completed in 1954 and the lake is managed by the office of "Lake and Cascades" Kazanlak Branch. The watershed covers an area of 861 sq. km, and has an average altitude of ca. 800 m and a mean river gradient of 31.4%. The area is built of granite and granite-gneiss, old Tertiary sediments, diluvial and alluvial deposits. One may find traces of tectonic activities - fissured rocks, dislocation zones with sources of hot spring, etc. Its northern part includes the highest peak of Balkan Mountains, where thick and prolonged snow cover is characteristic. Steep slopes favor surface erosion development.

The lake is about 11 sq. km in its surface area and the maximum depth reaches 40 m. It is located in a rich rural region that needs much clean water, and serves to regulate the seasonal turnoff of water supply according to the requirements of consumers - irrigation for fertile fields of both Kazanlak and Stara Zagora, chemical industry in the town of St. Zagora, and hydroelectric power plant.

Lake Dimitrov is also a great local centre for recreation and hot-spring cure because it is surrounded by a number of settlements and dense network of roads. There are good water-sport facilities including a paddle sport base on its northern bank.

C. PHYSICAL DIMENSIONS
- Surface area [sq. km]   11
- Volume [cubic km]   0.14*
- Maximum depth [m]   40
- Mean depth [m]   12.7
- Water level   Regulated
- Normal range of annual water
  level fluctuation [m]   24
- Length of shoreline [km]   26.3
- Residence time [yr]   0.6
- Catchment area [sq. km]   861

  * Maximum.

EUR-47 LAKE VORTSJARV

A. LOCATION
- Viljandi, Tartu and Valga Counties, Estonia.
- 58°05' 58°26'N, 25°24' 26°09'E ; 33.7 m above sea level.

B. DESCRIPTION

Lake Vortsjarv is the second largest lake of Estonia.

The lake depression was formed in the pre-glacial period, but was later transformed by the action of inland ice which partly eroded the lake wall and partly filled the depression with deposits. The present lake has existed since the Middle Holocene. The basic substratum is formed by Middle Devonian deposits, which are exposed on steep banks on the eastern shore of the lake. Elsewhere the lake shore is rather low. The bottom of the depression around the lake is covered with moraine, fluvio-glacial sand and gravel, lacustrine/alluvial sand, clay and peat. About two-thirds of the lake bottom are covered with mud lying on marl. The total volume of the mud and marl amounts to 3.6×10^9 million cubic m.

The number of main tributaries is 18, the Vaike-Emajogi River being the most important. The outflowing River Suur-Emajogi drains into Lake Peipus, the fifth widest lake (3,555 sq. km) in Europe. The hydrologic feature of the lake is characterized by intensive and prolonged high water level in spring, low water level in summer and winter, and a noticeable rise of water level in autumn. On an average, one year is needed for a complete change of lake water. The whole lake is prevailingly homothermal in summer, while there is persistent inverse stratification in winter. The surface water temperature remains quite even all over the lake, local differences not exceeding 2°C. Ice cover lasts for 135 days from November to April. Ice is the thickest in March.

The lake is situated at some distance from industrial centres, and the drainage basin is mainly used for crop production and cattle breeding. About 36% of the catchment area is covered by forests.

L. Vortsjarv has been strongly eutrophied, accumulating a great amount of biogenic substances. Oxygen deficit may sometimes take place under ice cover in the southern part of the lake and near the shore. Typical features of the lake water quality are its high buffer capacity and very large seston contents. The most important factors responsible for the present state of the lake are non-purified or only unsatisfactorily treated wastewater and excessive use of fertilizers in agriculture. Low water level brings about a rise in trophic level and is therefore dangerous. In order to keep the water level within an optimum range, it is planned to build a regulating lock at the head of the outflowing Suur-Emajogi River.

C. PHYSICAL DIMENSIONS

- Surface area [sq. km]   270.7
- Volume [cubic km]   0.760
- Maximum depth [m]   6
- Mean depth [m]   2.8
- Water level   Unregulated
- Normal range of annual water level fluctuation [m]   1.4
- Length of shoreline [km]   96
- Residence time [yr]   1
- Catchment area [sq. km]   3,100

EUR-48 LAKE DRUKSIAI

A. LOCATION

- Lithuania.
- 55°37'N, 26°38'E ; 141.6 m above sea level.

B. DESCRIPTION

Lake Druksiai is located in the northeastern part of Lithuanian Republic on the borderline between Lithuania and Belarus. Its northern part belongs to Belarus, where the lake is called Lake Drisvyaty. It belongs to the River Desna system spreading over the eastern slope of Baltic Hills and the lowland of Desna.

The landscape of the region is characterized by the relief formed by glacial action, consisting of picturesque mountain ridges, ravines, lakes and plains as well as by pine forests and vast water-meadows. In Desna basin, the crystalline bedrock lies at a depth of 750 m, and is overlaid by thick layers of sedimentary rocks belonging to Upper Proterozoic, Cambrian Ordovician, Silurian, Devonian and Quaternary horizons. The lithological composition of Quaternary sediments (90 m thick) deposited during the three glacial periods is diverse. Moraines of clay, clay loam, carbonate sapropel, sand, mixed sand and gravel, etc. have been detected.

Since 1984, the Ignalina Nuclear Power Plant (INPP) started operation using the lake as its cooling pond. The Scientific Base was established on the northern shore in 1978. The lake is now used for power generation, irrigation and fishery, and also for cultural and everyday needs.

C. PHYSICAL DIMENSIONS

- Surface area [sq. km]   49.0
- Volume [cubic km]   0.370
- Maximum depth [m]   33.3
- Mean depth [m]   7.6
- Water level   Regulated
- Normal range of annual water level fluctuation [m]   0.7
- Length of shoreline [km]   60.5
- Residence time [yr]   3
- Catchment area [sq. km]   564

EUR-49 LAKE NAROCH

A. LOCATION
- Belarus.
- 54°51'N, 26°46'E ; 165 m above sea level.

B. DESCRIPTION

Lake Naroch is the largest inland water body in Belarus. It belongs to the system of the River Vulija, a right-side tributary of the River Neman leading to the Baltic Sea.

The lake basin originates from the glacial action of the last Ice Age, and is bordered by 45 50 m high slopes of Sventsyanskaja Range on its north and northeast sides and Narochano-Vilenskaja lowland on the south side. Complicated bathy-orogenic processes led to the formation of many local hollows on the lake bottom reaching a maximum depth of 24.8 m. The lake shores are mostly sandy or shingly.

Atmospheric precipitation plays an important role as the source of lake water, accounting for about 45% of incoming water. The share of surface inflow is 35%. The turnover time of the lake water is eight years. The annual range of water level fluctuation is normally about 0.3 m (up to 0.7 m in some years). Transparency amounts to 10 m during the freezing period, but decreases to 5 7 m in summer. The lake water is homogeneously saturated with dissolved oxygen throughout the year, and has total mineral contents less than 200 mg /L.

Twenty-one percent of the lake area is covered by macrophytes consisting of 38 species. Phytoplankton flora contains 361 taxa, of which only 12 are dominants. There are 9 species of Cladocera, 13 species of Copepoda, 13 species of Rotatoria and 17 species of Infusoria. The community of macrozoobenthos consists of 60 taxa and that of fish of 25 species. Avifauna is remarkably rich and includes such species as Pandion haliaetus, Sterna albifrons and Podiceps ruficollis which are mentioned in the Red Data Book of the Republic.

Picturesque landscape and good water quality of L. Naroch create favorable sites for various kinds of recreation. There are many camping sites and sanatoria on the lake shore.

C. PHYSICAL DIMENSIONS
- Surface area [sq. km]   79.6
- Volume [cubic km]   0.710
- Maximum depth [m]   24.8
- Mean depth [m]   8.9
- Water level   Regulated
- Normal range of annual water
  level fluctuation [m]   0.3
- Length of shoreline [km]   41
- Residence time [yr]   8.0
- Catchment area [sq. km]   279

EUR-50 LAKE CHERVONOJE

A. LOCATION
- Belarus.
- 52°24'N, 27°58'E ; 136 m above sea level.

B. DESCRIPTION

Lake Chervonoje is one of the largest lakes in Belarus Republic. It is located in the watershed of the River Pripiat, a right-side tributary of the River Dnepr that drains into the Black Sea. The lake water originates partly from the seepage of groundwater in the enormous marshy lowland of Polesie.

Surface runoff from the catchment area is partially regulated by diking marsh systems and peat bogs for drainage or moisture supply. Though the shoreline is embanked, natural shores are low being sandy and peaty on the southern side of the lake. The lake water level has now been lowered by 0.4 m in comparison with the former natural level, and fluctuates with an annual range of 0.3 0.4 m. Deeper lake bottom is covered by siliceous ooze rich in decaying organic matter. An intensive sediment re-suspension due to wind force takes place in the ice-free period. Transparency of the lake water becomes as small as 0.1 m in summer. Dissolved oxygen in the lake water is exhausted at the end of the freezing period. Total mineral contents amount to 200 -240 mg /L, and the level of organic matter content is also high.

Eighteen species of macrophytes have been recorded in the lake, and 24% of its surface area are covered by their growth. There are 288 taxa of phytoplankton, their maximum biomass reaching 80 g/m^3. The species number and summer biomass of zooplankton amounts to 197 and 0.8 g/m^3, while those of zoobenthos to 107 and 22 g/m^2, respectively.

L. Chervonoje is intensively used. The lake water is pumped up freely throughout the year for fish farming. Drainage water from diked marshes and peat plots for agricultural uses is discharged directly into the lake from pumping stations. The extraction of lake sediments for industrial uses is estimated at 100,000 t/yr. Fish fingerlings, particularly of Carassius auratus, are released into the lake every year, and the annual fish production amounts to 15 kg/ha. There are villages such as Puchovichi, Liachovichi, etc. along the lakeshore.

C. PHYSICAL DIMENSIONS

- Surface area [sq. km]   40
- Volume [cubic km]   0.046
- Maximum depth [m]   4.5
- Mean depth [m]   1.2
- Water level   Regulated
- Normal range of annual water
  level fluctuation [m]   0.4
- Length of shoreline [km]   30.8
- Residence time [yr]   0.6
- Catchment area [sq. km]   353

EUR-51 LAKE LUKOMSKOJE

A. LOCATION

- Belarus.
- 54°40'N, 29°05'E ; 165.1 m above sea level.

B. DESCRIPTION

The Lake Lukomskoje belongs to the system of the River Ulla, a left-bank tributary of the River Zapadnaya Dvina flowing into Baltic Sea. The town of Novolukoml is situated on the picturesque river bank.

The lake's basin is in a glaciated zone of the last Ice Age. Lake shores are generally low (0.5-2.0 m in height). Foreshore shallows are usually covered by sand, or less frequently by shingle, while siliceous organic ooze spreads over deeper parts of the lake bottom.

The River Zytranka and several other streams flow into the lake. The outflow of water through the River Lukomka is regulated by a dam, by which the lake water level is raised by 1.5 m. The annual range of water level fluctuation is 0.4 0.8 m. Since 1969 the lake has been used as the cooling pool for thermal discharge from Lukomskaya Hydroelectric Power Station (2,400 MW). The water warmed up by 8 12°C is directly drained into the lake and 7% of its area are affected by the thermal pollution.

The whole lake water mass is fully mixed up and homogeneously oxygen-saturated during the ice-free period. Transparency amounts to 10 m during the freezing season and is reduced to 3 4 m in summer. The total mineral content of the lake water is 220 240 mg/L.

About 17% of the lake surface is covered by macrophytes, which consist of 31 species. The phytoplankton flora includes 101 species and has an average biomass of about 4 g/m^3. The number of species and biomass of zooplankton are 69 and 1.4 g/m^3, and those of zoobenthos (except Dreissena polymorpha) are

202 and 8/gm^3, respectively. The biomass of D. polymorpha is estimated to exceed 5,000 tons, and this mussel population filters an amount of water equivalent to the whole lake volume in less than two months. There are about 20 species of fish (dominants: Lucioperca lucioperca and Abramis brama) and crayfish in the lake.

C. PHYSICAL DIMENSIONS

- Surface area [sq. km]   36.7
- Volume [cubic km]   0.243
- Maximum depth [m]   11.5
- Mean depth [m]   6.6
- Water level   Regulated
- Normal range of annual water
  level fluctuation [m]   0.4
- Length of shoreline [km]   36.4
- Residence time [yr]   7.0
- Catchment area [sq. km]   179.0

EUR-52 LAKE UVILDY

A. LOCATION

- Cheliabinsk Region, Russia.
- 55°30'N, 60°30'E ; 273 m above sea level.

B. DESCRIPTION

Lake Uvildy is one of the largest lakes situated in the ancient Urals. Its drainage basin is of tectonic origin, and was formed in Miocene (20-25 million years ago) by the fault dislocation of the Eastern Urals anticline on the boundary of the Transurals Peneplain. It seems possible that its transformation proceeded further due to the tectonic movement during the Quaternary period.

The lake basin is 12.2 km long and consists of three sub-basins separated by submerged ridges and an island chain. The largest and deepest (maximum depth 37 m) southern sub-basin is called Marine Reach. The northern and western (Red Reach) sub-basins are bordered by Beriozovy Island, the largest of 52 islands on the lake.

Lakeshores are lightly cut and gently sloping in Marine Reach, while they are sharply cut and with a lot of islands in the other two sub-basins. The southwestern coasts of Red Reach are high and rocky with steep forested slopes, offering the most picturesque scenery. The western side of the two sub-basins are low and marshy, bearing birch and osier stands. Reeds grow along the littoral zone of the lake. The area occupied by macrophytes amounts to 10 sq. km. Stoneworts (Chara) grows on the lake floor down to a depth of 14 m. Deeper bottoms (to 16 m) are covered by a moss Fontinalis.

The catchment area is not wide, and is located on hilly eastern slopes of the Southern Urals, where pine and birch forests grow on gray forest podzol except for swampy depressions. The greater part of the catchment is drained by two tributary rivers flowing into the northern sub-basin, the Cheremshanka and the Kosaya.

The lake is oligotrophic and filled with transparent freshwater. In 1964-1967, the lake water was channeled eastward from Marine Reach via a small canal to the neighbouring Lake Malye Iradiaghy for supporting a fish-breeding nursery. The most significant consumption of the lake water started in the dry years of 1975 1976 to improve water supply to the city of Cheliabinsk by constructing a deep canal with a watergate that connected Lake Uvildy with Argazy Reservoir on the River Miass. This resulted in the subsidence of the lake's water level by 3.9 m and the decrease of the lake water volume by 0.245 cubic km.

L. Uvildy is intensively used as the site of recreation and health resort. The lake silt is used as medicinal mud in sanatoria located on the lake shore. Coastal radon springs are used for medical purposes as well.

C. PHYSICAL DIMENSIONS(1988)

- Surface area [sq. km]   60.6
- Volume [cubic km]   0.770
- Maximum depth [m]   37
- Mean depth [m]   12.7
- Water level   Regulated
- Normal range of annual water
  level fluctuation [m]   0.2 0.3
- Length of shoreline [km]   117
- Residence time [yr]   19
- Catchment area [sq. km]   144

EUR-53 RESERVOIR VORONEGSKOE

A. LOCATION

- Voronege Region, Russia.
- 54°40'N, 39°12'E ; 93 m above sea level.

B. DESCRIPTION

Reservoir Voronegskoe was formed on the River Voronege at 5.5 km upstream from its confluence with the River Don, based on the "Sojuzvodocanal Project" worked out by the State Designing Research Institute. It was put into operation in June 1972 by the State Committee of RSFSR Ministry of Land Improvement and Water Supply. The total cost of the reservoir was 27.5 million rubles.

The reservoir was mainly intended to reserve groundwater to be supplied to the city of Voronege,

and has successfully served as the reliable source of industrial and municipal water for the city. It also provides irrigation water to its catchment area and recreation sites and architectural beauty for urban residents.

This shallow reservoir is 35 km long, and is divided into five sections according to their morphology and hydrodynamics. Dam Section I is the widest and the deepest (mean depth 4.3 m and maximum depth 12 m). There, the height of wind wave may reach 1.3 m, while the annual mean current velocity is the least (0.8 cm/ sec). The mean depth is only 1.9 m in Section V, where the wave height is less than 0.5 m and the mean current velocity amounts to 1.6 cm sec 1. Shallows less than 1 m in water depth cover 16% of the total reservoir area, being mostly distributed in Section V as well as along the left bank and in bays of other sections. The transitional zone of medium depth (from 1 m to the lower limit of macrophyte growth 5 m) accounts for 64% of the reservoir surface and for 91% of its volume.

The catchment area is densely populated and used for industry and agriculture. There are large industrial centers such as Voronege and Lipetsk along the R. Voronege and a lot of towns, villages and residential areas.

C. PHYSICAL DIMENSIONS(1988)

- Surface area [sq. km]   70
- Volume [cubic km]   0.204
- Maximum depth [m]   12
- Mean depth [m]   2.9
- Water level   Regulated
- Normal range of annual water
  level fluctuation [m]   0.2
- Length of shoreline [km]   85
- Residence time [yr]   0.1
- Catchment area [sq. km]   21,390

EUR-54 RESERVOIR KUJBYSHEVSKOE

A. LOCATION

- Mari ASSR, Chuvash ASSR, Tatar ASSR, Ulianovsk Region and Samara Region, Russia.
- 56°10' 53°20'N, 47°30' 51°30'E ; 53 m above sea level.

B. DESCRIPTION

Reservoir Kujbyshevskoe on the River Volga is the largest riverine water body in Europe and is one of the most important components of the Volga-Kama cascade of reservoirs. Its dam (Volzhskaya Dam) was built near the city of Zhiguliovsk in accordance with the scheme made by the Institute of Hydroproject. The construction of this reservoir was began in October 1955 and completed in May 1957. This multi-purpose artificial water body carries out seasonal, week by and daily regulations of the flows of the Volga. Water discharged through Volzhskaya Dam flows into the Reservoir Saratovskoe which is the next stair in the Volga-Kama cascade.

The reservoir is located in the eastern part of Russian Plain. The middle course of the Volga where the reservoir is situated was formed several million years ago in Pliocene, and was flooded by the water of Paleo-Caspian Sea during its transgression period.

The reservoir is more than 400 km long, and consists of several sections or reaches, of which the largest is Cheremshan Bay with a water volume of more than 1 cubic km. There are many inlets near inflowing river mouths. The right (western) bank is high (up to 300 m) and steep. The submerged bed of the Volga runs near the right bank, forming a zone of maximum depth.

Major tributaries are the Rivers Viatka, Sviyagha and Bolshoy Cheremshan. Ninety-nine percent of the total inflowing water come from surface runoff, precipitation on the reservoir surface accounting for only 1%. On an average, the Volga contributes 43%, the R. Kama 38%, and the R. Viatka 11% of the total water influx. The input of the Volga water to the reservoir is controlled by six upstream dams and that of the Kama by three other dams.

The climate of the region is temperate, continental and transitional from humid to semi-arid climate. The northern part of the reservoir is in the forest zone, while its southern part belongs to the forest-steppe region. After the reservoir formation, daily mean temperature in the coastal area became lower by 1.5°C in spring, and rose by more than 2°C in autumn.

There are a lot of cities and towns along the shore of the reservoir. Some of them such as Kazan, Ulianovsk and Tolyatty have grown into large industrial centers of the country. Irrigated lands are widely developed in the catchment area. The growth of productivity in this region is associated with the increase of water use, which, however, negatively affects the environment and sanitary condition of the reservoir's water resources in turn.

C. PHYSICAL DIMENSIONS

- Surface area [sq. km]   5,900
- Volume [cubic km]   58
- Maximum depth [m]   41
- Mean depth [m]   9.8
- Water level   Regulated

- Normal range of annual water
  level fluctuation [m]   4-6
- Length of shoreline [km]   2,500
- Residence time [yr]   0.24
- Catchment area [sq. km]   1,200,000

EUR-55 LAKE DRIYVIATY

A. LOCATION

- Belarus.
- 55°37'N, 27°02'E ; 130 m above sea level.

B. DESCRIPTION

Lake Driyviaty belongs to the River Druika system (a left tributary of the River Zapadnaja Dvina in the Baltic Sea basin). The lake was originated by the glacial action in the last ice age (about 12,000 years ago). There are eleven small rivers and springs flowing into the lake and only one outlet, the River Druika. Improvement works carried out in 1930 resulted in the lowering of the lake's normal water level by 3 m and the present level fluctuates by 0.3-1 m in a year. The exchange time of the lake water is 2.6 years.

Lake shores are sandy, and the deepest part of lake bottom is covered by siliceous organic ooze. Thermal stratification does not exist during the ice- free period, when dissolved oxygen is also homogeneously distributed in the entire water column. The annual range of water transparency is 3-4.5 m. The total solid content of lake water is 240-320 mg/L.

There are 50 species of aquatic macrophytes that cover 17.4% of the lake surface. Hydrilla verticillata, Najas minor and N. flexilis are among the rare species. The species number of planktonic algae amounts to 169, and its total biomass up to 7 g/m^3, of which more than 50% are accounted for by blue- green algae. The species number and maximum biomass of zooplankton are 103 and 2-4 g/m^3. A marine relict species of amphipod, Pallasea quadrispinosa, that survived from the glacial period was discovered in the lake in 1964, and has been recorded in the Red Data Book of Belarus.

Zoobenthos fauna consists of 75 species and has a total biomass of about 10 g/m^2. The fish community is represented by about 20 species; the most important species are Abramis brama, Lucioperca lucioperca and Perca fluviatilis. The nesting of the swan Cygnus olor, also a Red Data Book species, in this lake is remarkable.

Picturesque landscape and good water quality areas of the lake are favorable for people's recreation. The town of Braslav is located on its northern shore.

C. PHYSICAL DIMENSIONS

Surface area [sq. km]	36.1
Volume [cubic km]	0.2235
Maximum depth [m]	12.0
Mean depth [m]	6.1
Water level	Regulated
Normal range of annual water level fluctuation [m]	0.7
Length of shoreline [km]	37.6
Residence time [yr]	2.6
Catchment area [sq. km]	459

African Developing Countries

AFR-01 LAKE CHILWA

A. LOCATION

- Southern, Malawi; and Niassa, Mozambique.
- 15°20'S, 35°40'E ; 622 m above sea level.

B. DESCRIPTION

Lake Chilwa (sometimes called Shilwa) is a shallow lake (maximum depth 2.7 m) on the border between Malawi and Mozambique in the southeastern part of the African continent. The water surface measures 1,750 sq. km. Being in a tectonic depression south of L. Niassa, at the southern end of the Great Rift Valley, it lacks an outflowing stream; thus the water level fluctuates widely due to the balance between rainfall and evaporation. Four steps of lacustrine terraces encircle the lake and indicate its development history. In the age when the highest terrace, now at an altitude of 650 m, was formed, the lake may have been nearly three times as large its present size, being then connected with the Indian Ocean by an outlet river.

The northern half of the lake is now fringed by a vast area of swampy vegetation dominated by a species of cattail, Typha domingensis, while alkaline mud deposits are found along the southernmost part. The drainage basin, with abundant production of rice, tobacco, groundnut and other crops, supports a population of about 400,000 people. Fishery is extensively carried on in the lake with an annual catch of some 20,000 tons.

C. PHYSICAL DIMENSIONS

Surface area [sq. km]*	ca. 1,750
Volume [cubic km]	ca. 1.8
Maximum depth [m]	ca. 2.7
Mean depth [m]	ca. 1.0
Water level	Unregulated
Normal range of annual water level fluctuation [m]	5-10
Length of shoreline [km]	ca. 200
Catchment area [sq. km]	7,500

* Including swamp area; open water area ca. 600 sq. km.

AFR-02 LAKE CHAD

A. LOCATION

- Lac and Chari Baguirmi, Chad; Nord, Cameroon; Borno, Nigeria; and Diffa, Niger.
- 12°20'-14°20'N, 13°00' 15°20'E ; 280 m above sea level.

B. DESCRIPTION

Being on the southern fringe of the Sahara Desert in north-central Africa, Lake Chad extends over the territories of four countries : Chad, Niger, Nigeria and Cameroon. Owing to the supply of river water from the highlands to the south, it remains a freshwater lake under the prevailing arid climate. Apparently no river flows out from the lake, though some water is said to percolate along the dry bed of the Gazal River to feed the oases of the Bodele Depression about 40 km to the northeast.

The water level is variable as it is influenced by the rainfall fluctuation both seasonally and annually. The lake size was five times its present size (ca. 20,000 sq. km) several thousand year ago, while the drought years in the 1970's made the northern half of the lake (Northern Basin) completely dry and turned the Southern Basin into a densely vegetated area with scattered swamps and open pools (Fig. AFR-02-01).

L. Chad is very shallow even in normal years, averaging 1.5 m in depth. It is fringed by a zone of swampy vegetation dominated by reeds (Phragmites spp.), papyrus (Cyperus papyrus) and cattail (Typha australis). These water plants often form dense thickets or floating mats even in the centre of the lake. Local inhabitants use the stems of papyrus as material for canoe making. There are many small islands formed by the invasion of moving sand dunes near the northeastern coast; some of them are inhabited and utilized as bases for fishing.

Besides the products of agriculture, livestock grazing and fishery, the drainage basin of L. Chad is known for its yield of natural soda, an activity that contributes to keeping the lake water fresh (Q2).

C. PHYSICAL DIMENSIONS

- Surface area [sq. km]   10,000-25,000
- Volume [cubic km]   72
- Maximum depth [m]   10-11
- Mean depth [m]
  (North)   4-8
  (South)   2-4
- Water level   Unregulated
- Normal range of annual water
  level fluctuation [m]   1
- Length of shoreline [km]   500-800
- Residence time [yr]
  (North)   2
  (South)   0.5
- Catchment area [sq. km]   2,426,370

AFR-03 LAKE SIBAYA

A. LOCATION

- Natal, South Africa.
- 27°20'S, 32°20'E ; 23.35 m above sea level.

B. DESCRIPTION

South Africa, near the boundary of Mozambique. The lake is surrounded by indented shorelines and has two elongated bays extending to the north and west. The surface area and mean depth are 77.5 sq. km and 12.6 m. It is separated from the sea by coastal dunes only 2 km in width, and was presumably derived from an old lagoon which later became isolated by sand deposition. The water level is now 23 m above the sea surface, and fluctuates widely depending on rainfall and evaporation, because of the lack of outflowing rivers.

L. Sibaya and its surrounding area are known for the wealth of fauna containing not a few rare species and more than 200 species of birds, hippopotamus, crocodile, etc. Some 1,500 inhabitants on the lake coast live on agriculture and fishery, keeping traditional ways of fishing. Fishery products are partly exported to the other districts.

In the drainage basin, natural forests still survive mainly on sand dunes, but have been destroyed steadily owing to firewood harvest and clearing for agriculture. On the north and south sides of the lake, on the other hand, plantations of eucalypt and pine are expanding partly for use as pulp wood

C. PHYSICAL DIMENSIONS

- Surface area [sq. km]   78

- Volume [cubic km]   0.981
- Maximum depth [m]   43.0
- Mean depth [m]   12.6
- Water level   Unregulated
- Length of shoreline [km]   126.9
- Catchment area [sq. km]   465

AFR-04 LAKE KARIBA

A. LOCATION

- Southern, Zambia; and Matabeleland North and Mashonaland West, Zimbabwe.
- 16°28'-18°04'S, 26°42'-29°03'E ; 485 m above sea level.

B. DESCRIPTION

In 1961, the damming of the Zambezi River was completed and one of the largest man-made lakes in the world was formed. The massive project was undertaken to provide hydroelectric power for the growing industries of Zimbabwe and Zambia. Two power stations, one on the Zambian bank and the other on the Zimbabwean side are in full operation. Covering an area of nearly 6,000 sq. km, the lake has become a year-round source of water for an abundance of animal and bird life, and a sunny playground for both local and foreign tourists. From the urban area of Kariba Township, near the dam wall, the lake extends westwards for 290 km with a width of 32 km.

The story of the creation of the lake and the building of Kariba Dam is an exciting account of modern engineering. But it is also the tale of the tragic but necessary removal of the Ba Tonga people, who held that the river god Nyaminyami would destroy the dam and allow the Zambezi to run free again. As well, it is the story of one of the most impressive wildlife rescue operations ever carried out in Africa. Over 5,000 animals were rescued, including 35 different mammal species and 44 black rhino. Frightened creatures ranging from elephant to snakes were captured for release into areas that now form Matusadona National Park and Chete Safari Area.

C. PHYSICAL DIMENSIONS

- Surface area [sq. km]   5,400
- Volume [cubic km]   160
- Maximum depth [m]   78
- Mean depth [m]   31
- Water level   Regulated
- Normal range of annual water
  level fluctuation [m]   2-3
- Length of shoreline [km]   2,164
- Residence time [yr]   3
- Catchment area [sq. km]   663,000

AFR-05 LAKE VICTORIA

A. LOCATION
- Mara, Muwanza and West Lake, Tanzania; North Buganda, South Buganda and Busoga, Uganda; and Nyanza and Western, Kenya.
- 0°21'N-3°00'S, 31°39'-34°53'E ; 1,134 m above sea level.

B. DESCRIPTION
Lake Victoria, the largest of all African Lakes, is also the second widest freshwater body in the world. Its extensive surface belongs to the three countries; the northern half to Uganda, the southern half to Tanzania, and part of the northeastern sector to Kenya. The lake occupies a wide depression near the equator, between the East and West Great Rift Valleys, but its drainage basin is relatively small, being slightly less than three times the lake's surface in area. The lake water is drained at a rate of about 600 m³/sec, at Jinja on the northern shore, into the Victoria Nile which flows northward via Lake Albert and the White Nile forming the uppermost reaches of the Nile River.

The lake shore is highly indented, and there are many isles in the lake, some of which, especially the Sesse Group, are known for their beautiful landscape, health resorts and sightseeing places. Abundant prehistoric remains found around the lake indicate the early development of agriculture. There are a number of coastal towns such as Kisumu (Kenya), Entebe (Uganda), Bukoba, Muwanza and Musoma (Tanzania), connected with each other by ship routes and also to the cities of the Indian Ocean coast by railways. The dam constructed in 1954 at Owen Falls on the Victoria Nile supplies electricity and water for various uses in Uganda and Kenya.

C. PHYSICAL DIMENSIONS
- Surface area [sq. km]   68,800
- Volume [cubic km]   2,750
- Maximum depth [m]   84
- Mean depth [m]   40
- Water level   Regulated
- Length of shoreline [km]   3,440
- Residence time [yr]   23
- Catchment area [sq. km]   184,000

AFR-06 LAKE TANGANYIKA

A. LOCATION
- Kigoma and Rukwa, Tanzania; Shaba and Kivu, Zaire; Northern, Zambia; and Burundi.
- 3°25'-8°45'S, 29°10'-31°10'E ; 773 m above sea level.

B. DESCRIPTION
Among the chain of lakes on the bottom of the Western Great Rift Valley, Lake Tanganyika is outstanding for its extraordinary north-south extension (670 km) and depth (1,470 m). It is the second largest of African lakes, the second deepest (next to L. Baikal) and the longest lake of the world. Its very ancient origin, only rivalled by such old lakes as Baikal, and a long period of isolation resulted in the evolution of a great number of indigenous organisms, including brilliantly colored cichlid fishes, well-known gastropods with the appearance of marine snails, and so on. Of the 214 species of native fishes in the lake, 176 are endemic; the number of endemic genera amounts to 30 in cichlids and 8 in non- cichlid fishes.

The surrounding areas are mostly mountainous with poorly developed coastal plains except on part of the east side. Especially on the western coast, steep side-walls of the Great Rift Valley reaching 2,000 m in relative height form the shoreline. The sole effluent river, the Lukuga, starts from the middle part of western coast and flows westward to join the Zaire River draining into the Atlantic.

Agriculture, livestock raising and the processing of these products as well as the mining (tin, copper, coal, etc.) are the main industries in the drainage basin of L. Tanganyika. Fishery products, the "Tanganyika sardine" (Stolothrissa tanganikae, Herring Family) in particular, are also important for local economy. Well-developed regular ship lines connect Kigoma (Tanzania), Kalemie (Zaire) and other coastal towns as essential part of the inland traffic system of east Africa.

C. PHYSICAL DIMENSIONS
- Surface area [sq. km]   32,000
- Volume [cubic km]   17,800
- Maximum depth [m]   1,471
- Mean depth [m]   572
- Water level   Unregulated
- Length of shoreline [km]   1,900
- Catchment area [sq. km]   263,000

AFR-07 LAKE NAKURU

A. LOCATION
- Rift Valley Province, Kenya.
- 0°22'S, 36°05'E ; 1,759 m above sea level.

B. DESCRIPTION
Lake Nakuru is a small, shallow, alkaline-saline lake located in a closed basin without outlets in the Eastern Rift Valley of equatorial East Africa. It is the

centre of a most familiar national park of Kenya known for its spectacular bird fauna (495 species), particularly the vast flock of lesser flamingo (*Phoeniconaias minor*).

Being in the Rift Valley where tectonic and volcanic activities as well as climatic changes have been very remarkable, the lake underwent drastic changes during the recent geological ages. About 10,000 years ago, Nakuru and its two neighbor lakes, Elmenteita and Naivasha (60 km south of Nakuru), formed a single deep freshwater lake, which however dried owing to the later desiccation of climate leaving the three separate lakes as remnants. The present maximum depth is about three meters, but the lake water level is still quite variable; the whole lake had been almost dried up several times during the past 50 years due to unknown reasons.

The lake is a soda-lake with a water pH value of 10.5 and an alkalinity of 122 meq/L. Main ions are sodium and bicarbonate-carbonate. The biota in the lake is very simple as in other saline lakes, consisting of phytoplankters dominated by blue-green algae and very poor planktonic and benthic fauna originally lacking fish. However, the lake is highly eutrophic owing to the vigorous growth of a planktonic blue-green alga, Spirulina platensis, which supports an immense number of alga.grazing lesser flamingo and an increasing population of the introduced fish, Sarotherodon alcalicum grahami, though, in the last several years since 1974, the planktonic productivity and the flamingo population decreased abruptly.

The lake's catchment area amounts to some 1,800 sq. km and is extensively utilized for agriculture and livestock raising. The city of Nakuru on the northernmost shore of the lake is a rapidly growing local centre of industry and agriculture. Effluents from the city's two sewage treatment plants are discharged into the lake. The potential danger of pollution is suspected, but it is not yet clear whether the pollution is responsible for the recent changes of the lake ecosystem.

C. PHYSICAL DIMENSIONS

- Surface area [sq. km]   40
- Volume [cubic km]   0.092
- Maximum depth [m]   2.8
- Mean depth [m]   2.3
- Water level   Unregulated
- Length of shoreline [km]   27
- Catchment area [sq. km]   1,800*

    * Including the lake area.

A. LOCATION

- Mashonaland West and Mashonaland East, Zimbabwe.
- 17°52'S, 30°56'E ; 1,363.6 m above sea level.

B. DESCRIPTION

Lake McIlwaine is a man-made lake and the fourth largest impoundment in Zimbabwe. It was formed in 1952 by the Hunyanipoort Dam and is situated on the Hunyani River some 37 km southwest of Harare. It is a lake of many aspects: being a popular recreational site, the City's primary water supply reservoir, a source of irrigation water to downstream farms, an important fishery ground, and, until the 1970s, the receptacle of Harare's sewage effluent. It is, in short, typical of so many urban lakes in Africa and throughout the world. Lake McIlwaine is also unique, being amongst the first of the major man-made lakes on the continent to suffer from what is known as cultural eutrophication, and the first to be rehabilitated to a mesotrophic state through a rational programme of lake management.

Lake McIlwaine's physical limnology is controlled by the climate. The primary factors determining the surface and internal movements of the water are air temperature and winds, with river inflows becoming significant during the rainy season. Maximum air temperatures are in October and November and maximum wind strengths are in September and early October. River inflows are moderate or large during the period from January to March and negligible during the months May to November. Lake levels normally vary within a range of about 2 m of full supply level per annum largely in response to abstraction by the City of Harare for water supply purposes and to satisfy downstream demands. The lake is fairly typical of most southern African manmade lakes in terms of its inorganic chemistry. Most inorganic ions follow similar seasonal trends, with maximum values being recorded in spring and summer, and minimum in winter. This pattern is closely related to the hydrological regime and reflects concentration by evaporation during the hot spring and summer months as well as dilution by riverine inflows during late summer and winter.

Because of its proximity to Harare, the lake is an important recreational centre and the surrounding land was proclaimed as a National Park soon after the lake was formed. Angling is a major attraction and a commercial fishery was established in 1956. From 1960, periodic algal blooms appeared in the lake and caused purification difficulties at the works. But, during the. years 1976-78, phosphorus concentrations in the lake decreased to pre- eutrophic levels by a nutrient diversion programme by the City of Harare.

C. PHYSICAL DIMENSIONS

- Surface area [sq. km]   26
- Volume [cubic km]   0.25
- Maximum depth [m]   27.4
- Mean depth [m]   9.4
- Water level   Regulated
- Normal range of annual water level fluctuation [m]   4.3
- Length of shoreline [km]   74
- Residence time [yr]   -
- Catchment area [sq. km]   2,227

AFR-09 LAKE GUIERS

A. LOCATION

- Senegal.
- 15°55'-16°25'N, 15°45'-16°00'W ; 0 m above sea level.

B. DESCRIPTION

The lake is located on the left bank of the Senegal River. It is the largest reserve of surface freshwater in the country. Embankments have been built at the northern and southern extremities. The lake is connected with the Senegal River by a canal. Its hydrological regime was submitted to the fluvial rising, but is now regulated by the dams constructed on the river. Its principal uses are: irrigation for sugar cane and production of drinking water. In the future the lake could serve as starting point of a canal to Dakar (250 km) for supplying water the town. This shallow lake has a lot of similarities with Lake Chad, but its size permits an easier study of the ecosystem.

C. PHYSICAL DIMENSIONS

- Surface area [sq. km]   175-280
- Volume [cubic km]   0.18-0.65
- Maximum depth [m]   2.5
- Mean depth [m]   1.3
- Water level   Regulated
- Normal range of annual water level fluctuation [m]   2.5
- Length of shoreline [km]   150
- Residence time [yr]   0.5

AFR-10 LAKE GEORGE

A. LOCATION

- Western, Uganda.
- 0°05'-0°05'S, 30°02'-30°18'E ; 914 m above sea level.

B. DESCRIPTION

Lake George lies in the western branch of the Great Rift Valley. It is a small shallow lake of about 250 sq. km with an average depth of 2.4 m. It is supplied by inflows from the Rwenzori mountain range and from the agricultural area towards the northeast; major inflows include Rumi, Mubuku and Nsonge from Rwenzori and Mpanga and Dura from the northeast. The outflow is the Kazinga Channel which drains toward Lake Edward. Thenorthern lake shore is lined with papyrus swamp. The level of water fluctuates very little. At an altitude of 914 m above sea level, Lake George has its main catchment area in the Rwenzori range. Apart from the agricultural lands in the northeast, there are no major sources of allochthonous material. The lake experiences two rainy seasons with rainfall peaks in May and October and the monthly means range from 3 to 194 mm. The lake is highly productive and lucrative fishery goes on. The lake has been fairly well investigated.

C. PHYSICAL DIMENSIONS

- Surface area [sq. km]   250
- Volume [cubic km]   0.8
- Maximum depth [m]   4.5
- Mean depth [m]   2.4
- Water level   Unregulated
- Normal range of annual water level fluctuation [m]   0.1
- Residence time [yr]   0.3
- Catchment area [sq. km]   9,705

AFR-11 LAKE ALBERT

A. LOCATION

- Haut-Zaire, Zaire; and Western, Uganda.
- 1°00'-2°20'N, 30°20'-31°30'E ; 615 m above sea level.

B. DESCRIPTION

Lake Albert is a typical Rift Valley lake lying at an altitude of 615 m between two parallel escarpments, that on the western side rising abruptly to nearly 2,000 m above the water surface. The lake is about 150 km long, with an average width of about 35 km, and a maximum depth of 56 m within 7 km of the mid-western shore. The main inflow is at the south end via the Semliki River which comes from Lake Edward through the western edge of the great Ituri rain forest in Zaire, augmented by streams from the northern slopes of the Rwenzoris. On its course through the forest are several kilometers of rapids which are an effective barrier to faunal interchange between the two lakes. Most of the lateral inflows into the lake from the escarpments are seasonal and contribute very little, since their catchments are small. Owing to an accident of geological history, the overflow from Lakes Victoria and Kyoga, known as the Victoria Nile, originated by uptilting of the Victoria basin in the late Pleistocene and made its way via a previous river valley to a low point along the Rift wall to plunge over the Murchison Falls and to reach Lake Albert at its very northernmost end almost directly into the outflowing Albert Nile.

The water of the Victoria Nile is much less saline than that of Lake Albert. It has therefore been possible to demonstrate by conductivity measurements that even in times of floods the river water does not affect the lake beyond about 10 km from the north end. The Victoria Nile thus serves to maintain the level but has no other influence on the water of the lake except at its northern end though its rate of flow is considerably greater than that of the Semliki. The hydrology and ecology of the lake would have been different if the Victoria Nile had flowed into it near the south end, or alternatively, had joined the Albert Nile further north where it could have had no controlling influence on the level of the lake. In the latter event a small reduction in the rainfall in the Albert and Edward basins and thus a smaller inflow from the Semliki, could result in an excess of evaporation over inflow with a consequent fall in level and stoppage of the outflow. The level of Lake Albert is now maintained above the exit partly by the Victoria Nile which functions in the manner of the inflow to a constant level water still.

C. PHYSICAL DIMENSIONS

- Surface area [sq. km]   5,300
- Volume [cubic km]   280
- Maximum depth [m]   58
- Mean depth [m]   25
- Water level   Unregulated
- Normal range of annual water
  level fluctuation [m]   0.5

A. LOCATION

- Kivu, Zaire; and Southern, Uganda.
- 0°53'S, 29°34'E ; 912 m above sea level.

B. DESCRIPTION

Lake Edward is one of the great lakes of Africa lying in the western Rift Valley. Its length is about 65 km and the maximum width is 38 km. The deepest region is a trench only 5 km from the western shore from which the escarpment rises precipitously to highlands exceeding 2,500 m in altitude. The eastern side of this trench is much less steep and rises with an almost uniform gradient for more than 30 km under water to the Uganda shore.

The Main inflows to Lake Edward are the Nyamugasani River, which drains the southwestern end of the Rwenzoris, and Ishasha, Rutshuru and Rwindi Rivers from the Kigezi and Rwanda highlands and the Virunga volcanoes in the south. The annual contribution from the Kazinga Channel is probably small compared with that from the rivers. The amount of water flowing through the lake, exclusive of evaporation, can be seen at the outflow via the Semliki River at Ishango in the northwest which is 30-40 m wide. The water leaves the lake as a rapid and turbulent stream about 3 m deep over rocks and boulders. It is so clear that the hippopotamus can be observed under water and large numbers of BaRbus are seen facing the current.

The eastern half of Lakes Edward and George is surrounded by the Rwenzori National Park of Uganda. The western half of Lake Edward, including the outflowing Semliki River, is encompassed by the Parc National de Zaire. This whole vast region of national parks from Lake Albert to Kivu - the Great Rift Valley with its lakes, game plains and precipitous escarpments, the glaciated Rwenzoris and partially extinct Virunga volcanoes, the tropical rainforests of Semliki Valley, the mountain forests above 3,000 m and the alpine highlands above 3,800 m - present some of the most dramatic and beautiful scenery in Africa and, with its great variety of organisms and of conditions of existence, is of extreme interest to land and water ecologists.

C. PHYSICAL DIMENSIONS

- Surface area [sq. km]   2,325
- Maximum depth [m]   112
- Mean depth [m]   17*
- Catchment area [sq. km]   12,096
  * Uganda part.

AFR-13 LAKE NYASA (LAKE MALAWI)

A. LOCATION
- Niassa, Mozambique; Malawi; and Ruvuma, Tanzania.
- 9°30'-14°30'S, 34°51'-34°57'E ; 500 m above sea level.

B. DESCRIPTION
Lake Nyasa is the most southerly of the great African Rift Valley lakes. It is about 560 km long and has a greatest width of about 75 km. In contrast with Lake Tanganyika, it consists of a single basin with greatest depth of about 706 m near the western shore about 45 km north of Nkhata Bay. It lies between 9°30' and 14°30' S at an altitude of about 500 m in a tropical climate. However it lies far enough south of the equator to experience marked seasonal variations in wind, temperature and precipitation.

The lake occupies part of the southern end of the Rift Valley system and is to a large extent delimited by faults, particularly to the north and on the eastern coast. In these areas the shores are steep and depths in excess of 200 m are found close inshore. At the southern extremity and along the southern half of the west coast the shoreline is more gently shelving. From here the bottom rises gradually to north and south and, except for a ridge some 20 m high at 10°25'S, there is no trace of separate basins as in Lake Tanganyika. In further contrast to Lake Tanganyika, where a depth of 200 m is found within 20 km of the southern extremity of the lake, in Lake Nyasa such a depth is not encountered within 110 km of the southern end.

C. PHYSICAL DIMENSIONS
- Surface area [sq. km]   6,400
- Volume [cubic km]   8,400
- Maximum depth [m]   706 (2)
- Mean depth [m]   292
- Water level   Regulated
- Normal range of annual water level fluctuation [m]   0.7-1.8
- Length of shoreline [km]   245
- Catchment area [sq. km]   6,593

AFR-14 CABORA BASSA RESERVOIR

A. LOCATION
- Tete Province, Mozambique.
- 15°29'-16°00'S, 30°25'-32°44'E ; 314 m above sea level.

B. DESCRIPTION
Cabora Bassa, a new impoundment in the middle Zambezi River, was closed in December 1974, filling rapidly to 12 m below full supply by May 1975. The principal objective of the construction is the production of 3,870 MW of electricity, making Cabora Bassa the largest power-producing barrage in Africa.

The lake, with five basins, lies along a west-east axis almost parallel to prevailing southeasterly winds. Limnological records, from several stations along the lake axis, indicated homoisothermal conditions until September, the hot day season. From then until records ceased in December, thermocline and oxyclines were present in the deeper eastern basins. Hydrogen sulphide was recorded in hypolimnial waters towards the end of the year. Open water of the shallow, wind- and wave-swept eastern basins remained oxygenated throughout the year.

Water transparency increased five-fold from April to December, increasing too from east to west. pH was alkaline becoming more acid in cool winter months and in bottom waters of stratified basins. Conductivity ranged from 95 to 119 μS/cm with higher values in shallow lake margins. Chemical content of surface waters showed little seasonal or spatial variation and was, in general, comparable with pre-impoundment levels.

Duration of the initial 'productive phase' will probably be shorter than Kariba due to more rapid lake water exchange but indications are that productivity will be higher in the maturation phase.

C. PHYSICAL DIMENSIONS
- Surface area [sq. km]   2,739
- Volume [cubic km]   55.8
- Maximum depth [m]   157
- Mean depth [m]   20.9
- Water level   Regulated
- Length of shoreline [km]   246
- Residence time [yr]   0.5
- Catchment area [sq. km]   56,927

AFR-15 LAKE KYOGA

A. LOCATION
- North Buganda, Northern, Eastern and Busoga, Uganda.
- 1°00'-2°00'N, 32°10'-34°20'E ; 914 m above sea level.

B. DESCRIPTION
A complex of earth movement, which began in the Miocene and eventually resulted in the faulting of the Western Rift Valley, caused the reversal of the previous east-west drainage (1). River Kafu once flowing westwards began to flow eastwards. Lake Kyoga was

then formed by ponding-back of the Kafu river. The lake lies in the flooded branches of the low west-flowing Kafu river. It receives the outflow from the Victoria Nile and is drained northward and then westward over the low northern end of the Rift escarpment (the Murchison Falls) to Lake Albert.

The lake occupies a very shallow saucer-like depression. Depth does not exceed 5.7 m and greater part is less than 4 m. Large areas less than 3 m are covered by a continuous growth of water lilies. Shoreline is everywhere fringed with papyrus and other swamps sometimes forming a belt of several miles width between land and the open water. The lake is divided into three environments: the open water deeper than 3 m; the water less than 3 m deep which is covered completely with a growth of water lilies; the swamps chiefly papyrus, which fringe the shoreline.

The fish fauna of the lake is more akin to Lake Victoria than to Lake Albert. The majority of 46 species recorded are found in Lake Victoria. The lake lacks any large predatory fish except a native species; hence abundance of Haplochromis and other small defenceless species. Nile perch was stocked in the late fifties. The fishery accounted for 60% of national production in 1983. It is Government strategy to start cropping Engraulicypris abundant in the lake.

There are numerous floating papyrus islands in the lake. In stormy weather, they are blown about the lake. This is hazardous to set nets. Crocodiles were abundant in the lake. Fishermen of surrounding communities practice long line fishing, inshore weed fishing or river fishing with primitive traditional gears. The lake provides papyrus which is widely used for making mats, roof thatch, fishing floats and rafts. Most of the operational factories around the drainage basin are now defunct; hence pollution (industrial) is not a problem.

C. PHYSICAL DIMENSIONS

- Surface area [sq. km]   1,720
- Maximum depth [m]   5.7
- Water level   Unregulated
- Normal range of annual water
  level fluctuation [m]   3.8
- Catchment area [sq. km]   75,000

AFR-16 VOLTA LAKE

A. LOCATION
- Ghana.
- 6°15'-9°10'N, 0°20'-1°40'E ; 85 m above sea level.

B. DESCRIPTION
The Volta Lake is a man-made lake created after the River Volta was dammed at the Akosombo gorge. The lake is dendritic in shape and has a generally north-south orientation with an average length and width of 400 km and 25 km respectively. It has a catchment of 385,185 sq. km, excluding its own area of 8,730 sq. km. Nearly 60% of this area lies outside of Ghana.

The lake was created to store up water primarily to generate hydro-electricity. Additionally it was envisaged that it would improve inland water transport, boost fishing, ensure enough water for domestic and industrial use and for irrigation, etc. The project was implemented by Impregilo (Italian Civil Engineering Firm) under the supervision of the Volta River Authority of Ghana, at the cost of £ 70 million, and was completed in 1966.

C. PHYSICAL DIMENSIONS
- Surface area [sq. km]   8,502
- Volume [cubic km]   148
- Maximum depth [m]   75
- Mean depth [m]   18.8
- Water level   Regulated
- Normal range of annual water
  level fluctuation [m]   2-3
- Length of shoreline [km]   4,800
- Residence time [yr]   4.3
- Catchment area [sq. km]   385,180

AFR-17 ZEEKOEVLEI

A. LOCATION
- Western Cape Province, South Africa.
- 34°03'S, 18°31'E ; 5.2 m above sea level.

B. DESCRIPTION
Zeekoevlei is the largest (256 ha) freshwater lake in South Africa, situated on the Cape Flats near Cape Town in the Western Cape Province. The Cape Flats are a low-lying, sandy region which was originally submerged beneath the sea and which separate the mountainous Cape Peninsula from the mainland. The prevailing climate is a Mediterranean, winter-rainfall type. Zeekoevlei is an important regional recreational venue. The lake is a shallow (mean depth 1.9 m), polymictic and hyper-eutrophic urban-impacted system, which has year-round non-limiting concentrations of nitrogen and phosphorus, with mean annual value of 3.6 and 0.55 mg/L respectively. Nutrient loading from the catchment occurs during the winter via the Big and Little Lotus Rivers. Of these, the Big Lotus River

delivers in excess of 80% of the annual hydraulic flow, and non-point source catchment pollution results in mean annual concentrations of 2.2 mg/L N and 0.64 mg/L P in this influent water. The lake overflows only during the winter into a canal leading to the sea. Lake levels fluctuate by an average of 0.5 m between winter and summer.

The vlei is fringed by dense growth of the emergent aquatic macrophytes Typhacapensis and The vlei contains no submerged macrophytes but is subject to isolated infestation by the floating water hyacinth, Eichhornia crassipes. Phytoplankton diversity is poor and the phytoplankton assemblage is dominated year round by the blue-green alga Microcystis. Growth of this alga completely masks the periodic characteristics of the sub-dominant taxa of Chlorophyta and Bacillariophyta. Typical mean annual chlorophyll a and Secchi disk transparencies are, respectively, 200 μg/L and 0.25 m. Maximal growth and water blooms of Microcystis are experienced during the spring.

The prolific growth of blue-green algae, coupled with restrictions of the natural hydraulic flushing of the lake as consequence of the construction of an outlet weir in 1948, have resulted in massive accumulations of organically rich sediments. These currently comprise 21% of the volume of the lake 1,100,000 cubic m, and are thought to play an integral role in the internal nutrient cycling and self-sustaining nature of the system during the dry summer season. Since 1990 Zeekoevlei has been the focus of a management investigation conducted by the Cape Town City Council to ascertain viable options for the lake's future rehabilitation.

C. PHYSICAL DIMENSIONS

- Surface area [sq. km]   3
- Volume [cubic km]   0.005
- Maximum depth [m]   5.2
- Mean depth [m]   1.9
- Water level   Regulated
- Normal range of annual water
  level fluctuation [m]   0.5
- Length of shoreline [km]   12.6
- Residence time [yr]   0.2
- Catchment area [sq. km]   80

AFR-18 OGUTA LAKE

A. LOCATION
- Imo State, Nigeria.
- 5°41' 5°44'N, 6°41' 6°50'E ; <50 m above sea level.

B. DESCRIPTION
Oguta Lake is the largest natural lake in Imo State and is supposed to have originated from a natural depression. This region is located within the equatorial rain forest belt with an average annual rainfall of 3,100 mm, but most of the rain forest has been replaced by oil palm plantations especially around the lake.

The lake has a high diversity of phytoplankton community. It contains as many as 258 species of phytoplankton which fall in 107 genera (Omin, 1983). Despite this diversity of phytoplankton, the estimated level of primary productivity of 160-279 mg C/m³ day (Egi, 1983) is generally low. This may be the reason for the low level of fishery production estimated at 12.5 metric tons/yr (Ita & Balogun, 1983).

The lake is of immense value to the people of Oguta, Orsu, Nkwesi and Awo. In fact, the lake is the identity and pride of the Ogutaman. They draw their water from it. They ob-tain 80% of their protein from it. It has been observed that a total of 2,403 full-time fishermen and 154 part-time fishermen operate in the lake. The lake serves as a septic pool for domestic urban sewage. The local people also dredge the lake for sand which is used for the construction industry. The Oguta Lake Motel with a tourist resort is a 3-star hotel aimed at attracting tourists to Oguta. In the colonial era, the Oguta Lake was a port for the evacuation of palm products. The relics of the jetties used by the United African Company (U. A. C.) still exist today. During the civil war, the Oguta Lake was a marine base for the Biafran Navy.

C. PHYSICAL DIMENSIONS

- Surface area [sq. km]   1.8[*1]
                                     2.5[*2]
- Maximum depth [m]   8.0
- Mean depth [m]   5.5
- Water lever   Unregulated
- Normal range of annual water
  level fluctuation [m]   9.3 7.0
- Length of shoreline [km]   10

[*1] Dry season. [*2] Wet season.

AFR-19 ASWAN HIGH DAM RESERVOIR

A. LOCATION
- Aswan, Egypt ; and Northern, Sudan.
- 20°27' 23°58'N, 30°07' 33°15'E ; 183 m above sea level.

B. DESCRIPTION
Aswan High Dam Reservoir extends for 500 km along the Nile River and covers an area of 6,000 sq.

km, of which northern two-thirds (known as Lake Nasser) is in Egypt and one-third (called Lake Nubia) in Sudan.

The dam, completed in 1968 at a distance of 7 km south of Aswan City, is a rockfill dam made of granite rocks and sands and provided with a verticalcutoff wall consisting of very impermeable clay. The structure is 2,325 m long, 111 m high over the original river bed, and 40 m and 980 m wide, respectively, at its crest and bottom. Nile flow is allowed to pass only through the open-cut channel at the eastern side of the dam, where six tunnel inlets provided with steel gates are constructed for discharge control and water supply to power plants. An escape is also provided at the western side of the dam to permit excess water discharge.

The long reservoir has 100 side arms called khors, more on the eastern shore than on the western shore. The total capacity of the reservoir (162 cubic km) consists of the dead storage of 31.6 cubic km (85-147 m a.s.l. of lake water level), the active storage of 90.7 cubic km (147-174 m) and the emergency storage for flood protection of 41 cubic km (175-182 m). The reservoir is surrounded by rocky desert terrain. To the west is the great Sahara Desert, and the Eastern Desert on the east side extends to the Red Sea.

The Aswan High Dam contributed greatly to the economic development of Egypt by supplying 15% more irrigation water and about 2,000 MW hydroelectricity and protecting the lower reaches of the Nile from flood disasters. On the other hand, however, its environmental impacts were serious. The rapid siltation near the head of the reservoir may dam up the narrow Nile valley in Nubia in a relatively short time. Whereas floods have been prevented along the Nile, the erosion increased along its lower courses and the transgression of Nile delta on the Mediterranean coast is taking place. The loss of soil fertility and the increase of soil salinity are noticed in cultivated fields along the Nile owing to the cease of annual silt and flood water supply.

C. PHYSICAL DIMENSIONS

- Surface area [sq. km]   6,000
- Volume [cubic km]   162
- Maximum depth [m]   110
- Mean depth [m]   70
- Water level   Regulated
- Normal range of annual water
  level fluctuation [m]   25
- Length of shoreline [km]   ca. 9,000
- Catchment area [sq. km]   2,849,000

A. LOCATION

- Gamo Gofa, Ethiopia; and Rift Valley and Eastern, Kenya.
- 2°23'4°35'N, 35°50'36°44'E ; 360.4 m above sea level.

B. DESCRIPTION

Lake Turkana is situated in the Great Rift Valley in the northwestern part of Kenya. Volcanic activity was frequent during the creation of the Rift Valley and lavas from the Quaternary and Tertiary ages cover much of the floor of the valley in Kenya. The lavas are mainly of alkaline type, which has important implications for the chemical composition of lakes in this area. In the Lake Turkana basin, Tertiary volcanic rocks are found in the south and along most of the western side of the lake, while a later lava flow (Pleistocene) forms a barrier in the southern end of the lake.

Quaternary sediments dominate the western and northern side of the lake. L. Turkana is in an arid and hot area. The mean annual rainfall in most of the lake surroundings is less than 250 mm. The occurrence of rainfall is very erratic and unpredictable, although the probability of rainfall is the highest during the "long rains" in March May. The air temperature recordings at Lodwar show a seasonal pattern with the lowest temperatures in July August, a wide range between 19.5 and 39.9°C, and a mean daily temperature of 29.26°C. The lake is exposed to frequent strong winds, the prevailing wind direction being from the southeast.

The main tributary is the River Omo, which enters the lake from the north and contributes more than 90% of the total water influx. Other rivers are temporary, flooding only during sporadic rains. The second largest river, Turkwel River, is now being dammed for hydroelectric power generation at Turkwel Gorge ca. 150 km west of the lake.

L. Turkana has no outlet, and water is lost from the lake mainly by evaporation. The evaporation rate has been estimated at 2,335 mm/yr. The water level of this closed basin lake is determined by the balance between the influx from rivers and groundwater and the evaporation from the lake surface. Therefore the level is sensitive to climatic variations, and subject to marked seasonal fluctuations as well as to long-term periodical changes.

The development of phytoplankton is limited by the availability of nitrate and light. Light limitation was caused by turbid water and vertical mixing. The sustainable yield of traditionally exploited fish from open lake was estimated to be 15,000 - 30,000 t/yr.

C. PHYSICAL DIMENSIONS

- Surface area [sq. km]   6,750
- Volume [cubic km]   203.6
- Maximum depth [m]   109
- Mean depth [m]   30.2
- Water level   Unregulated
- Normal range of annual water
  level fluctuation [m]   ca.11.5
- Residence time [yr]   12.5
- Catchment area [sq. km]   130,860

Latin America and the Caribbean Developing Countries

NAM-41 LAKE AMATITLAN

A. LOCATION

- Amatitlan, Guatemala.
- 14°28'N, 90°36'W ; 1,188 m above sea level.

B. DESCRIPTION

Lake Amatitlan (amatl = letter, titlan = mail in the pipil language) is the fourth largest water body in Guatemala, located close to the south of the capital city (alt. 1,500 m) at an altitude of 1,188 m above sea level. The lake consists of two basins connected by a narrow constriction, where a dry dock was constructed to let the railway pass through. This separated the lake into two water bodies with different physical, chemical and biological charac-teristics. The western basin receives all pollution loads coming from the southern part of the capital city as well as from the whole catchment area via the Villalobos River. The water of the same basin is drained by the Michatoya River, which is used for hydroelectric power generation.

The lake is directly and negatively affected by the rapidly growing impacts from the capital area, through 1) population growth, 2) consumption of forest trees for fuel, 3) inadequate land use, 4) industrial development in the catchment area, 5) lack of environment consciousness and environmental education among the inhabitants, 6) almost no administrative/legal control for environmental protection, and 7) absence of proper foresight and management program.

Despite these circumstances, L. Amatitlan and surrounding valleys, mountains and nearby volcanoes present a unique landscape, making the area a recreation park for a lot of visitors. The lake has also been used in other multiple ways. In pre-Columbian days, it was a place for rituals where offerings were deposited. During the colonial times, the lake was a center of fisheries and its catchment area was the most important site of production of cochineal, which was the main product for export when industrial chemicals had not yet replaced the natural dye. The lake water is also being used for domestic use, irrigation and industrial activities.

C. PHYSICAL DIMENSIONS

- Surface area [sq. km]   15.2
- Volume [cubic km]   0.286
- Maximum depth [m]   33
- Mean depth [m]   18
- Water level   Unregulated
- Normal range of annual water
  level fluctuation [m]   1.5-2.3
- Catchment area [sq. km]   368

NAM-59 LAKE CHAPALA

A. LOCATION

- Jalisco, Mexico.
- 20°06'20°18'N, 102°42'103°25'W ; 1,524 m above sea level.

B. DESCRIPTION

Lake Chapala is the largest natural lake in Mexico, located 42 km south of the metropolitan area of Guadalajara. Hydrologically it belongs to the Rio Lerma Lago de Chapala Rio Santiago drainage system, one of the most important in Mexico. The main tributary R. Lerma supplies almost half of the water input, while the R. Santiago drains the lake water to the Pacific Ocean.

This region, the Mesa Central Region, is a highly unstable geological zone. The lake forms part of an east west oriented graben which is a Tertiary lake system where the majority of once existed lakes are now dry or almost dry. The geological history of the lake is poorly known. It is thought that the present lake basin and the R. Santiago outflow originated in the middle Pleistocene or the late Pliocene. The original drainage was probably from the west end of the lake directly to the Pacific Ocean, but uplifting blocked that flow establishing the present R. Santiago drainage. Terraces provide evidence of lake water level variation due to climatic changes during the Pleistocene.

The catchment area is large as compared with the lake area, amounting to 52,500 sq. km. Sixteen percent of this area drains directly into the lake via small streams and runoff, while the remainder belongs to the watershed of R. Lerma. The climate is moderate, tropical and sub-humid with a single summer rainy season. Winter rains are less than 5% of the annual precipitation. Average annual evaporation (1,910 mm) greatly exceeds annual precipitation (781 mm in average).

Principal uses of the lake are irrigation, tourism, recreation and fisheries. In addition, it is the main water source for Guadalajara City with a population in excess of 4.5 million. The city used 2.108×10^8 m^3 of water in 1986, and water demands are increasing at a rate of 4% per year owing to urban, agricultural and industrial development. Principal industries in the lake's drainage basin are chemical, petrochemical and food processing. However, 93% of the water consumption in the basin are for agriculture. Predominantly untreated wastewaters are released to the R. Lerma. In the lower part of the river near the lake, much of the organic loading comes from pig farms.

C. PHYSICAL DIMENSIONS

- Surface area [sq. km]   1,112
- Volume [cubic km]   7.9
- Maximum depth [m]   10.5
- Mean depth [m]   7.2
- Water level   Regulated
- Normal range of annual water
  level fluctuation [m]   1.2
- Length of shoreline [km]   15
- Residence time [yr]   10.2
- Catchment area [sq. km]   52,500

NAM-60 LAGO XOLOTLAN

A. LOCATION

- Leon and Managua, Nicaragua.
- 12°30'N, 86°45'W ; 37.8 m above sea level.

B. DESCRIPTION

Lago Xolotlan, also known as Lake Managua, is situated in the Nicaraguan hydrographic depression or Nicaraguan rift valley, which is separated from the Pacific Ocean by a strip of lowlands, to the northwest of Lake Nicaragua, the largest lake in Central America. The two lakes put together cover almost 10% of the country's total area.

The depression is probably a graben structure

formed in the late Tertiary or Quaternary period, though the origin of these two lakes is often described as tectonic or volcanic. There is considerable volcanic activity along the rift valley, and part of it is employed for geo-thermal energy generation.

Lake Managua is endorheic, or a closed lake system in which evaporation approximately equals inflow, and its water level is controlled primarily by evaporation. According to the Nicaraguan Institute of Natural Resources and Environment (IRENA), there are stratigraphic evidences that the lake water level was once higher than the present level by 10 15 m. The lake would then have formed a single great inland water body together with L. Nicaragua. A broad river had connected the two lakes until the 16th century. The remnant of this connection, the Rio Tipitapa was a free-flowing stream as late as in 1840, but ceased to function as a regular outflow by 1850 and now serves as only an occasional overflow mechanism. The total inputs of water are so closely balanced with the average evaporation (2,270 mm/yr) that the overflow across the threshold of the Rio Tipitpa of 40.75 m has occurred only three times (1933, 1955 and 1982) in recent history.

The lake's mean depth is 7.8 m and the deepest point (26 m) is found in a pit near the volcanic Momotombito Island. A greater part of the drainage basin is located to the north of the lake and drained by three major tributary rivers, Rio Viejo, Rio Sinecapa and Rio Pacora. The total inputs of water varies widely within the drainage basin, geographically, annually and seasonally.

The "dirty dozen" of pesticides from agricultural and pasture lands contaminate the lake. Untreated sewage of one million population of Managua City on the southern shore is also poured into the lake. About 300 small industries discharge their effluents containing mercury, lead other heavy metals and pollutants. Inflowing sediments are mostly fine particles and rich in organic matter. Furthermore, wastes of geothermal energy plants as well as hot spring water containing rich arsenic salts, boron and other substances enter the lake.

C. PHYSICAL DIMENSIONS

- Surface area [sq. km]   1,016
- Volume [cubic km]   7.97
- Maximum depth [m]   26
- Mean depth [m]   7.8
- Length of shoreline [km]   200
- Residence time [yr]   Endorheic
- Catchment area [sq. km]   6,668

SAM-01 REPRESA DO LOBO (BROA RESERVOIR)

A. LOCATION
- Sao Paulo State, Brazil.
- 22°12'S, 47°51'W ; 710 m above sea level.

B. DESCRIPTION

Broa Reservoir is a man-made lake at the centre of San Paulo State of Brazil created in a tropical savanna (cerrado) region in 1936 by damming up the Itaqueri River, a small tributary of the Rio Parana. At present, however, the lake is turned into an area of environmental protection because of its importance as a recreation area of scenic beauty and of scientific activities in and around the lake. Large scientific and educational projects are now in progress.

The lake is 7.5 km long and has a very flat basin with a mean water depth of 3 m. A maximum depth of 12 m is observed near the dam site. The water level fluctuates within a range of 1.5 m, being high in April at the end of rainy season and low in September at the end of dry season. A large portion of its catchment area is covered by sandy soils. which are very aged and extremely infertile. The lake water is also oligotrophic and low in nitrogen level, and certain heavy metals often limit phytoplankton production.

Since the lake is located only 100 km apart from large reservoir systems of S. Paulo State and its water remains relatively free from eutrophication and pollution, it serves as an important standard system for comparison with the large eutrophied reservoirs. The limnology of this reservoir was opened by Brazilian scientists in 1971. Several climatological, hydrological, biological and water chemistry aspects were studied. The researches also cover the ecology, physiology and chemistry of almost all organisms present in the lake. The number of scientific papers so far published regarding this lake now amounts to approximately 200. including several masters and doctoral theses prepared at the University of S. Paulo and Federal University of S. Carlos. The Centre for Hydrological Researches and Applied Ecology, University of S. Paulo, is currently engaged in scientific projects including the modelling of Broa Reservoir system. Educational programs using the lake area as a natural laboratory have also started since 1985.

C. PHYSICAL DIMENSIONS
- Surface area [sq. km]   7
- Volume [cubic km]   0.022
- Maximum depth [m]   12.0
- Mean depth [m]   3.0
- Water level   Regulated
- Normal range of annual water level fluctuation [m]   1.5
- Length of shoreline [km]   18.3
- Residence time [yr]   0.1
- Catchment area [sq. km]   280

SAM-02 LAGO NAHUEL HUAPI (LAKE NAHUEL HUAPI)

A. LOCATION
- Rio Negro Province, Argentina.
- 40°40'-41°10'S, 71°10'-71°50'W ; 740-767 m above sea level.

B. DESCRIPTION

Nahuel Huapi is a glacial lake located along the eastern slope of Southern Andean Range with a maximum length of 67 km and a maximum width of 10 km. Thelake resembles in its shape "a gigantic amoeba with enormous tentacles extending in all directions to form (1)" a number of arms or fjords. It is also encircled by many smaller lakes. Mountains fringe almost all its coastline; there is a succession of bays and coves, shingle and sandy beaches, perpendicular rocky cliffs, steep promontories, and wooded isthmuses and peninsulas.

The lake offers one of the nicest landscapes in South America, and has been included since 1909 in Nahuel Huapi National Park, the largest of Argentine national parks (785,000 ha). The international city of San Carlos de Bariloche, growing up very fast on the southeastern margin of the lake, attracts every year lots of tourists with pleasant summer weather and winter sports.

The report of a Swedish South-American expedition in 1953-1954 (1) states that "the luxuriant forests of Austrocedrus and Nothofagus surrounding its solitary fjords contrast with the scanty aquatic macrophytes" and that "the scarcity of the latter is partly dependent on the very limited shallow water areas..." This situation, however, changed in the last years when a rapid cultural eutrophication was observed in some small and less deep inlets of the lake, particularly near the city of Bariloche, though the main body of Nahuel Huapi remains oligotrophic. Thus, a lot of macrophytes, especially Scirpus californicus, cover those inlets and are expanding in some arms. Those arms are also rich in nutrients and phytoplankton owing to the result of human activities. Protective measures should be taken before the eutrophication and other kinds of pollution spoil the value of the National Park, where themunicipal authorities of Bariloche have jurisdiction of administration.

C. PHYSICAL DIMENSIONS
- Surface area [sq. km] — 646
- Maximum depth [m] — >300
- Water level — Unregulated
- Length of shoreline [km] — 357
- Catchment area [sq. km] — 2,758

SAM-03 EZEQUIEL RAMOS MEXIA RESERVOIR

A. LOCATION
- Rio Negro Province, Argentina.
- 39°50'S, 66°20'W ; 381 m above sea level.

B. DESCRIPTION

Ezequiel Ramos Mexia Reservoir is a man-made lake in the Southern Andean Range, about 600 km away from Bahia Blanca. The lake was formed in 1972 by the damming of Limay River, which flows out from Lake Nahuel Huapi. The Limay Valley is formed by the 10-30 m thick layer of well-graded pebbles mixed with 30% of sand. The stratigraphic structure of the lake district consists of three kinds of sediments; a) Cretaceous sediments emerging continuously on both sides of the reservoir, b) Cenozoic sediments of conglomerates of variable sandy and clayey matrix, and c) recent sediments of fine to very fine sands forming dunes up to 7 m high on the northeastern side of the reservoir.

The lake water is soft, neutral to slightly alkaline, basically bicarbonate- calcic. The chlorophyll concentration and primary production are relativel low because of the low concentrations of nutrients (inorganic nitrogen and total phosphorus) and the short residence time. Therefore, the reservoir may be classified as an oligo-mesotrophic lake.

C. PHYSICAL DIMENSIONS
- Surface area [sq. km] — 816
- Volume [cubic km] — 20.2
- Maximum depth [m] — 60
- Mean depth [m] — 24.7
- Water level — Regulated
- Length of shoreline [km] — 346
- Residence time [yr] — 1
- Catchment area [sq. km] — 24,420

SAM-04 LAGO TITICACA (LAKE TITICACA)

A. LOCATION
- Puno, Peru; and La Paz, Bolivia.
- 14°07'-17°08'S, 68°02'-71°06'W ; 3,812 m above sea level.

B. DESCRIPTION

Lake Titicaca is the largest freshwater lake in South America, located on the border between Peru and Bolivia between the two snowy mountain ranges of East and West Cordillera in the central Andes. The lake is 8,372 sq. km wide, including both the deep main basin (Lago Mayor) and the shallow sub-basin (Lago Pequeno), and its altitude (3,812 m) is unrivalled among large lakes of this size class in the world.

The distribution of old coastal terraces indicates that a huge body of water reaching as far south as the Uyuni Depression once existed during an inter- glacial period of the Pleistocene, but the lake's size has been greatly reduced due to the increasing aridity of climate and the formation of an effluent stream. The water of Titicaca is now drained via the Rio Desaguadero into Lago Poopo, which, however, has no outlet to the sea.

The whole catchment area on the high plateau of Altiplano remains almost treeless, and is covered by coarse grasses with scattered fields of potato, barley, quinoa (Chenopodium quinoa) and the other local crops. The lake is fringed by a swampy zone of totora (Scirpus tatora), which is indispensablefor the life of inhabitants on the shore, furnishing materials for the famous reed-boats and floating gardens where they grow potatoes.

The line between Puno (Peru) at the northwestern end of the lake and Guaqui (Bolivia) on the southwestern shore is an important shipping route for Bolivia. an inland country without seaside territory. Recent development of cities with manufacturing industry and a few sightseeing sites are going to affect the quality of the lake water to a certain extent.

C. PHYSICAL DIMENSIONS
- Surface area [sq. km] — 8,372
- Volume [cubic km] — 93
- Maximum depth [m] — 281
- Mean depth [m] — 107
- Water level — Unregulated
- Length of shoreline [km] — 1,125
- Residence time [yr] — 1,343
- Catchment area [sq. km] — 58,000

SAM-05 LAGO DE VALENCIA (LAKE VALENCIA)

A. LOCATION
- Aragua and Carabobo, Venezuela.
- 10°05'-10°16'N, 67°35'-67°52'W ; 405 m above sea level.

B. DESCRIPTION

Lake Valencia is the largest natural freshwater lake of Venezuela. It is located in the central-north part of the country, which is the most densely populated. Lake Valencia lies on an east-west tectonic depression between two ranges of mountains: Cordillera de la Costa on the north and the Serrania del Interior in the south. The graben originated probably at the end of the Tertiary. As it developed, flowing waters of river Valencia were dammed and the lake was first established in the late Pliocene. Peeters (1968) recognizes four different evolutionary periods for Lake Valencia. They are related to the alternation of humid and dry climate. Thirteen thousand years ago the lake basin was probably dry (Bradbury, et al., 1981). The lake drained into a tributary of Orinoco River until the beginning of the 18th century. However, due to a negative water balance the level of the lake declined very fast (7.5 m/yr, Bockh, 1956). The lake became endorheic about 250 years ago, when the discharge level (427 m) was exceeded due to desiccation. Intensive human intervention of the watershed and a reduction of groundwater flow have been mentioned for causing that rapid decline of the lake level. A minimum was achieved in 1976 (400.8 m above sea level). However, the lake level has recovered to 405 m with water provided from another watershed for urban consumption. Incoming untreated wastewater from domestic, agricultural and industrial activities of about 2 million people contribute to eutrophication, contamination and salinization of the lake. The use of the lake as water source for domestic activities and for irrigation is restricted by the high salt content (electric conductivity ca. 2000 μmhos/cm). Commercial fishing and recreation are also very limited by the precarious sanitary conditions of the water. Permanent algal blooms, high fish mortality, stench, etc. prevent the practice of aquatic sports and tourism.

C. PHYSICAL DIMENSIONS
- Surface area [sq. km]   350
- Volume [cubic km]   6.3
- Maximum depth [m]   39
- Mean depth [m]   18
- Water level   Unregulated

- Length of shoreline [km]   117
- Residence time [yr]*
- Catchment area [sq. km]   2,646
  * No surface outflow (endorheic).

SAM-06 SAN ROQUE RESERVOIR

A. LOCATION
- Province of Cordoba, Argentina.
- 31°21'S, 64°30'W ; 600 m above sea level.

B. DESCRIPTION

San Roque Reservoir is located in the Provionce of Cordoba at 600 m above sea level in Punilla Valley. It was created by the construction of the dams - the first one was built in 1888 and the second one, only a few meters distant from the former dam, replaced it in 1944 - for supplying tap water to the city of Cordoba, covering irrigation water needs, controlling floods, hydroelectric power generation and recreational purposes. The Cosquin and San Antonio Rivers and Las Mojarras and Los Chorrillos Streams flow into the reservoir, which is drained by the Suquia.

The reservoir is situated on an inverse fault by which Punilla Valley was formed. The risen botck (eastern side) corresponds to the Sierras Chicas. Geologically, it lies on a metamorphic crystalline basement covered by continental tertiary sediments, though there are different types of intrusion in its margilal parts, such as granite and diorite in the western margin, crystalline schist and limestone in the eastern margin, and quarternary deposits in the northern and southern margin.

The catchment area lies in a moderate subtropical climate with an average annual precipitation of 650 mm and an average humidity of 65%. San Roque Reservoir plays an important role as the source of water for domestic uses in Cordoba city as well as for industries and irrigation. Its significance as hydroelectric power generator depends on the requirements from industrial and other sectors. Besides, it has encouraged the development of recreational activities in the territory's central area, e. g. sport-fishing, various water sports, motor boat races, cruising, etc. More than 50% of facilities for tourist reception in Cordoba Province are concentrated in the Valley of Punilla. Villa Carlos Paz area-an entrance gate to Cordoba Mountains-has the highest tourist density, and offers a variety of bathing sites.

C. PHYSICAL DIMENSIONS
- Surface area [sq. km]   17

- Volume [cubic km] — 0.19
- Maximum depth [m] — 25.0
- Mean depth [m] — 11.0
- Water level — Regulated
- Normal range of annual water
  level fluctuation [m] — 8.0
- Length of shoreline [km] — 54.5
- Residence time [yr] — 0.1-0.7
- Catchment area [sq. km] — 1,750

SAM-07 LAGO LACAR (LAKE LACAR)

A. LOCATION
- Neuquen, Argentina.
- 40°11'S, 71°32'W ; 630 m above sea level.

B. DESCRIPTION

Lake Lacar is located at approximately 40 degrees of south latitude and 71 degrees of west longitude in the province of Neuquen. The lake is embeded in the Andes Mountains Range and surrounded by a mountainous region, ranging 1,600 to 1,900 m. This stretched area contains in its interior the lake, which is a lacustrine hollow that occupies the lowest zone. The basin of the lake extends towards the east up to San Martin de los Andes and Maipu. Towards the west the Nonthue lake forms its natural prolongation, being separated from the principal flow by a narrow valley. Towards the northwest it extends through the valley of Hua-Hum River, which cross the boundary with the Republic of Chile and goes into the Chilean territory.

Lake Lacar, as well as other basins which have a glacial origin, is characterized by the typical erosion of the ice in its surroundings. Its water surface is placed at 630 m above sea level. Several rivers and streams come from the mountainous zone which is adjacent to the drawdown occupied by the lake and they come out through the Hua-Hum River. It has been estimated that the hydrographic basin of this drawdown has an area of 1,048 sq. km. No flux measurements are made in this river as it turns impossible to reach it by land. The only information available is the estimation made by Engineer Figueroa Bunge (CFI, 1961) who said that it had a mean flux of 50 cubic m/sec at the boundary between Argentina and Chile.

The drainage basin of the lake is almost uninhabited, with the only exception of the northeast coast where San Martin de los Andes city is located. This city has about 12,000 inhabitants and its economy is based on tourism. The main activities are sport and recreational, the most important of them are hunting, fishing, sailing,

ski and other aquatic sports.

C. PHYSICAL DIMENSIONS
- Surface area [sq. km] — 55
- Volume [cubic km] — 9.2
- Maximum depth [m] — 277
- Mean depth [m] — 167
- Length of shoreline [km] — 69.5
- Residence time [yr] — 5.8
- Catchment area [sq. km] — 1,048

SAM-08 LAGO YPACARAI

A. LOCATION
- Cordillera and Central, Paraguay.
- 25°14'-25°22'S, 57°17'-57°22'W ; 64.1 m above sea level.

B. DESCRIPTION

Lake Ypacarai is a shallow and swampy natural lake located some 30 km east of Asuncion, the capital of Paraguay. It has a surface area of approximately 60 sq. km and a maximum depth of 3 m. The catchment basin of 833 sq. km is largely covered by pastures and crop fields. There are some 20 inflowing tributaries of various sizes, while only one river, Rio Slado, drains the lake joining the Paraguay River at about 20 km downstream. An extensive area of wetlands with luxuriant growth of emergent and submerged plants develops near the lake's outlet and maintains the lake water level effectively within a narrow range of fluctuation.

Since natural water bodies are particularly valuable for this flat inland country, Lake Ypacarai district offers one of the best sites for tourism and outdoor recreation in Paraguay, with abundant facilities for visitors and summer houses around the lake. The lake water is also used for drinking water supply and irrigation. The lake has recently suffered from progressive eutrophication owing to the nutrient discharge from surrounding crop fields, livestock farms, residential areas, deforested lands and large-scale land development. An international multi-disciplinary research project has been launched since 1987 by the national government to cope with this problem.

C. PHYSICAL DIMENSIONS
- Surface area [sq. km] — 60
- Volume [cubic km] — 0.115
- Maximum depth [m] — 3.0
- Mean depth [m] — 2.0
- Water level — Unregulated
- Normal range of annual water
  level fluctuation [m] — 0.2

- Length of shoreline [km]   ca. 40
- Residence time [yr]   0.2*
- Catchment area [sq. km]   833
  * 81 days.

SAM-09 LAGUNA DE ROCHA

A. LOCATION
- Rocha municipality, Uruguay.
- 34°33'-34°41'S, 54°12'-54°22'W; ca. 0 m above sea level.

B. DESCRIPTION

Uruguay has several coastal lagoons in the southeastern and eastern part of the country. Many of them, including Laguna de Rocha, are comprised in the Biosphere Reserve designated by Man and the Biosphere Program (MAB) of UNESCO.

Like most recent lagoons, Laguna de Rocha was formed through the rise of sea level during the last 6,000-8,000 years. It is separated from the Atlantic Ocean by a sand bar, which is sometimes opened by wave action and thixotropy as well as artificially. The intrusion of salt water during open-bar periods produces a clear gradient of salinity that controls physical and chemical water parameters. There are five inflowing rivers, of which the Arroyo Rocha (average flux 13.4 cubic m/sec) and the Las Conchas are the most important. This lagoon is known for its production of fish, crab, shrimp and molluscs harvested by fisherman families living on its southern shore.

The Limnology Department, Faculty of Sciences, Univ. de la Republica, has been studying the lagoon system since 1986 and is currently constructing a limnology station which is expected to serve also as an operative centre for researches on other coastal lagoons.

C. PHYSICAL DIMENSIONS
- Surface area [sq. km]   72
- Volume [cubic km]   0.04
- Maximum depth [m]   1.4
- Mean depth [m]   0.6
- Catchment area [sq. km]   1,312

SAM-10 SOBRADINHO RESERVOIR

A. LOCATION
- Sobradinho, Bahia, Brazil.
- 9°35'S, 40°50'W ; 392.5 m above sea level.

B. DESCRIPTION

This is the largest reservoir in Brazil in terms of surface area, situated in the north of the State of Bahia. The dam was built in the hydrologic basin of the River Sao Francisco at a distance of 748 km from its source and 1,912 km from its estuary on the Atlantic coast. The power generation was started on 31 November 1979. It covers an area of 4,225 sq. km with mean depth of 8.6 m and a maximum depth of 30 m. At the maximum elevation of 392.5 m above sea level, the reservoir accumulates 34.1×10^9 cubic m of water with a regulated discharge rate of 1,060 m3/sec.

The geological formation of the region consists of very ancient rocks of the Brazilian shield, igneous or highly metamorphosed and dating back to the Precambrian era. The soils are predominantly latosol, quartz sand and lithosol. The climate is semi-arid, characterized by very high evaporation rate. Mean annual rainfall ranges between 400 mm and 800 mm and mean annual temperature of 26-27°C is affected by the water body of the reservoir. The prevailing vegetation consists of caranauba (a type of palm tree), hypoxerophilous and hyperxerophilous shrubs of medium height, and low shrubs. When the water level becomes low, wet areas around the reservoir are cultivated.

C. PHYSICAL DIMENSIONS
- Surface area [sq. km]   4,220
- Volume [cubic km]   34.1
- Maximum depth [m]   30
- Mean depth [m]   8.6
- Water level   Regulated
- Normal range of annual water level fluctuation [m]   4.5
- Length of shoreline [km]   1,690
- Residence time [yr]   0.35
- Catchment area [sq. km]   498,425

SAM-11 LAKE TODOS LOS SANTOS

A. LOCATION
- Los Lagos, Chile.
- 41°08'S, 72°12'W ; 189 m above sea level.

B. DESCRIPTION

Lake Todos los Santos is located in the Andean pre-mountain range in the Araucanian lake district of southern Chile within the latitudinal range of 39-42°S. Lakes in the district have many biotic and abiotic characteristics in common, but differ in the extent of their oligotrophy.

L. Todos los Santos has a surface area of 178.5 sq. km and a large volume owing to its great depth reaching a maximum of 337 m. The catchment area of the lake is fairly wide, being 17 times as wide as the lake surface.

Its origin is both glacial and volcanic. During in the Ice Age, two glacier arms, one flowing down southward through the present Negro River valley and the other in the opposite direction through the Blanco River valley, converged in the central valley and advanced westward excavating the tertiary valley to form the depression now occupied by Lakes Todos los Santos and Llanquihue. After the disappearance of the ice, the action of Osorno and Calbuco Volcanoes divided the two lake basins with volcanic matters. Matters from Tronador Volcano also reached the lake via Blanco River glacier.

The lake is warm monomictic and oligotrophic. The concentration of major nutrients are low. The highest carbon assimilation rate per unit amount of chlorophyll occurs in winter, but the primary production reaches its highest level at the beginning of summer, though the productivity itself is low.

C. PHYSICAL DIMENSIONS

- Surface area [sq. km]   178.5
- Volume [cubic km]   34.4
- Maximum depth [m]   337
- Mean depth [m]   191
- Length of shoreline [km]   125
- Residence time [yr]   4
- Catchment area [sq. km]   3,036

SAM-12 LAKE SALTO GRANDE

A. LOCATION

- Entre Rios, Argentina; and Artigas and Salto, Uruguay.
- 29°43' 31°12'S, 57°06' 57°55'W ; 35 m above sea level.

B. DESCRIPTION

Lake Salto Grande is an artificial lake built on the Uruguay River, which forms the boundary between Argentina and Uruguay, at about 450 km from Buenos Aires and about 500 km from Montevideo. The reservoir is 144 km long and about 9 km wide, covering an area of 783 sq. km. Its western shore belongs to the Province of Entre Rios of Argentina, and the eastern shore is shared by two provinces of Uruguay. The catchment area covers 224,000 sq. km extending over the territories of the two countries.

The impoundment was initiated in 1973 after a long period of negotiation between the two countries since 1964. The reservoir was constructed and managed by the Comision Tecnica Mixta de Salto Grande in which Argentina and Uruguay participate evenly in both operational and financial aspects. The creation of the reservoir resulted in the submergence of a town with 22,000 inhabitants, though the town has been relocated at some distance from the dam site. The produced electricity is supplied to both countries. The supply to Uruguay side very often surpasses the whole consumption in Montevideo.

Because of its proximity to such cities as Concordia (Argentina) and Salto (Uruguay), L. Salto Grande is an important recreational center. The surrounding area made a public park with various facilities (an airport, harbors, auditoria and camping sites) soon after the reservoir was formed. Since there are vast flat plain with many residential areas in the upstream of the reservoir, accelerated soil erosion in the rainy season and resultant siltation offer a prevailing problem in spite of the afforestation efforts around the reservoir.

C. PHYSICAL DIMENSIONS

- Surface area [sq. km]   783
- Volume [cubic km]   5.0
- Maximum depth [m]   33
- Mean depth [m]   6.4
- Water level   Regulated
- Normal range of annual water level fluctuation [m]   0.8
- Length of shoreline [km]   1,190
- Residence time [yr]   0.031
- Catchment area [sq. km]   224,000

Annex

Annex 1 Problems of selected lakes and reservoirs of the world

Information mainly based on *Survey of the state of world lakes*, Vols.1-5 (ILEC/UNEP, 1988-93).

Type of water
F : Freshwater
B : Brackish water
S : Saline water (including soda lake)

Origin
M : Man-made reservoir
T : Tectonic lake (formed with the tectonic movement)
G : Glacial lake (formed with scouring of glacier movement)
V : Volcanic lake (formed with falling of crater)
D : Dammed lake (Formed naturally by damming with rock scrapes of glacier, lava of volcano and/or landslide)
F : Fluvial lake (formed by silt carried by river)
R : Regressed lake (formed by decreasing of sea level)
L : Lagoon (formed with sand drift along coast)

Utilization
W: Water source(D, drinking water; I, industry; A, irrigation)
N : Transportation
F : Fisheries
E : Hydro-power generation
R : Recreation and Tourism

○ : Presence of problem/measure(those without marks do not necessarily mean absence of the problem/measure)

ASIA

Country	Lake Name	Type	Origin	Utilization	Major problems						Measures			Remarks
					Eutrophi-cation	Toxic Pollu-tion	Acidi-fica-tion	Silta-tion	Water level change	Bio-logical change	Legis-lative measure	Basin wide measure	In-lake measure	
S.Korea	Pal-dang Res.	F	M	P,W(D)	○									Occurrence of red tide and algal bloom.
P.R.China	Dongting-hu	F	F	W,F,N				○			○	○	○	Important as flood buffering reservoir. though suffering from sedimentation. Dredging along navigation routes.
	Tai-hu	F	S	W,F,N,R	○	○	○				○	○		Eutrophication at northern part. Pollution by industrial discharge.
	Xi-hu	F		R,F	○					○	○	○	○	Inflow of urban sewage. Dilution. Dredging. Historic touristic site.
	Dian-chi	F	T	W,N,F	○	○		○		○	○	○		Rapid eutrophication. Algal bloom. Inflow of urban/industrial discharge.
	Chao-hu	F	F	N,W,	○	○		○		○	○	○	○	Pollution from mining and industries. Algal bloom.
	Poyang-hu	F	F	N,W,F				○			○		○	Important as flood buffering reservoir. Lake tends to enlarge.
	Hongze-hu	F	F	F,W,N		○		○			○		○	Pollution by heavy metals and agrochemicals. Dredging. Intended eutrophication for fisheries
	Er-hai	F		W,P	○			○	○	○	○			Artificial water level reduction. Abnormal submerged weed growth.
	Qinghai-hu	S		W(A)				○			○			Water level decrease. Increase of salinity level and mineralization.
	Dong-hu	F	F	F,N,R,W	○						○	○	○	Eutrophication by urbanization.
	Po-mang Res.	F	M	P,W(A)							○			
	Ya-er-hu	F		F		○				○				Toxic pollution by agrochemical factories.
Taiwan	Feitsui Res.	F	M	W	○						○	○		Improvement of trophic state from eutrophic to mesotrophic by basin measures.
Philippines	L. Laguna	B		W(A),F	○	○	○			○		○	○	Over-aquaculture. Increased siltation.
	L. Buhi	F	V	W,F,N,P	○			○						

240

Country	Lake Name	Type	Origin	Utilization	Major problems						Measures			Remarks
					Eutrophication	Toxic Pollution	Acidification	Siltation	Water level change	Biological change	Legislative measure	Basin wide measure	In-lake measure	
Thailand	L. Sonkhla	F	L	W,F,R,N	○	○		○						Under development pressure.
	L. Boraped	F	M	F,W,R	○			○						Important as flood buffering reservoir. High fish productivity. Siltation. Overgrowth of water hyacinth.
Nepal	L. Phewa	F	D	R,F,W(A)				○						
	L. Rara	F		R				○						
Cambodia	L. Tonle Sap	F	F	F,N	○			○						Important as flood buffering reservoir of the Mekong basin.
Malaysia	L. Bera	F	F	F,N										
Indonesia	Jatiluhur Res.	F		W	○									
	L. Toba	F	V	R,P,WX					○					Touristic place.
	Saguling Res.	F	M	W,P,R,F	○			○				○	○	Inflow of untreated sewage from upstream city. Erosion by illegal farming.
	Ogan-Komering Lebaks	F	F	W,N,F			○	○						Threats from irrigation and reclamation. introduction of exotic fishes; over fishing
	L. Kerinci	V,T		F						○			○	Water hyacinth increased as a result of eutrophication, though decreasing recently.
	L. Maninjau	V		W,E,F,R						○				Good water quality; introduction of exotic species; oligotrophic
	L. Singkarak	T		W,F,R				○						Reduction of water quality in the past decade.
	Rawa Danau	F	V	W,F	○			○		○	○			Changes in Biodiversity in Nature Reserve; application of pesticide and poisons
	L. Tempe	F	F	F,W,N	○			○		○	○			Use of bunga (man-made circles of floating vegetation) for fishing; high level of aluminum which may be harmful to human body.
	L. Matano	T		W,E						○	○	○		Deepest lake in Southeast Asia; threats to indigenous species from Nickel mining area and hydro-electricity.
	L. Towuci	T		W,E					○		○			The second largest lake in Indonesia; threats from Nickel mining; deforestation
India	L. Loktak	F		F,W				○						
	L. Dal	F		W,F,R	○			○			○			Inflow of untreated urban discharge.
	L. Surinsar	F	D	R						○		○		High pollution level due to the activities of ONGC prospecting for oil; disturbance from tourism; threats to charophytes
	L. Manasbal			F,W,R,N	○					○	○			The deepest valley lake in Kashmir; eutrophication by human pressure and excessive growth of submerged weeds; decrease in species diversity
	Lower L.		M	W,R	○			○						Highly eutrophicated and grossly polluted lake by sewage inflow; convertion to 'septic tank'; constructionally defect dam
	L. Nainital			W,E,R				○						Extinction of Ceratiumhirundinella; accelerated pollution by inflow of pollutants.
	L. Pulicat	B	L	F,R				○						Producing salt; siltation problem which harmful to wide variety of flora and fish
	L.Chilka (B.W.)	B	L	F										The biggest island-lake in India; important habit for migratory birds

Country	Lake Name	Type	Origin	Utili-zation	Major problems						Measures			Remarks
					Eutrophi-cation	Toxic Pollu-tion	Acidi-fica-tion	Silta-tion	Water level change	Bio-logical change	Legis-lative measure	Basin wide measure	In-lake measure	
	Kanhargaov Res.	M		W,F				○						Serious siltation problem; significant pollution without waste water treatment
	L. Fateh Sagar	M		I,D,R,F	○						○		○	Unusual algal bloom; Encroachment of urban area; degradation of water quality and possible danger to human health
	L. Kolleru	F	F	F	○			○						
Sri Lanka	L. Beira	F		W	○							○	○	Damping of solid waste. Dilution. Dredging.
Russia	L. Baikal	F	T	W,F,R		○				○		○		Pollution by pulp industries.
	Caspian Sea	S	T	F,W,N,R		○				○				Quick water level rise in recent years.
	Brahtuk Res.	F	M	W	○									
Kazakhstan	L. Balkhash	S	T	W,F		○			○	○		○		Water level decrease by power generation and irrigation. Pollution by agrochemicals. Increase of salinity. Reduction of fishery production.
Kazakhstan/ Uzbekistan	Aral Sea	S	T	F,W(I)		○	○	○	○					Disastrous shrinking by mismanagement of irrigation. Increase of salinity and subsequent ecological catastrophe. Damage to human health. Soil salinization.
Kyrgystan	L. Issykkool		T						○					
Armenia	L. Sevan	F			○				○					Temporal eutrophication by water level decrease. Decrease of phosphorus concentration.
Israel	L. Kinneret	F		W,R							○	○	○	Successfully managed by legislation.

Caspian Sea ; Russia/Iran/Azerbaijan/Turkmenistan/Kazakhstan

OCEANIA

Country	Lake Name	Type	Origin	Utili-zation	Major problems						Measures			Remarks
					Eutrophi-cation	Toxic Pollu-tion	Acidi-fica-tion	Silta-tion	Water level change	Bio-logical change	Legis-lative measure	Basin wide measure	In-lake measure	
New Zealand	L. Taupo	F	V	R,W							○	○		Successful basinwide management.
	L. Rotorua	F	V	R	○	○				○	○	○	○	Experienced abnormal weed growth.
Australia	L. Burley Griffin	F	M	W,R							○			Artificial lake in Cambera constructed for better landscape. Regulations for landscape conservation.

AFRICA

Country	Lake Name	Type	Origin	Utili-zation	Major problems						Measures			Remarks
					Eutrophi-cation	Toxic Pollu-tion	Acidi-fica-tion	Silta-tion	Water level change	Bio-logical change	Legis-lative measure	Basin wide measure	In-lake measure	
Egypt	Aswan High Dam	F	M	P,W(A),F,N	○				○		○			Spread of sistosomiasis following dam construction. Decrease of downstreamfishcatch.
	L. Maryut	F			○									Pollution by urban and industrial discharge. No flood-flushing effect after the High Dam construction.
Kenya	L. Nakuru	S	T	R						○	○	○		Rich avifauna. Inflow of urban discharge from Nakuru City. Introduction of exotic fish.
	L. Victoria	F	T	F,W,N,R	○						○	○		Recent invasion of water hyacinth. Possible extinction of endemic fishes by introduction of exotic commercial species.
Senegal	L. Guier	F	M	W(A),P F	○					○				Spread of sistosomiasis.
Chad	L. Chad	F	T	F,W,N					○					Desertification. Delay of rehabilitation due to war state.
Ghana	L. Volta	F	M	P,N,F,W (D,I,A),R	○			○			○			
Tanzania	L. Tanganyika	F	T	F,N				○						
Malawi	L. Nyasa	F	T	W,N,R,F										
Zimbabwe	L. Kariba	F	M	P,F,R,W(D)					○					
	L. McIlwaine	F	M	W(A),F,R							○	○		Algal bloom and overgrowth of water hyacinth. Water quality being improved by diversion of sewage.
Uganda	L. George	F		F	○									
	L. Albert	F	T	W,F	○									
Mozambique	L. Chilwa	F	T	F										
South Africa	L. Sibaya	F	L	F										Rich biodiversity.
Cameroon	L. Nyos	F	V											Eruption of carbon-dioxide gas.

Aswan High Dam Res., Egypt/Sudan; L. Victoria, Uganda/Tanzania/Kenya; L. Chad, Chad/Cameroon/Niger/Nigeria; L. Tanganyika, Tanzania/Zaire/Zambia/Burundi; L. Nyasa(Malawi), Malawi/Tanzania/Mozambique;L. Kariba, Zimbabwe/Zambia; L. Albert, Uganda/Zaire; L. Chilwa, Mozambique/Malawi.

EUROPE

Country	Lake Name	Type	Origin	Utili-zation	Major problems						Measures			Remarks
					Eutrophi-cation	Toxic Pollu-tion	Acidi-fica-tion	Silta-tion	Water level change	Bio-logical change	Legis-lative measure	Basin wide measure	In-lake measure	
Russia	L. Ladoga	F	M	W,R	○						○	○		Closing down of an industrial complex.
	Mozhaysk Res.	F	M	W,R							○			
Italy	Lake Orta	F	G	R		○					○		○	Acidification by industrial discharge. Success of liming operation.
	L. Lugano	F	G	R	○						○			
	L. Maggiore	F	G	W,R,N	○						○	○		Improvement of eutrophication by sewage diversion.
Slovenia	L. Bled	F		W	○						○		○	Eutrophication being stabilized. Dilution. Sewage construction.
Switzerland	L. Leman	F	G	W,R,F	○						○	○	○	Water quality being improved. Stringent regulation for wastewater discharge.
	L. Baldegger	F	G		○						○		○	Aeration.
	L. Sempacher	F	G		○						○		○	Aeration.
	L. Tailleres	F			○						○		○	Aeration
	L. Zurich	F	G	W,R,F,N	○					○	○		○	Recovered to mesotrophic state by physical measures.
France	L. Bourget	F		R,W	○						○	○	○	Use of boats for collecting floating wastes.
Netherlands	L. Ijsell	F	M	W	○						○	○	○	Dilution. Aeration.
	L. Tjeuke	F	M	W,R	○						○			
Austria	L. Neusiedler	F	T	W,R,F	○					○	○	○	○	Conservation of reed beds.
	L. Lunzer	F	G	R	○					○		○		Partially eutrophicated.
	L. Atter	F	G	R							○	○		
Hungary	L. Balaton	F	T	W,R	○						○	○	○	Construction of an artificial wetland for nutrient trap.
Sweden	L. Malaren	F	G	R,F	○						○	○		Thorough waste water treatment
	L. Trummen	F		R,F	○					○	○	○		Successful eutrophication control. Diversion. Dredging.
	L. Hjalmaren	F		W,N,R,F	○						○			
	L. Vattern	F		W,N,R,F		○					○			
Denmark	L. Esrom	F	G	R	○						○	○		
Finland	L. Inari	F	G	W,F						○	○			Water level decrease by hydro-power and subsequent influence to aquatic biodiversity
	L. Pielinen	F	G	W,R,N,F	○						○			
	L. Paijanne	F	G	W(D),R,N	○						○			Water quality being improved.
Norway	L. Mjosa	F	G		○						○	○	○	Water quality being improved.
U.K.	L. Windermere	F	G	W	○						○			
	L. Ness	F	G	R							○			Pollution by tourism and livestock farming being worried
	L. Shiel	F	G	W,R										
	L. Lomond	F	G	N,R										
	L. Windsor	F		R	○									
Ireland	L. Ree	F	G	W,R	○						○			
	L. Derg	F	G	W,N,R,F	○						○			Water quality being improved.
Germany	L. Boden	F	G	W	○	○	○				○	○	○	Successful international management. Heavy metal pollution. Siltation at river mouth.
	L. Great Plon	F		W	○						○	○	○	
	L. Sternberger	F	G	R,F										Water quality being improved.
	L. Stechlin	F	G	W(I),R,F							○	○		
	L. Ammer	F	G	R,F							○	○		Water quality being improved.

L. Leman(Geneva), Switzerland/France; L. Neusiedler, Austria/Hungary; L. Boden(Constance), Germany/Switzerland/Austria

THE AMERICAS

Country	Lake Name	Type	Origin	Utilization	Major problems						Measures			Remarks
					Eutrophication	Toxic Pollution	Acidification	Siltation	Water level change	Biological change	Legislative measure	Basin wide measure	In-lake measure	
Canada	L. Winnipeg	F	G	R	○									Eutrophication by natural loadings.
	L. Saint-Jean	F	G	P,W,F,R,N			○	○						Acidification of neighboring small lakes. Siltation. Lakeshore erosion.
Canada/USA	L. Ontario	F	G	W(I) N,R,F	○	○				○	○	○	○	Serious toxic contamination by PCB and heavy metals. Symptom of water quality improvement.
	L. Huron	F	G	W(I) F,N,R		○				○	○	○	○	
	L. Erie	F	G	W(I) N,R,F	○	○					○	○	○	
	L. Superior	F	G	W(I) N,R,F		○		○			○	○	○	
U.S.A.	L. Michigan	F	G	W(I) N,R,F	○	○	○				○	○	○	Ban of phosphate-containing detergent. Lakeshore erosion.
	L. Mead	F	M	P,R	○						○			
	L. Washington	F	G	N,R	○						○	○		Successful eutrophication control by sewage diversion.
	L. Tahoe	F		R,W	○						○	○	○	Successful example of stringent basin management.
	L. Mono	S		W					○					Water level decrease by water intake from inflowinf rivers.
	L. Conesus	F	G	W,R	○						○	○	○	Dredging as flood control measure
	L. Hemlok	F	G	W(D),R							○	○		Stringent management as water source. Relocation of cottages.
	L. Chicot	F	F	F,R		○					○	○	○	Agrochemical contamination.
	L. Okeechobee	F	S	W(D),N,R	○						○	○	○	Wetland lake. Surrounded by dyke for water use.
	Twin lakes	F	G	W(A,I),R							○	○	○	Eutrophication by domestic sewage
	L. Mendota	F		R	○	○							○	Relocation of residents by dam construction. Anaerobic water by decomposition of submerged tropical forest.
Brazil	Tukurui Res.	F	M	P	○									
	L. Baleia	F			○									Serious eutrophication
	Patos Res.	F / S		W(I) / N,P	○	○		○			○	○		
	Parana River reservoirs	F	M	P	○			○						Eutrophication by urban discharge and fertilizers.
	Lobo Res.	F	M	R							○	○		Logging of basin forests.
Bolivia	L. Titicaca	F	T	W,F,N,R							○			
Argentina	San Roque Res.	F	M	W(I),R,P	○	○	○		○		○	○		Occurrence of algal bloom. Acidification by industrial discharge.
	L. Nahuel Huapi	F	G	R,N,W	○						○			Development of tourism. Symptom of partial eutrophication.
	Ezequiel Ramos Mexia Res.	F	M	W,N,R										
Columbia	L. Tota	F		W	○			○			○	○		
Venezualla	L. Valencia	F	T	W,R	○	○			○		○			Serious eutrophication by livestock farming.
	L. Maracaibo	S	T,L			○								Contamination by oil spill.
Paraguay	L. Ypacarai	F	M	W(I),R	○			○			○	○		Inflow of industrial and livestock discharges.
	Itaipu Res.	F	M	R,P									○	Anaerobic water
	Yacireta Res.	F	M	P										(under construction.) Dispute on appropriate EIA.

245

JAPAN

Country	Lake Name	Type	Origin	Utilization	Major problems						Measures			Remarks
					Eutrophi-cation	Toxic Pollu-tion	Acidi-fica-tion	Silta-tion	Water level change	Bio-logical change	Legis-lative measure	Basin wide measure	In-lake measure	
Japan	Abashiri L.	B	L	W(D),R	○						○	○	○	Outbreaks of water bloom.
	Mashu L.	F	V	R							○			Touristic place. World record of transparency in 1911.
	Saroma L.	B	L	F,R							○			Various kinds of aquaculture
	Akan L.	F	D	F,R							○			Touristic place.
	Shikotsu L.	F	V	F,R							○			
	Toya L.	F	V	W(DAI),R							○			
	Ogawara L.	B	R	W(A),F,R							○			Large-scale comprehensive industrialdevelopment project planned nearby.
	Towada L.	F	V	F,R,E							○	○	○	
	Yuda Res.	F	M	W(A),T,E							○			
	Kamafusa Res.	F	M	W(DAI), F,R,E	○						○	○	○	Designated under the Clean Lakes Law.
	Hachiro Res.	F	L	W(A),F, R	○							○		Outbreak of water bloom by construction of salinity barrier.
	Misakubo Res.	F	M	W(A,I), R	○						○	○		Moldy smell of water occurred in spring since 1988.
	Inawashiro L.	F	T	W(A)F, R,E							○	○	○	Naturally acid lake by inflow of acid river water.
	Okutadami Res.	F	M	F,R,E							○	○		The largest artificial lake in Japan.
	Kasumigaura L.	F	R	W(DAI), F,R	○						○	○	○	Large-scale Integrated Measures for Water Quality Conservation under way.
	Chuzenji L.	F	D	W(D) R,E	○						○	○		Occurrence of bad smell of water since 1981 by phytoplankton *Urogrena*.
	Oze-numa L.	F	D	F,R,E							○	○		Measures by integral type of septic tank system promoted.
	Inba-numa L.	F	F	W(A)I, F,R	○						○	○	○	Serious eutrophicated by urbanizationin surrounding area.
	Okutama Res.	F	M	W(D), R,E	○						○	○		Occurrence of red tide and water bloom.
	Sagami Res.	F	M	W(DA)I, F,R,E	○						○	○	○	Moldy smell of water, filtration problem in water purification.
	Kurobe Res.	F	M	W(A),F, R,E							○	○		High touristic value. Potential of environmental degradation by tourists.
	Kahoku-gata L.	F	L	W(A),F,R							○	○		Small-scale integrated type of septic tank system promoted.
	Mikata-goko Ls.	F	R	F,R	○						○	○	○	Partially brackish. Touristic damage caused by water bloom.
	Yamanaka L.	F	D	W(A),F,R,E							○	○		
	Hamana L.	B	L	F,R	○						○	○	○	Famous for eel aquaculture.
	Suwa L.	F	T	F,R	○						○	○	○	Diversion of sewage.
	Agigawa Res.	F	M	W(D),I, F,R,E	○						○	○	○	Outbreak of red tide in 1992/93. Multi-purposes dam.
	Miyagawa Res.	F	M	W(A),E							○	○	○	Utilization for irrigation after power generation.
	Biwa L.	F	T	W(DAI), F,R,E	○					○	○	○	○	Large-scale integrated measures for water quality conservation under way.
	Sengari Res.	F	M	W(DA), F	○						○	○	○	Filtration problem in water purification. Aeration and water mixing.
	Kazaya Res.	F	M	R,E	○						○		○	Sometimes outbreak of red tide. Artificial lake for power generation only.
	Togo-ike L.	F		F,R										Touristic pollution by visitors at spa. Temporal outbreak of water bloom.
	Shinji L.	B	L	W(A), F,R	○						○	○	○	Agricultural reclamation in the adjoining lake being suspended.

Country	Lake Name	Type	Origin	Utili-zation	Major problems						Measures			Remarks
					Eutrophi-cation	Toxic Pollu-tion	Acidi-fica-tion	Silta-tion	Water level change	Bio-logical change	Legis-lative measure	Basin wide measure	In-lake measure	
	Kojima Res.	F	M	W(A), F,R	○						○	○	○	Decrease of fishery and agricultural productivities by water quality deterioration.
	Abu Res.	F	M	R,E	○						○	○		Floating wastes causing degradation of tourism value.
	Nagayasuguchi Res.	F	M	W(DA)I, F,R,E	○									Outbreak of red tide in summer.
	Manno-ike Res.	F	M	W(A), F,R							○	○		The oldest agricultural reservoir built more than 1,000 years before.
	Yanase Res.	F	M	W(DA)I, R,E							○	○		Nutrient loadings mainly from natural forests. Touristic place.
	Nagase Res.	F	M	W(A), F,R,E	○						○	○		Nutrient loadings mainly from natural forests. Temporal outbreak of red tide.
	Hyugakami Res.	F	M	W(A), F,R,E	○						○	○		Multi-purpose dam.
	Kitayama Res.	F	M	W(A), R,E	○						○	○		
	Ichifusa Res.	F	M	W(A),E							○			
	Ikeda L.	F	V	W(A), F,R	○						○			Water quality deterioration by industrialization.

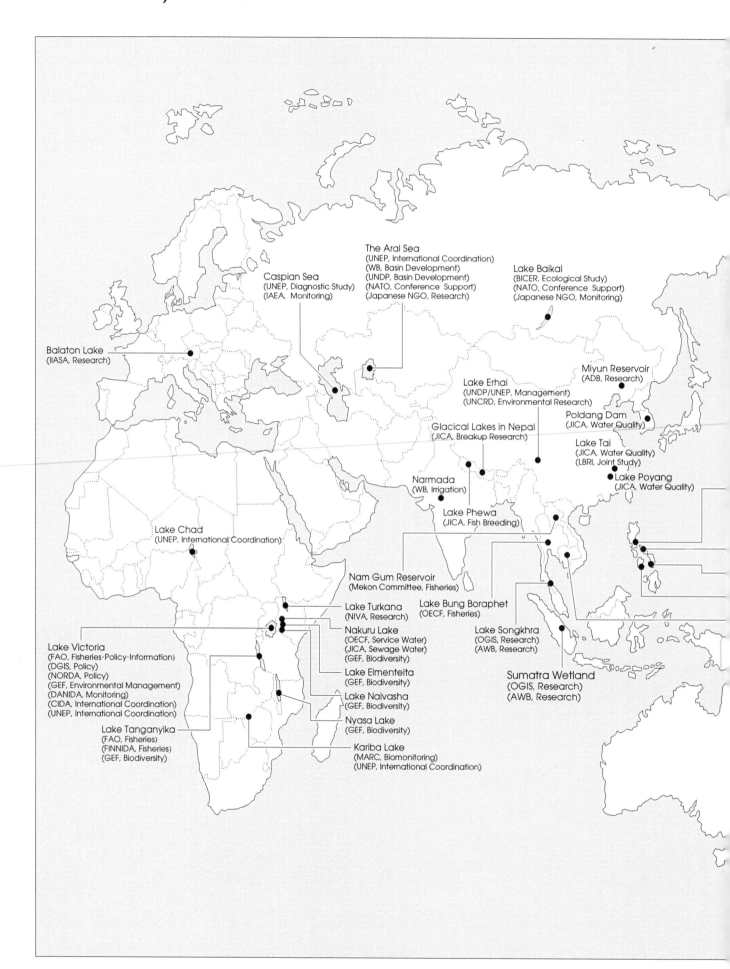

Balaton Lake
(IIASA, Research)

Caspian Sea
(UNEP, Diagnostic Study)
(IAEA, Monitoring)

The Aral Sea
(UNEP, International Coordination)
(WB, Basin Development)
(UNDP, Basin Development)
(NATO, Conference Support)
(Japanese NGO, Research)

Lake Baikal
(BICER, Ecological Study)
(NATO, Conference Support)
(Japanese NGO, Monitoring)

Lake Erhai
(UNDP/UNEP, Management)
(UNCRD, Environmental Research)

Miyun Reservoir
(ADB, Research)

Poldang Dam
(JICA, Water Quality)

Glacical Lakes in Nepal
(JICA, Breakup Research)

Lake Tai
(JICA, Water Quality)
(LBRI, Joint Study)

Lake Poyang
(JICA, Water Quality)

Narmada
(WB, Irrigation)

Lake Phewa
(JICA, Fish Breeding)

Lake Chad
(UNEP, International Coordination)

Nam Gum Reservoir
(Mekon Committee, Fisheries)

Lake Bung Boraphet
(OECF, Fisheries)

Lake Turkana
(NIVA, Research)

Nakuru Lake
(OECF, Service Water)
(JICA, Sewage Water)
(GEF, Biodiversity)

Lake Songkhra
(OGIS, Research)
(AWB, Research)

Lake Victoria
(FAO, Fisheries·Policy·Information)
(DGIS, Policy)
(NORDA, Policy)
(GEF, Environmental Management)
(DANIDA, Monitoring)
(CIDA, International Coordination)
(UNEP, International Coordination)

Lake Elmenteita
(GEF, Biodiversity)

Lake Naivasha
(GEF, Biodiversity)

Nyasa Lake
(GEF, Biodiversity)

Sumatra Wetland
(OGIS, Research)
(AWB, Research)

Lake Tanganyika
(FAO, Fisheries)
(FINNIDA, Fisheries)
(GEF, Biodiversity)

Kariba Lake
(MARC, Biomonitoring)
(UNEP, International Coordination)

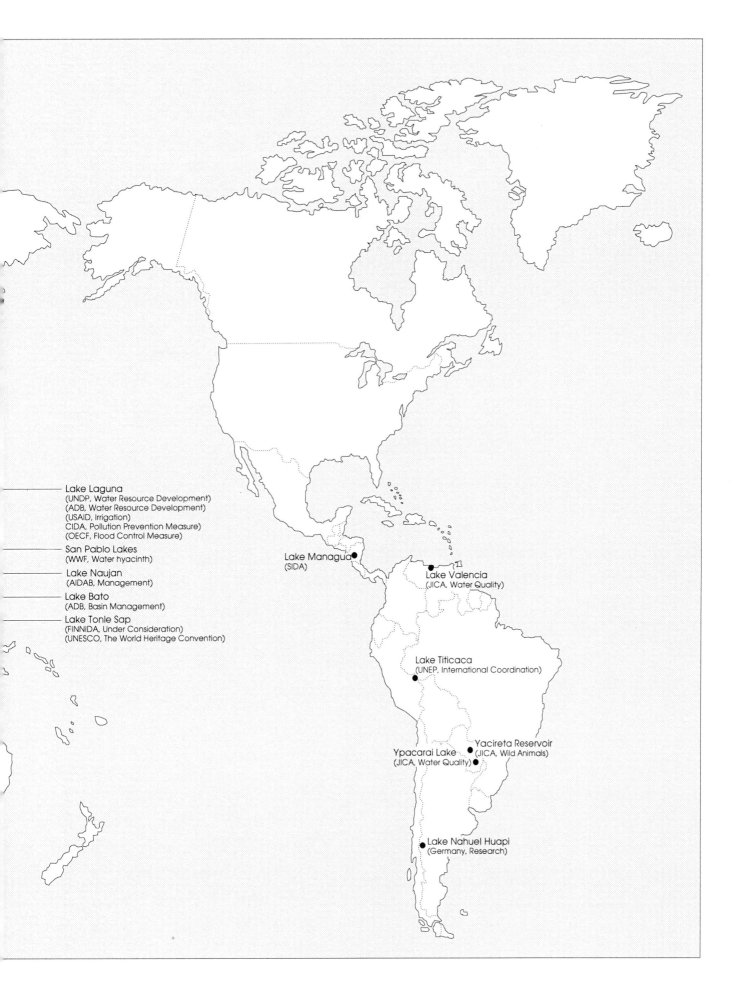

Lake Laguna
(UNDP, Water Resource Development)
(ADB, Water Resource Development)
(USAID, Irrigation)
CIDA, Pollution Prevention Measure)
(OECF, Flood Control Measure)

San Pablo Lakes
(WWF, Water hyacinth)

Lake Naujan
(AIDAB, Management)

Lake Bato
(ADB, Basin Management)

Lake Tonle Sap
(FINNIDA, Under Consideration)
(UNESCO, The World Heritage Convention)

Lake Managua
(SIDA)

Lake Valencia
(JICA, Water Quality)

Lake Titicaca
(UNEP, International Coordination)

Yacireta Reservoir
Ypacarai Lake (JICA, Wild Animals)
(JICA, Water Quality)

Lake Nahuel Huapi
(Germany, Research)

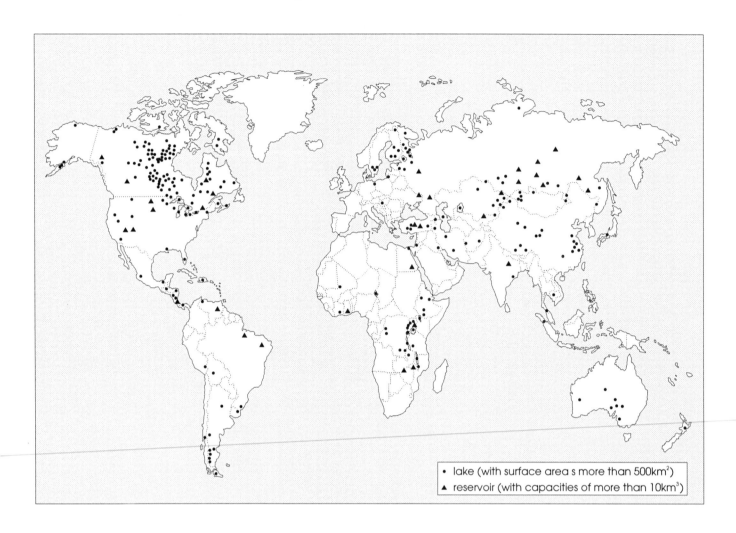

- lake (with surface area s more than 500km^2)
- ▲ reservoir (with capacities of more than 10km^3)

Annex 4 Distribution of lakes/reservois listed on *Survey of the State of World Lakes* Vols.1-5, 1988-1993, UNEP/ILEC

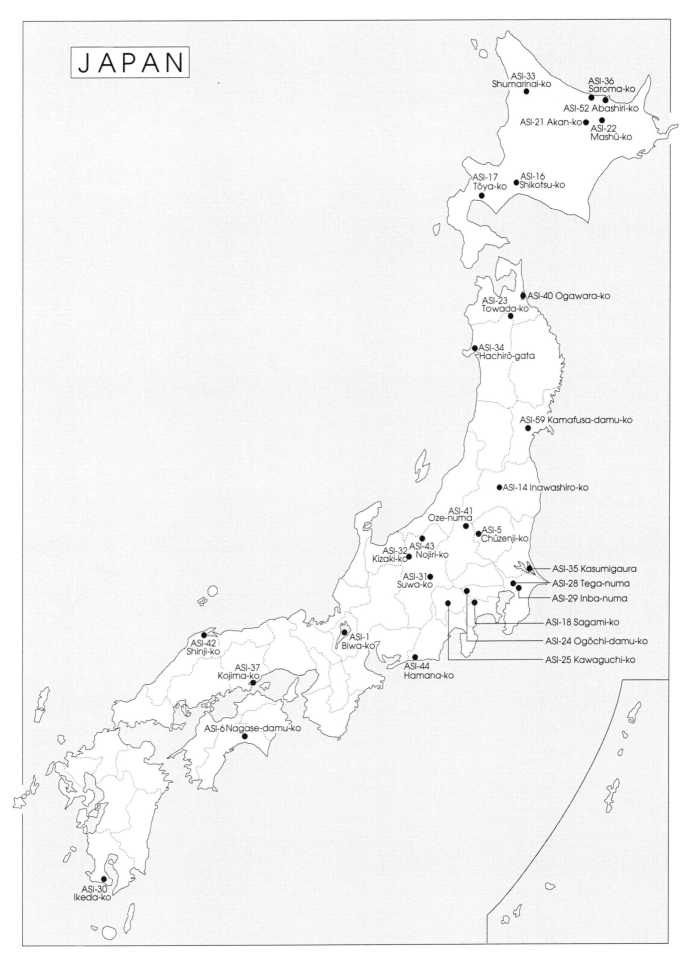

JAPAN

ASI-33 Shumarinai-ko
ASI-36 Saroma-ko
ASI-52 Abashiri-ko
ASI-21 Akan-ko
ASI-22 Mashû-ko
ASI-17 Tôya-ko
ASI-16 Shikotsu-ko
ASI-40 Ogawara-ko
ASI-23 Towada-ko
ASI-34 Hachirô-gata
ASI-59 Kamafusa-damu-ko
ASI-14 Inawashiro-ko
ASI-41 Oze-numa
ASI-5 Chûzenji-ko
ASI-32 Kizaki-ko
ASI-43 Nojiri-ko
ASI-31 Suwa-ko
ASI-35 Kasumigaura
ASI-28 Tega-numa
ASI-29 Inba-numa
ASI-18 Sagami-ko
ASI-24 Ogôchi-damu-ko
ASI-25 Kawaguchi-ko
ASI-42 Shinji-ko
ASI-1 Biwa-ko
ASI-37 Kojima-ko
ASI-44 Hamana-ko
ASI-6 Nagase-damu-ko
ASI-30 Ikeda-ko

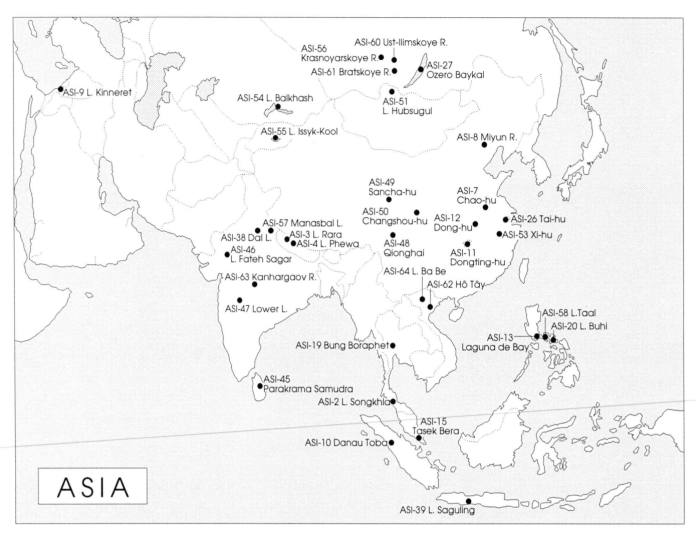

ASI-60 Ust-Ilimskoye R.
ASI-56 Krasnoyarskoye R.
ASI-61 Bratskoye R.
ASI-27 Ozero Baykal
ASI-9 L. Kinneret
ASI-54 L. Balkhash
ASI-51 L. Hubsugul
ASI-55 L. Issyk-Kool
ASI-8 Miyun R.
ASI-49 Sancha-hu
ASI-7 Chao-hu
ASI-50 Changshou-hu
ASI-57 Manasbal L.
ASI-12 Dong-hu
ASI-26 Tai-hu
ASI-38 Dal L.
ASI-3 L. Rara
ASI-53 Xi-hu
ASI-46 L. Fateh Sagar
ASI-4 L. Phewa
ASI-48 Qionghai
ASI-11 Dongting-hu
ASI-63 Kanhargaov R.
ASI-64 L. Ba Be
ASI-62 Hô Tây
ASI-47 Lower L.
ASI-58 L.Taal
ASI-20 L. Buhi
ASI-13 Laguna de Bay
ASI-19 Bung Boraphet
ASI-45 Parakrama Samudra
ASI-2 L. Songkhla
ASI-15 Tasek Bera
ASI-10 Danau Toba
ASI-39 L. Saguling

ASIA

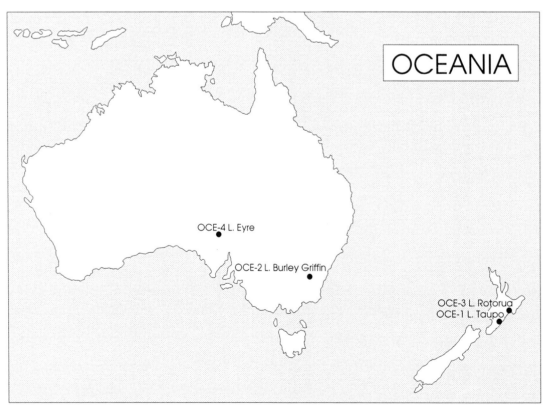

OCEANIA

OCE-4 L. Eyre
OCE-2 L. Burley Griffin
OCE-3 L. Rotorua
OCE-1 L. Taupo

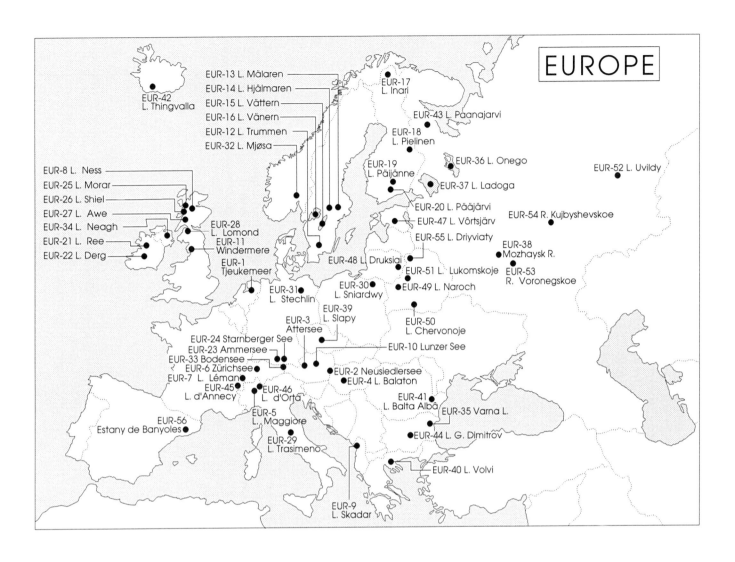

EUROPE

EUR-13 L. Mälaren
EUR-14 L. Hjälmaren
EUR-15 L. Vättern
EUR-16 L. Vänern
EUR-12 L. Trummen
EUR-32 L. Mjøsa

EUR-17 L. Inari

EUR-43 L. Paanajarvi

EUR-18 L. Pielinen

EUR-36 L. Onego

EUR-52 L. Uvildy

EUR-42 L. Thingvalla

EUR-8 L. Ness
EUR-25 L. Morar
EUR-26 L. Shiel
EUR-27 L. Awe
EUR-34 L. Neagh
EUR-21 L. Ree
EUR-22 L. Derg

EUR-19 L. Päijänne

EUR-37 L. Ladoga

EUR-54 R. Kujbyshevskoe

EUR-20 L. Pääjärvi
EUR-47 L. Võrtsjärv
EUR-55 L. Driyviaty

EUR-38 Mozhaysk R.

EUR-28 L. Lomond
EUR-11 Windermere
EUR-1 Tjeukemeer

EUR-48 L Druksiai

EUR-51 L. Lukomskoje
EUR-49 L. Naroch

EUR-53 R. Voronegskoe

EUR-31 L. Stechlin

EUR-30 L. Sniardwy

EUR-50 L. Chervonoje

EUR-3 Attersee

EUR-39 L. Slapy

EUR-24 Starnberger See
EUR-23 Ammersee
EUR-33 Bodensee
EUR-6 Zürichsee
EUR-7 L. Léman
EUR-45 L. d'Annecy

EUR-10 Lunzer See

EUR-46 L. d'Orta

EUR-2 Neusiedlersee
EUR-4 L. Balaton

EUR-41 L. Balta Albã
EUR-35 Varna L.

EUR-56 Estany de Banyoles

EUR-5 L. Maggiore

EUR-44 L. G. Dimitrõv

EUR-29 L. Trasimeno

EUR-40 L. Volvi

EUR-9 L. Skadar

AFR-19
Aswan High Dam R.

AFR-9 L. Guiers

AFR-2
L. Chad

AFR-16
Volta L.

AFR-18
Oguta L.

AFR-20 L. Turkana

AFR-11 L. Albert
AFR-10 L. George
AFR-12 L. Edward

AFR-15 L. Kyoga

AFR-7
L. Nakuru

AFR-5
L. Victoria

AFR-6
L. Tanganyika

AFR-13
L. Nyasa

AFR-14
Cabora Bassa R.

AFR-1
L. Chilwa

AFR-4
L. Kariba

AFR-8
L. McIlwaine

AFR-3 L. Sibaya

AFR-17 Zeekoevlei

AFRICA

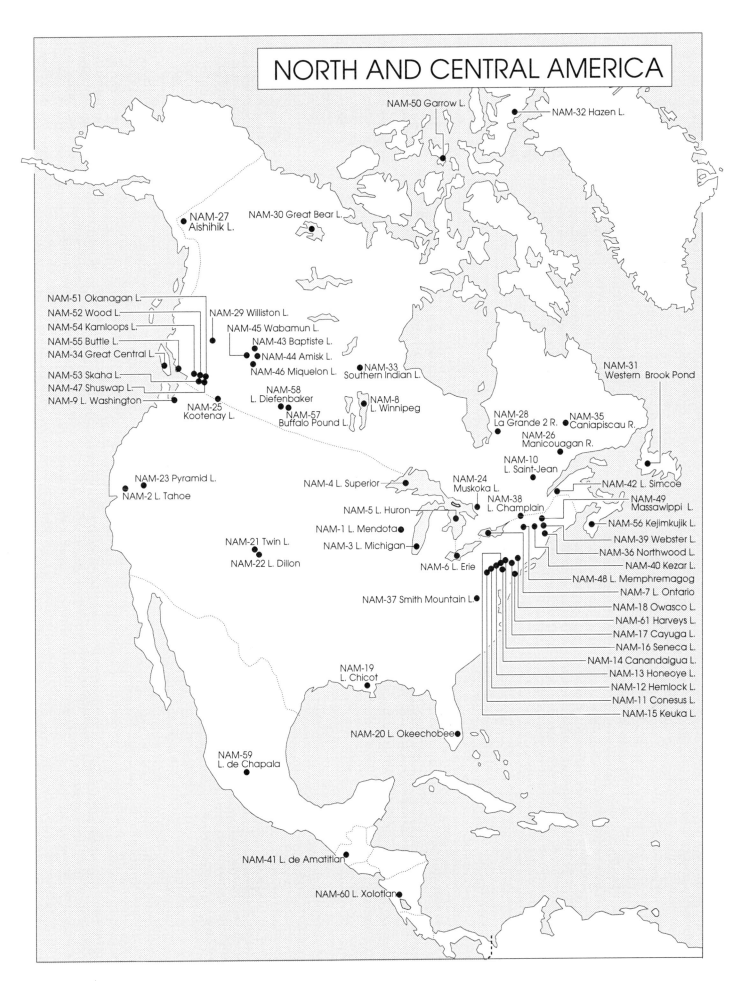

NORTH AND CENTRAL AMERICA

NAM-50 Garrow L.

NAM-32 Hazen L.

NAM-27 Aishihik L.

NAM-30 Great Bear L.

NAM-51 Okanagan L.
NAM-52 Wood L.
NAM-54 Kamloops L.
NAM-55 Buttle L.
NAM-34 Great Central L.
NAM-53 Skaha L.
NAM-47 Shuswap L.
NAM-9 L. Washington

NAM-29 Williston L.
NAM-45 Wabamun L.
NAM-43 Baptiste L.
NAM-44 Amisk L.
NAM-46 Miquelon L.

NAM-33 Southern Indian L.

NAM-31 Western Brook Pond

NAM-25 Kootenay L.

NAM-58 L. Diefenbaker
NAM-57 Buffalo Pound L.

NAM-8 L. Winnipeg

NAM-28 La Grande 2 R.
NAM-35 Caniapiscau R.
NAM-26 Manicouagan R.

NAM-10 L. Saint-Jean

NAM-23 Pyramid L.
NAM-2 L. Tahoe

NAM-4 L. Superior

NAM-24 Muskoka L.

NAM-42 L. Simcoe
NAM-49 Massawippi L.

NAM-5 L. Huron

NAM-38 L. Champlain

NAM-1 L. Mendota

NAM-56 Kejimkujik L.
NAM-39 Webster L.
NAM-36 Northwood L.
NAM-40 Kezar L.
NAM-48 L. Memphremagog
NAM-7 L. Ontario
NAM-18 Owasco L.
NAM-61 Harveys L.
NAM-17 Cayuga L.
NAM-16 Seneca L.
NAM-14 Canandaigua L.
NAM-13 Honeoye L.
NAM-12 Hemlock L.
NAM-11 Conesus L.
NAM-15 Keuka L.

NAM-21 Twin L.
NAM-22 L. Dillon

NAM-3 L. Michigan

NAM-6 L. Erie

NAM-37 Smith Mountain L.

NAM-19 L. Chicot

NAM-20 L. Okeechobee

NAM-59 L. de Chapala

NAM-41 L. de Amatitlan

NAM-60 L. Xolotlan

SOUTH AMERICA

SAM-5 L. de Valencia

SAM-10 Sobradinho R.

SAM-4 L. Titicaca

SAM-1 Represa do Lobo

SAM-8 L. Ypacarai

SAM-12
L. de Salto Grande

SAM-6 San
Roque R.

SAM-9 Laguna de Rocha

SAM-7
L. Lacar

SAM-3
Ezequiel Ramos Mexia R.

SAM-11 L. Todos Los Santos

SAM-2
L. Nahuel Huápi